Electrical Product Compliance and Safety Engineering

For a complete listing of titles in the *Artech House Technology Management and Professional Development Series,* turn to the back of this book.

Electrical Product Compliance and Safety Engineering

Steli Loznen

Constantin Bolintineanu

Jan Swart

ARTECH HOUSE

BOSTON | LONDON
artechhouse.com

Library of Congress Cataloging-in-Publication Data
A catalog record for this book is available from the U.S. Library of Congress.

British Library Cataloguing in Publication Data
A catalogue record for this book is available from the British Library.

Cover design by John Gomes

ISBN 13: 978-1-63081-011-5

© 2017 ARTECH HOUSE
685 Canton Street
Norwood, MA 02062

10 9 8 7 6 5 4 3 2 1

Contents

Foreword

The developments of modern technology are increasingly rapid and becoming more complex and more sophisticated. Nowhere is this more evident than in the electrical products used for communication and information technology; the medical, household, controller, measuring, and machinery applications that result from that technology, and the associated software, hardware, and wireless and system technologies that are incorporated in these products. No longer are single electrical products or components the norm; instead, they are incorporated into processes such as design, manufacturing, and marketing to accomplish required goals for effectiveness and safety.

Management is defined as the setting of strategies and the coordination of activities using human, financial, and other resources to accomplish objectives. It follows then that for all organizations or individuals who might be involved in the development of these products from concept onward, it is imperative to put an effective management process in place. This book does not explicitly discuss such a management system, but throughout, it outlines elements that must be considered in the management of electrical product development and implementation. Indeed, to develop and manufacture electrical products, it is necessary to develop a culture of compliance and safety.

This book focuses on the product compliance and safety engineering needed to ensure the effectiveness of the design, testing, manufacturing, and marketing of electrical products. The book's three authors tap their vast experience and knowledge to significantly benefit readers with a detailed outline of the practical elements and solutions necessary to effectively manage the development and provision of electrical products and systems.

The provision of safe and effective electrical products for users is the basis for electrical products standards and regulations worldwide. Designing products in compliance with these standards—including compliance with product-specific standards and overarching standards such as standards on risk management—will help alleviate problems during the certification process and in marketing. It will also help to prevent costly project delays due to design changes and/or test failures. The authors bring this to the fore in the first three chapters, which outline the basis for this book and provide an overview of regulations and standards and their effects on market access.

Subsequently, the authors analyze the elements and concepts of product compliance and safety science and, in the process, comprehensively identify the issues that need to be addressed to manage the development of electrical products and systems. The discussion of these issues—which include international regulations and product safety standards, risk management, compliance testing, and manufacturing for safety—provides not just a checklist for simply meeting compliance requirements but rather, more positively, the elements or milestones that need to be considered in the management of electrical product development.

This book is an excellent and much needed dissertation on product compliance and safety engineering for electrical products and systems, and its publication will help fulfill the industry's need to have well prepared professionals in field of compliance and safety engineering.

Furthermore, it is the responsibility of management and those involved in any way in the development and application of these products and systems to understand and address the compliance and safety issues discussed in this book. That responsibility is quite simply the provision of the safety and effectiveness that society deserves, and that these products and systems aim to deliver.

Alfred M. Dolan
Professor Emeritus
University of Toronto
May 2017

Preface

Product compliance and safety may help practitioners to develop more profitable products, to more completely satisfy customers, to reduce the risk of liability, and to build confidence in meeting the requirements of standards and regulatory bodies. We believe that this book will serve as a guide for electrical product compliance and safety professionals to develop a successful attitude and approach—and a winning concept.

We hope that you will both benefit and learn from this book, which represents a multiyear effort. The relevance of the book's content may change over time as standards change or are updated, as new standards are developed, as new safety concerns are discovered, or as new technologies are introduced in different applications. Therefore, readers should always use the book as a benchmark and then further verify the relevance and currency of standards and determine whether new or additional standards exist.

The book details why you need to understand compliance and safety engineering for electrical products and how to use the information provided. Product compliance and safety science is a broad and multidisciplinary field (encompassing electrical, electronic, mechanical, chemical, materials, and general engineering issues) governed by a well-established philosophy. Accordingly, this book analyzes sets of concepts, principles, and methods and then distills them to give readers an accurate understanding of product compliance and safety, highlighting the ways in which these concepts, principles, and methods need to be applied.

The following list is a summary of what you will find in this book:

- International regulation;
- Product safety standards;

- Failure analysis;
- Risk management;
- Product safety concepts;
- Selection of components;
- Product construction;
- Testing for compliance and safety;
- Manufacturing a safe product.

This book is intended for compliance and safety professionals responsible for designing, implementing, managing, testing, manufacturing, and marketing electrical products. The book's primary audience is comprised of design, quality assurance and control, testing, regulatory, manufacturing, service, sales, and marketing practitioners. No major background in electrical and electronics engineering is required, but a familiarity with specific topics will get you started right away. The book is also intended for instructors and students in the electrical and electronics departments of engineering universities—and it will add to their syllabus a topic that has previously been neglected. The information provided may also benefit current product compliance and safety professionals, who may lack a formal education in the subject and can hence turn to this book as an opportunity for professional growth.

The book is structured as follows:

- Chapter 1 examines the need for electrical product compliance and safety, by referring to product compliance and safety in the 21st century, electrical product safety legislation and liability, designing for safety, and safety cost estimation.

- Chapter 2 introduces international regulations and global market access regulations, addressing regional regulations and how they differ, CE marking, national recognized testing laboratories (e.g., NRTL, IECEE CB scheme, and product certification marks), and the ISO registration process.

- Chapter 3 addresses product safety standards and standardization, detailing standards and their structure; conformity to standards, and types of products safety standards and their objectives. It also lists the primary standards development organizations.

- Chapter 4 covers the electrical products safety philosophy, analyzing the concepts of safety, reliability, product safety, perception of risk, failure, single-fault safe, redundancy, and safety factors, and concluding with the differences between work safety and product safety.

- Chapter 5 introduces the methods for failure analysis: FMEA, FTA, HAZOP, AEA, and ETA.

- Chapter 6 discusses risk management for product safety by detailing the process: identification of hazards, estimation of the risk, risk evaluation, and risk control. Chapter 6 also covers functional safety and standards used for risk management.

- Chapter 7 deals with electrical products safety concepts: means of protection; the insulation diagram; safe current and voltage limits; leakage currents; spacing, or air clearance and creepage distances; grounding; fire, electrical, and mechanical enclosures; ratings; types of circuits; normal load; and abnormal operating conditions.

- Chapter 8 is dedicated to the selection of components: semiconductors, passive components, temperature control devices, motors and fans, thermoplastic materials, terminal blocks, connectors, and internal wiring.

- Chapter 9 examines batteries, detailing secondary and primary batteries, including the main applicable standards, with particular attention paid to battery safety design.

- Chapter 10 addresses power sources and their associated components: power supply plugs, connectors, and cord sets; fuses and fuse holders; power entry modules; and switches, varistors, transformers, and power supplies.

- Chapter 11 describes typical product construction requirements: enclosures, circuit separation, grounding and bonding, resistance to fire and flame rating, interlocks, moving parts, parts subject to pressure, and constructive aspects related to EMC. In addition, the chapter discusses serviceability.

- Chapter 12 looks at markings, indicators, and accompanying documents describing internal and external marking, safety labels; the marking of controls and instruments; the color of indicators; user's manual and installation instructions; and safety instructions, cautions, and warnings.

- Chapter 13 addresses human factors and product safety, focusing on operator and service personnel, human factors, and ergonomic hazards.

- Chapter 14 details testing for compliance and safety. Topics include types of product basic safety and EMC tests, information typically required for product basic safety and EMC testing, work safety in a product basic safety and EMC testing laboratory, equipment used for product basic safety and EMC testing, general testing conditions, product basic safety testing, EMC testing, and software testing.

- Chapter 15 examines the manufacture of a safe electrical product with attention paid to the manufacturer's responsibilities, the supply chain, manufacturability, integration, and routine tests (production line testing).
- Chapter 16 covers education and training for compliance and product safety professionals, analyzing compliance and product safety engineering in senior design courses, training resources development, and professional certification.
- The included glossaries of terms and acronyms serve as a quick reference to deal with issues at hand.

Although we have made every effort to ensure the accuracy and currency of the book at the time of writing, errors and documentation bugs sometimes arise from any mass of technical details. Furthermore, we have relied on documents and materials whose accuracy we cannot guarantee. However, we have exercised great care in our presentation of the content. Ultimately, readers are responsible for their usage of the book's content.

We hope that this book will raise awareness of product safety hazards and, consequently, help our readers to avoid dangerous situations and meet safety requirements for the benefit of all: manufacturers, users, and service personnel.

We are grateful to Aileen Storry and the staff at Artech House who provided us with helpful input and reviews. Because the reviewers chose to remain anonymous, we can only thank them collectively for their professionalism and correctness.

1

Why Do We Need Electrical Product Compliance and Safety?

1.1   Product Compliance and Safety in the Twenty-First Century

It is unanimously accepted that manufacturers around the world have a responsibility to provide products that satisfy the safety expectations of society. The growing field of safety as a global function acts as a cross-functional discipline that has a direct impact on people's lives. The term *safety* has many different connotations, and it can be related to many different concepts such as occupational health and safety, road safety, or product safety.

Most people accept that product safety issues are important in customer and professional areas, engineering, management, and other fields. Further, product safety is now a global issue, because markets are global.

What is safety? There are many different definitions of safety, but the most agreed upon is the "freedom from unacceptable risk of harm (i.e., death, injury, occupational illness, or damage to or loss of equipment or property, or damage to the environment)," [1] meaning as a judgment of the acceptability of risk, and risk, in turn, as a measure of probability and severity of harm to entities such as human health or the environment. An object is safe if its risks of harm are judged to be acceptable. It should be clear that safety and risk are inextricably linked. Typically, safety requirements arise from an understanding of hazards that need to be addressed; each safety requirement, if satisfied, mitigates one or more hazards.

The increase in the quantity and complexity of products means an increase in potential hazards that can endanger the safety of persons or properties when they are installed, used, and maintained for their intended purpose.

Product safety plays a fundamental role in guiding design and risk acceptance decisions related to conformity to applicable local regulations, standards, and codes. Specifically, new technological development is generating the emerging science of product safety, which will help prevent adverse events by improving the applications of safety means used in the entire life cycle of a product, from idea to decommissioning, for whom benefits relative to risks are maximized. This new science will also give us the tools to prevent adverse events by rapidly identifying safety problems before they can cause injury.

For a good understanding of this book, it is important to comprehend the following terms [1]:

- *Product:* A composite, at any level of complexity, of materials, components, and software. The elements of this composite entity are used together in the intended functional requirement to perform a given task. All products must be fit for purpose, be of satisfactory quality, and fit their description. This means that the products must fulfill the purpose customers have been led to expect and satisfy the reasons that led them to buy it.

- *Electrical product:* Any current-using equipment or accessory that uses low-voltage or high-voltage electricity.

- *Accessory:* A device, other than current-using equipment, associated with current-using equipment or with the wiring of an electrical installation.

- *Low voltage:* Voltage normally exceeding extra low voltage (a maximum 50-V rms ac or 120-V dc between conductors or between a conductor and Earth) but normally not exceeding—between conductors—1,000-V rms ac or 1,500-V dc, or—between a conductor and Earth—600-V rms ac or 900-V dc.

- *High voltage:* Voltage normally exceeding low voltage.

Note: The values of extra low voltage and low voltage can differ from the above limits depending on the application and type of the electrical product. See Section 7.3 for details.

- *Safe product:* A product that, under normal or reasonably foreseeable conditions of use including duration, service, installation, use, and maintenance requirements, presents only the minimum risks compatible with the product's use considered to be acceptable and consistent with a high level of protection from the associated risks involved with that product.

- *Product compliance:* A product's conforming to rules, such as specifications, policies, standards, or laws. Manufacturers aim for product compliance and thus take steps to comply with relevant laws and regulations.

- *Product safety:* The application of engineering and management principles, criteria, and techniques to optimize all aspects of safety within the constraints of functional effectiveness, time, and cost throughout all phases of the product life cycle.

To employ the concepts of product safety, it is necessary to understand what product safety is and what product safety strives to do. The fundamental objective of product safety is to identify, eliminate or control, and document product hazards.

Absolute safety is not possible because complete freedom from all hazardous conditions is not possible. Therefore, safety is a relative term that implies a level of risk that is both perceived and accepted.

Product safety as a discipline employed from the initial design steps through product disposal is an optimized level of risk that is constrained by cost, time, and operational effectiveness (performance) requiring that risk be evaluated and the level of risk accepted or rejected. This is the basic origin of product safety's requirement for both engineering and management functions.

Sometime product safety is confused with product reliability; however, even the most reliable product may not necessarily be safe. Product reliability is necessary but is not sufficient alone to ensure the safety of a product.

Product safety views the probability that the system will fail in a way that results in harm and predicts the severity of this harm.

Reliability engineering views probability alone by ignoring severity and views the probability that the product will operate with unimpaired performance, but it ignores the potential for coexisting faults and common cause threats that can generate harms.

A safe product is achieved through the implementation and careful execution of a product safety program. The objectives of a product safety program are to ensure the following:

- That safety, consistent with operational requirements, is designed into the product in a timely, cost-effective manner;

- That hazards are identified, evaluated, and eliminated, or that the associated risk is reduced to a level acceptable throughout the entire life cycle of a product;

- That historical safety data, including lessons learned from other products, is considered and used;

- That minimum risk is sought in accepting and using new designs, materials, and production and test techniques;

- That actions taken to eliminate hazards or reduce risk to a level acceptable are documented;

- That changes in design, configuration, or operational requirements are accomplished in a manner that maintains an acceptable level of risk;

- That consideration is given to safe and ease in the disposal of any hazardous materials associated with the product;

- That significant safety data is documented as "lessons learned" and submitted to data banks, design handbooks, or guidance documentation.

- That hazards identified after production are minimized consistent with program restraints.

Product safety programs are a response to ethical demands made by society on industry in general. Engineers have a special responsibility in this social context, as they are involved with high-energy sources, hazardous materials, and new technologies that offer both tremendous benefits to society and the potential for accidents.

1.1.1 Product Safety Process

Before discussing the various aspects of product safety, one must understand the general product safety process [2, 3]. The product safety process is a logical engineering approach for reaching product safety objectives. Figure 1.1 shows a simplified model of the product safety process, and the steps of the product safety process are described as follows.

- *Step 1—Product initialization:* This represents lessons learned and knowledge gained from previous products similar to the one under consideration. Of particular interest is previous action taken to correct design features that have resulted in accidental damage, loss, or harm. This action includes design changes, production/operational retrofits, and operating/maintenance procedures changes.

- *Step 2—Product specification:* This step clearly defines the product under consideration. The product elements must be specified as early as possible and revised as required during the product life cycle. Product definitions must also include major product interfaces such as product

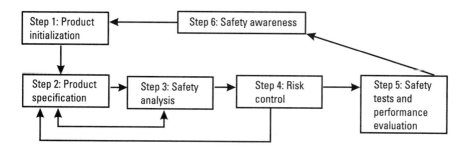

Figure 1.1 Product safety process.

operating conditions, environmental conditions, and the human role in product operation. The object of good product specification is to set limits for the following steps in the process and to reduce complex products to manageable parts.

- *Step 3—Product safety analysis:* This is the heart of the product safety process and demands a comprehensive, methodical analysis of the product and its elements. The search for possible product hazards and hazardous situations with rigorous brainstorming aim to achieve before-the-fact accident prevention. To be comprehensive, the analysis must consider every undesired event that might occur to the product and either the conditions that produce the undesired event or the consequences from it. The result is a high degree of confidence that no failures or errors have been left untreated in the search for potential hazards. A thorough analysis should identify possible hazards and hazardous situations; estimate the associated risks for each; determine the probability of occurrence of harm and classify its severity; evaluate the risk levels establishing which risks are unacceptable based on these results; and suggest possible risk control actions based on the risk/benefit analysis. The risk control actions should also be incorporated into the analysis and be examined to evaluate them for effectiveness. (Refer to Chapter 6 for more information on risk analysis). It is essential to maintain a closed-loop hazard identification and tracking product so that all identified hazards are followed through the risk control action.

  This type of documentation, while not part of the analysis, is the administrative work over which the product safety program lies and is essential in assuring completed action on identified hazards as well as following the progress of benefits derived from the product safety program. It is important in this step that one avoid confusing the risk management process with failure analysis methods. These methods are essential in the identification of hazards and hazardous situation but are not a complete risk management.

• *Step 4—Risk control to eliminate or control hazards:* Nothing that has been done so far in the product safety process will prevent hazards. The process produces no useful results until action is actually taken to eliminate or control the hazards that have been identified. However, all steps taken up to this point have been designed so that the most appropriate action can be taken. The project manager is responsible for this step. This responsibility includes the decision and direction for action, plus the allocation of resources required to do the job. This is perhaps the most critical step in the entire process because it is here that practical results are actually achieved. Any action taken in this step will modify or change some element of the product.

The modification involves both hardware and software. Initial assumptions on operating conditions can be amended or basic specifications can be changed. Because the product is modified, the initial specification of the product and its elements in step 2 must be revised. The process is then repeated, as required, until any additional hazards introduced by product modification are acceptable. These repeated steps ensure that actions taken to correct one hazard do not induce more hazards elsewhere in the product.

• *Step 5—Safety tests and performance evaluation:* Most, if not all, development programs for electrical products include testing to verify performance and the demonstration of product compliance with regulations, standards, and code safety requirements. They are conducted to assure the user that a product performs as required and to reveal any safety inadequacies. When the test results (related to identified hazards) are within the limits specified by the safety requirements, the residual risks are presumed to be acceptable Such, the subjects hazard no need additional implementation of risk control means.

• *Step 6—Safety awareness:* In those areas where effectiveness evaluation and tests indicate that the product safety process has produced the desired results, assurance that the product safety objective has been met increases correspondingly. This increased assurance is then applied the next time we go through the process, as an element of product qualification, or in applying the process to another product. In this manner, we continually build on past successes while correcting deficiencies.

1.2   Electrical Product Safety Legislation and Liability

General product safety (GPS) is regulated by GPS regulations, which apply to all products (new and secondhand). Product-specific legislation continues to take precedence in areas where the provisions have similar objectives to GPS regulations.

GPS regulations maintain the general duty placed on producers and distributors to place on the market (or supply) only products that are safe in normal or reasonable foreseeable use. The principal responsibility for day-to-day enforcement of such regulations lies with local authorities. GPS regulations presume that certain technical standards conform with general safety requirements, meaning that products that comply with them are deemed to be safe.

Engineers, designers, and other technical personnel involved in product development need to apply the principles of product safety engineering to the design, manufacturing, and marketing of products. To build safe and secure products, organizations need to have well-defined processes and methods for planning, design, development, testing, implementation, and disposal.

Generally, the manufacturers or importers of products are liable, but if other suppliers, such as retailers, cannot identify the manufacturer or importer, they may be deemed liable for the damages. Manufacturers, importers, or suppliers could be held liable in any legal action for harm caused to consumers or businesses as a result of unintended side effects or the failure of manufactured or supplied products.

Manufacturers, importers and suppliers ensure that products are safe by taking on the following responsibilities:

- Warning consumers about potential risks;
- Providing information to help consumers understand the risks;
- Monitoring the safety of products;
- Taking action immediately if a safety problem is found.

The resale of electrical products after reconditioning or repair is subject to the control of GPS regulations, and the suppliers of reconditioned products should ensure that these products comply with the applicable safety requirements and are issued with valid certificates of safety compliance.

Manufacturers may reduce their exposure to product liability action by using the following practices:

- Conducting regular reviews of product designs and production;
- Implementing and reviewing quality assurance procedures;

- Testing products regularly to relevant standards, including batch testing;
- Conducting appropriate marketing;
- Providing clear and thorough user instructions;
- When necessary, conducting prompt voluntary recalls of any products that are defective or unsafe.

Furthermore, manufacturers, importers, suppliers, and other liable entities should be sure that they are covered by product liability insurance. Insurance provides valuable protection to businesses against any costs or compensation awarded. Although such insurance is not legally required, it could mean the survival of the business when a claim related to the product safety is made.

The current trend in the European Union is toward self-certification (by CE marking) of products by the manufacturers. This means that, when permitted by law (directives), manufacturers claim by self-declaration the compliance of the product with relevant directives (all that apply), and are subject to process audits (postmarket surveillance) by regulators. Manufacturers take the risk that after the release of a product, regulators will determine that the product is unsafe.

North America uses third-party certification [using the evaluation services of a nationally recognized testing laboratory (NRTL)], to demonstrate compliance to safety standards and to electrical codes [*National Electrical Code* (NEC) and *Canadian Electrical Code* (CEC)]. Periodic follow-up service conducted by NRTLs at manufacturing locations monitors the preservation of the safety parameters in electrical products.

Opinion is divided on which of the above methodologies is more effective to ensure the safety of products on the market. Both methodologies have many pros and cons.

In both cases, the responsibility for ensuring compliance with the regulations rests with the manufacturer of the product in question. Failure to comply with regulations can result in prosecution. If a finished product contains a defect in a particular component, both the product manufacturer and component manufacturer may be liable. Customers can sue retailers under laws on the sale of unsafe products. A distributor, such as a shop, may not be liable if it can identify the original manufacturer.

In the United States, responsibility for the safety of consumer products, with the exception of food, pharmaceuticals, and medical devices [regulated under the auspices of the Food and Drug Administration (FDA)] and automobiles [regulated by the National Highway Traffic Safety Administration (NHTSA)], falls to the U.S. Consumer Product Safety Commission (CPSC), which regulates the sale and manufacture of more than 15,000 different consumer products. Since 2011, the CPSC has also maintained a public database of public complaints of safety problems connected with any of the 15,000 kinds of consumer goods it regulates (www.saferproducts.gov). This database provides a growing and potentially rich database for understanding trends in consumer product safety.

Authority for European consumer product safety is provided under the framework of the *General Product Safety Directive*. A rapid alert system, RAPEX, allows for the rapid exchange of information on dangerous consumer products between member countries and the European Union, with the exception of food, pharmaceutical, and medical devices, which are covered under other mechanisms.

1.3 Designing for Safety

Despite product safety legislation and standards, many products still present unacceptable risks. Many of the defects that result in safety problems for electrical products can be attributed to a lack of quality processes during product development, including engineering and design.

To prevent such situations one needs to promote a coherent product safety culture, including a stronger emphasis on risk assessment at the design stage, going beyond minimum standards and encouraging the integration of product safety management systems with other systems dealing with health, safety, quality, and the environment.

Designing a product with the applicable safety requirements in mind will help alleviate problems during the certification process. It will also help prevent costly project delays due to design changes and/or test failures.

Do not forget that most accidents are not the result of unknown scientific principles but rather of the failure to apply well-known, standard engineering practices. Accidents will not be prevented by technological fixes alone, but preventing them requires control of all aspects of the development and operation of the product.

The process of product certification can be simplified if applicable safety requirements are incorporated into design at every stage of product's development. This, in turn, can reduce the cost of redesign and accelerate time to market.

The following steps facilitate the integration of compliance into a new product:

• Identifying the markets in which the product will be sold;

• Implementing the applicable product safety standards;

• Training design engineers in the basics of compliance;

- Ensuring that compliance engineers work side-by-side with designers, providing deeper expertise when needed and information about the latest changes to standards and regulations;

- Making sure that safety requirements (both components and construction requirements) are incorporated into the design phase;

- Performing early design reviews and early testing on the first prototypes to lower the risk during final compliance testing;

- Ensuring that project schedules accommodate all compliance-related requirements.

Critical reviews of a product design identify hazards that can be controlled by modifying the design. Modifications are most readily accepted during the early stages of design, development, and testing. Previous design deficiencies can be exploited to prevent their recurrence. Inherent safety requires both engineering and management techniques to control the hazards of a product.

Safety requirements must be consistent with other program or design requirements. The evolution of a product design is a series of trade-offs among competing disciplines to optimize relative contributions. Safety competes with other disciplines; it does not override them.

1.4   Safety Cost Estimation

How much does a product safety program cost? The implication of that question is whether product safety is worth the expense. Fortunately, the costs of product safety programs are quite small in proportion to overall project costs. In fact, most projects need only one or two product safety personnel in the company. One person can monitor several product projects simultaneously.

A specific assessment of product safety payoff is difficult at best. One can hardly "measure" something that does not happen, such as an accident that has been prevented. The evaluation of safety work in positive terms is extremely difficult. When an accident does not occur, it is impossible to prove that some particular design feature prevented it.

Approaches other than absolute measurement can be significant as long as a reasonableness test is applied. Data concerning material failure accidents could be compared on a relative basis. Additionally, the cost of all documents requested (e.g., regulations and standards) could be considered. The prices of testing for compliance may also be included in the total safety costs.

References

[1]   ISO/IEC Guide 51, *"Safety Aspects—Guidelines for Their Inclusion in Standards,"* 2014.

[2]   U. S. Air Force Safety Agency, *System Safety Handbook*, 2000.

[3]   MIL-STD-882, *Standard Practice for System Safety*, U.S. Department of Defense, 2012.

Selected Bibliography

Amarendra, K., and R. A. Vasudeva, "Safety Critical Systems Analysis," *Global Journal of Computer Science and Technology*, Vol. 11, Issue 21, 2011

Baram, M., *Liability and Its Influence in Designing for Product and Process Safety*, Safety Science 45, 2007, pp. 11–30.

Drogout, F., et al., "Safety in Design—Can One Industry Learn from Another," *Safety Science 45*, 2007, pp. 129–153.

Fadier, E., and C. De la Garza, "Safety Design: Towards a New Philosophy," *Safety Science 44*, 2006, pp. 55–73.

Flaherty, E., "Safety First: The Consumer Product Safety Improvement Act of 2008," *Loyola Consumer Law Review*, Vol. 21, 2008, pp. 372–384.

Hale, A., B. Kirwan, and U. Kjellen, "Safe by Design: Where Are We Now?," *Safety Science 45*, 2007, pp.305–327.

Jordan, P. A., "Medical Device Manufacturers, Standards and the Law," *Sensible Standards*, 2012.

Leveson, N., *Safeware System Safety and Computers*, Reading, MA: Addison Wesley, 1995.

McDermid, J. A., "The Cost of COTS," *IEE Colloquium—COTS and Safety Critical Systems*, London, 1998.

Pidgeon, N., "Safety Culture: Key Theoretical Issues," *Work and Stress*, Vol. 12, No. 3,1998, pp. 202–216.

Ponsard, C., et al., "Early Verification and Validation of Mission Critical Systems," *Formal Methods in System Design*, Vol. 30, No. 3, 2007, pp. 233.

U.S. Consumer Product Safety Commission, *"Report to Congress Pursuant to Section 212 of the Consumer Product Safety Improvement Act of 2008,"* Report *to Congress*, 2009.

2

International Regulations and Global Market Access

2.1 Regional Regulations: How They Differ

The process for demonstrating that quality, safety, reliability, compatibility, interoperability, efficiency, and effectiveness meet the requirements of standards, regulations, and other specifications is called *conformity assessment* (CA). ISO/IEC 17000 defines CA as: demonstration that specified requirements relating to a product, process, system, person, or body are fulfilled.

Placing a product on the international market represents a challenging task for any marketing department. This is a process that, most of the time, represents a complex and difficult road. Trying to obtain full (or as complete as possible) global market access involves many resources.

A manufacturer or a supplier of any electrical product needs to seek and understand the imposed conditions for each intended market. These conditions differ from market to market, from country to country, and even from one state to another within the same country.

Whether we like it or not, the concept of a global market is becoming increasingly relevant. At the same time, within the last couple of years, the concept of globalization has—not surprisingly—started to evolve as well in the field of regulatory approvals. However, due to specific circumstances, we do not foresee global acceptance of market access.

From the point of view of electrical products manufacturers, it is important to first know the following information:

- Intended market(s);

- Specific requirements applicable to each of the targeted markets;

- The simplest and correct ways to obtain approvals for each intended market;

- The steps involved in maintaining the received approval(s).

The main error committed by manufacturers (or suppliers) of electrical products regarding the above-specified information is *not* obtaining all the information during the product definition phase (i.e., prior to the start of the product design process). The marketing department is then often faced with the difficult task of placing a product on the market as is (e.g., a product that was not designed properly for an intended market).

We often hear questions like, "Why is it not acceptable for Australia, since we already have an Underwriters Laboratories (UL) approval for our product?" or statements like, "We have this product listed/certified for North America, and our customer from South Africa wants it." We have to understand that each market may have its own supplementary requirements to the requirements of the market or markets for which the product was approved and that without fulfilling those specific requirements, the product will remain noncompliant.

Such situations are possible for the following reasons:

- Some markets impose conditions specific to their region, and these are in line with their specific legislation (e.g., electrical code, particular environmental conditions, and local standards);

- Other markets are trying to protect themselves against international competition or to take advantage of the companies that are exporting their products in that country.

The conditions specific to each market are accounted for by product safety design. Examples are found within the national deviations specified within documents such as regulations, standards, norms, and technical information letters.

All of the documents gathered by product safety engineers or regulatory specialists should be part of a product's definition before the schematics and the components design stage of the product are considered.

Having gathered all of the market requirements properly, hardware engineers should use the most stringent conditions to cover the widest range of possibilities, and the end result will be beneficial for the product and for the company that places the product on the market.

The design should be flexible to lower the cost of the product. For example, printed circuit boards (PCBs) should be designed in a manner that respects the requirements for creepage distances and air clearances as specified by the most stringent market, even if the same boards will be used for products intended to be placed on markets where requirements do not exist or are less stringent.

Flexible options in the design of the PCBs (e.g., choice of components) will allow manufacturers to use less expensive components for some of the markets, and the costs will increase only for the most severe markets. For example, in the design of a relay that provides separation between telecommunications network voltage (TNV) circuits and safety extra low voltage (SELV) circuits, a PCB layout that accepts different patterns will allow the use of cheaper components for some of the markets; it will be populated with more expensive components only for the markets that require those conditions.

A question we have heard repeatedly is, "How can a product that is compliant or safe for market A be noncompliant for market B?" This represents an obstacle for a marketing department and may generate headaches for the design team.

There are many reasons for these disparities in compliance requirements. For example, a piece of a product may be used in different environmental conditions: There are countries where the humidity and ambient temperature are lower than in other countries or where the product will be used within an environment where electric lightning is more severe than in other parts of the world. Similarly, there are countries where dust may play a significant role during the life of a product, affecting product safety and insulation requirements in the context of an aging product. Additionally, there are differences among countries with respect to technical culture and the attitude of the end user toward electrical product safety.

In such conditions, the task of any product safety engineer or regulatory specialist is to ensure that the design team is aware of all the regulatory conditions and to state those conditions clearly at the product definition stage. Different markets have different requirements according to their regulations; conversely, there are no regulations that will be able to cover all markets. Examples include local electrical codes and everything that follows from them (e.g., wiring regulations, power systems, and mains voltages). A very simple and clear example of this situation is represented by appliance couplers.

Regional conditions will differ in time as well. It is a natural process, and its dynamics are related to the experience of each market; the dynamics of changes to standards are driven and controlled by the feedback that comes from field issues.

Normally, no market offers lifetime approval for any product. There are several reasons for this, and it is a continuous process of evolution. Thus, product safety engineers and regulatory specialists must understand how to deal with these changes and how to build the approval for the products for which they are responsible.

Approvals are granted in different forms for different markets: Where a very rigid approach is used, local authorities require local certification of the product.

On the other hand, there are countries that encourage commerce and display more flexibility. Such flexibility, however, should not be used as an excuse to make a product less safe. We have observed that more flexible markets are often exposed to less compliant products as manufacturers tend to take shortcuts; as a result, their shipments could be put on hold at the borders. The flexibility of a market increases speed to market, reducing and managing costs. In our opinion, this ought at the same time to lead to improvement in product safety and risk management.

Manufacturers, importers, or suppliers seeking to bring their electrical products to any market will clearly reduce the challenges in managing the approval process by stating, from the beginning of product design, the applicable standards and requirements as well the national differences. Once the process of placing an electrical product on the market starts, exporters should be fully aware of all the imposed specific technical requirements to be fulfilled, such as the following:

- Product testing and certification;
- Shipment inspection requirements;
- Routine test requirements that it may be necessary to prove that they were done;
- Marking, documentation, and language in which the accompanying documents shall be submitted.

Even if most of the requirements are known at the beginning, it is necessary to understand that the access to a market is not a one-time deal: The complex regulatory framework in most countries is constantly being updated and expanded, and thus, the product will need to adapt accordingly.

Bringing electrical and electronic products to market in different countries is not complicated, but if the applicable requirements are not stated from the design stage, noncompliant products may result. Consequently, manufacturers will need to redesign or reengineer products, resulting in delays and loss of customers and revenue. Moreover, once arriving at customs, a batch of noncompliant products may be impounded or denied access, exposing manufacturers, importers, or suppliers to potential legal consequences.

Thus, it is important to pay attention to all of the following involved parameters, as applicable:

- Country- and market-specific regulatory requirements;

- Types of acceptable compliance processes;

- Language translation acceptance of the documentation;

- Local assistance and connection with authorities having jurisdiction and approval agencies and contacts from whom it will be possible to obtain local guidance;

- Preparation and submission of testing and approval applications;

- Testing coordination and scheduling;

- Understanding of the conditions of acceptability and limitations.

2.2   CE Marking

One of the most interesting and useful marks for a manufacturer is the CE mark. It offers an open door to the European Union market. The letters *CE* are the abbreviation of the French phrase *Conformité Européene,* which translates to European conformity. The term initially used was *EC mark,* which was officially replaced by "CE marking" in Directive 93/68/EEC in 1993. *CE marking* is now used in all EU official documents. *CE Mark* is another term that is used, but it is not the official term.

CE marking on a product implies a declaration by the manufacturer that the product complies with the essential requirements of the relevant European health, safety, and environmental protection legislation, as these are described within the applicable EU product directive(s).

The EU product directives describe the "essential requirements," including "performance levels" to which products must comply. The products shall fulfill the "essential requirements" generally by compliance with harmonized standards that are the technical specifications (European standards or harmonization documents) established by several European standards agencies (e.g., CEN and CENELEC). These are published in the *EU Official Journal* (OJ) for each directive. When "essential performance" is not covered by harmonized standards, then specific validation processes must be applied.

By affixing the CE marking on a product (product /component) the manufacturer officially indicates that the product may be legally placed in any country that belongs to the EU, assures free movement of it within the EU, and, in the case of a nonconforming product, permits the withdrawal of it from the EU market.

Each electrical product that falls under the scope of one of the European directives, shall be evaluated and found in compliance with the applicable requirements for it and shall bear the CE mark. The European directives were adopted by the member countries of the EU with the aim of harmonizing the laws of the member states relating to electrical products designed for use within EU countries.

It is important to understand that affixing the CE mark on a product does not give it a certification/listing. It merely represents a self-declaration of an "economic operator" and has no further implications as in the case of a certification/listing. However, it implies the same level of responsibility and liability for the economic operator that is making the product available for the EU market using compliance with one or more of the EU directives.

One of the most commonly used EU directives for electrical products is the *Low Voltage Directive* (LVD). It applies to all electrical products designed for use with a voltage rating of between 50 and 1,000V for alternating current and/or between 75 and 1,500V for direct current. Voltage ratings refer to the voltage of the electrical input or output, not to voltages that may occur inside the product.

The term *electrical product* is not defined in the directive. Therefore, it is to be interpreted according to the internationally recognized meaning of this term. The definition in the *International Electrotechnical Dictionary* of the International Electrotechnical Commission (IEC) is: "any item used for such purposes as generation, conversion, transmission, distribution or utilization of electrical energy, such as machines, transformers, apparatus, measuring instruments, protective devices, wiring material, appliances."

Depending on the conformity assessment procedure chosen to show compliance with applicable requirements, an evaluation shall be performed; the report issued as a result of the evaluation will be used as a backup of the declaration of conformity (DoC). It is the responsibility of the manufacturer to provide a complete file with technical documentation.

The technical documentation must include details of the design, manufacture, and operation of the electrical product insofar as these details are needed to assess the conformity of the electrical product with the requirements of the directive. Accordingly, it should contain the following:

- A general description of the electrical product;
- Design and manufacture drawings plus diagrams of items such as components, subassemblies, and circuits;
- Descriptions and explanations needed to understand the above mentioned drawings and diagrams plus the operation of the electrical product;
- A list of the standards used, in full or in part, and a description of the solutions employed to meet the safety aspects of the directive when standards have not been applied;
- The results of design calculations and of checks carried out;

• Test reports (which may be available and which could be issued by either the manufacturer or a third party).

Once the product is found to comply with the applicable requirements of a directive, specific requirements and a DoC are signed and issued by the manufacturer of the product.

As per the requirements of the annex of the LVD, the DoC must include the following:

1. The name and address of the manufacturer;
2. A description of the electrical product (e.g., fail safe transformer class 2 or model);
3. References to harmonized standards on which conformity is declared (e.g.:, EN 60742 and EN62368);
4. Where appropriate, reference to the specifications on which conformity is declared;
5. Identification of the signatory who has been empowered to enter into commitments on behalf of the manufacturer.
6. The last two digits of the year in which the CE marking was affixed (for the first time on the declared product).

The CE marking is considered a mark that meets certain requirements from the point of view of the shape and dimensions and durability. At the same time, we have found that some exemptions are allowed by directives. In our engineering judgment, the CE marking should be affixed on the product in such a manner that it will be visible after installation of the product. In fact, any marking is more useful if it is visible after installation, as it avoids the need to uninstall the product for reviewing the ratings or the model of the product when spare parts are needed.

2.3 NRTLs

In the United States, regulatory requirements and federal laws are found in the *Code of Federal Regulations*. The regulations for product safety approvals of electrical devices are specified in CFR21-1910, Subpart S. The mandatory federal requirements specify that all electrical appliances and devices shall be "listed" by an NRTL for the purpose for which they will be used. The term "listed" means controlled, monitored, and otherwise placed under formal surveillance by the approval agency or testing laboratory.

An NRTL is a term defined in North America and "represents a testing facility recognized by the Occupational Safety and Health Administration (OSHA) as primarily private sector organizations that provide product safety testing and certification services to manufacturers" [1]. OSHA is part of the U. S. Department of Labor.

The above definition is valid for the North American market only. Generally speaking, other countries that have similar regulatory bodies have locally equivalent testing laboratories that work with the local Authorities Having Jurisdiction (AHJ). An AHJ is defined as "an organization, office, or individual responsible for enforcing the requirements of a code or standard, or for approving product, materials, an installation, or a procedure." In North America, it is known that "where public safety is primary, the [AHJ] may be a federal, state, local, or other regional department or individual such as a fire chief; fire marshal; chief of a fire prevention bureau, labor department, or health department; building official; electrical inspector; or others having statutory authority. For insurance purposes, an insurance inspection department, rating bureau, or other insurance company representative may be the [AHJ]. In many circumstances, the property owner or his or her designated agent assumes the role of the [AHJ]; at governmental installations, the commanding officer or department official may be the [AHJ]" (www.nfpa.org).

An NRTL should not be confused with an AHJ; it provides its clients with an evaluation of a particular product or material, certification/listing, label, or acceptance, using the following controls and/or services:

1. Evaluation of the product and/or materials according to the applicable standards;

2. Implementation of control procedures for identifying the certified/listed and labeled product or materials;

3. Inspection of the production line process of the certified/listed items at factories with the purpose of assuring conformity with the standard(s) that were used during the initial evaluation;

4. Field inspections to monitor and to assure the proper use of its identifying mark or labels on products.

In our engineering judgment, there are two categories of NRTLs in the context of certification/listing of product:

- NRTLs that test and evaluate the product safety of the product;
- NRTLs that carry out conformity assessment testing and evaluation.

Clients of the NRTLs are not aware of these different categories, and the majority of manufacturers are not fully aware of the fact that in case of a non-conformance, the liability regarding even a certified/listed product falls entirely within the manufacturer's or supplier's responsibility.

In North America, along with UL, CSA, and Intertek, there are several other labs designated as NRTLs, including TUV and NEMKO.

2.4 Certification Body (CB) Scheme

The *CB Scheme* is an international system for mutual acceptance of test reports and certificates related to the safety evaluation of "electrical and electronic components, equipment and products." As of today, it is operated under the umbrella of the IEC—within the area known as the System of Conformity Assessment Schemes for Electrotechnical Equipment and Components (IECEE). (This scheme was originally operated by the CEE, the former European "International Commission for Conformity Testing of Electrical Equipment"; it was integrated into IEC in 1985).

IEC is one of the oldest professional/technical organizations in the world. Founded in 1906, it is one of the global developers of international standards for the entire world. In fact, IEC is the world's leading organization for the preparation and publication of international standards for "all electrical, electronic, and related technologies." These are known collectively as electrotechnology.

The CB Scheme, developed by the IEC as a multilateral agreement among participating countries and certification organizations, aims to facilitate trade by promoting harmonization of national standards with international standards and cooperation among accepted national certification bodies (NCBs) worldwide.

The equipment categories in which the IECEE works, are [2] listed as follows:

- BATT, or batteries;
- CABL, or cables and cords;
- CAP, or capacitors as components;
- CONT, or switches for appliances and automatic controls for electrical household appliances;
- E3, or energy efficiency;
- ELVH, or electric vehicles;
- EMC, or electromagnetic compatibility;
- HOUS, or household and similar equipment;

- HSTS, or hazardous substances;
- INDA, or industrial automation;
- INST, or installation accessories and connection devices;
- LITE, or lighting;
- MEAS, or measuring instruments;
- MED, or electrical equipment for medical use;
- MISC, or miscellaneous;
- OFF IT, office equipment and information technology;
- POW, or low-voltage, high-power switching equipment;
- PROT, or installation protective equipment;
- PV, or photovoltaics;
- SAFE, or safety transformers and similar equipment;
- TOOL, or portable tools;
- TOYS, or electric toys;
- TRON, or electronics and entertainment.

It has been observed over the years that this type of evaluation brings clear advantages for manufacturers of products for which the ratings are acceptable worldwide. While less than a half of all countries are part of the CB Scheme, it is a positive development that almost a half of the world is able to work together under the IEC umbrella using the CB Scheme.

Unfortunately, at the same time, by falsely flagging national differences or other organizational special interests, we have faced barriers during the process of acceptance even in countries that are part of the CB Scheme system. The rejections came from NCBs, and we have concluded that it was likely due to their national financial interests.

The CB Scheme does not represent a universal acceptance passport, but it is certainly the largest and most useful umbrella scheme to covers access in all countries that are part of the system and that are involved within the applicable standard.

Without a doubt, it is the best system for fraud protection, and thus, it brings a higher degree of confidence. All participants are seeking a well-defined discipline from the point of view of mutual respect.

The CB Scheme by its nature (being one of the expensive ways to walk on the road of regulatory compliance) brings a higher level of assurance regarding the quality of the products that are evaluated within this system. Additionally, manufacturers that adopt this approach for evaluation of their products or components are regarded more positively in the world of trade. Another positive aspect of the CB Scheme is that the regulatory bodies involved in the system inspire confidence that local consumers are better protected when using products subjected to this type of evaluation, raising the level of consistency regarding testing and evaluation of products, and access to the global market based on worldwide accepted criteria.

Use of the CB Scheme may help participating countries to reduce barriers of trade to an acceptable level and, thus, meet the political obligations they assumed as signatories of international trade agreements. Certainly, from the point of view of manufacturers, the CB scheme may reduce delays and costs involved in multiple testing since a product can be certified once by a single NCB, and then this certification can be accepted by others worldwide, usually without the need for further product assessment. Accordingly, markets can be expanded in time, and the time to bring a product to market may be reduced.

The main benefit of a CB Scheme goes ultimately to the consumer or end user: Anyone using a product that has been evaluated using the IECEE CB Scheme has the assurance that the goods purchased will perform to expectations based on reasonably safe characteristics when used as intended.

The operating units of the IECEE are the NCBs. They employ testing laboratories, known as CB testing laboratories (CBTLs).

The procedure for obtaining a certificate is not very complicated, but due to the length of the process and due to specific demands in each country, it can become a very difficult task. A manufacturer submits product samples to a CBTL for a third-party testing to product-specific IEC standards, as well as against any technical national differences from IEC standards that apply in those countries identified for certification (intended markets).

These national differences are specified in the IECEE website for the specific IEC standards. As an example, for IEC 60335-1:2010 the IEC standard for Household and similar electrical appliances—Safety—Part 1: General requirements, for eight countries (Australia, Canada, France, Mexico, New Zealand, Norway, Spain, and Switzerland) are indicated national differences. It is also possible to use associated testing laboratories (ACTLs) or even to perform the testing within the customers' testing facilities (CTFs).

Then, the CBTL conducts product evaluation and testing to assess compliance with the applicable technical requirements specified in the IEC standards. As a curiosity, the IEC standard with the biggest number worldwide of CBTLs able to conduct tests is the IEC 60950:2005 Information technology equipment—Safety—Part 1: General requirements, followed by IEC 60335-1:2010, the IEC standard for Household and similar electrical appliances—Safety—Part 1: General requirements.

If a product meets all technical requirements of the applicable IEC standards, the CBTL issues a CB test report in a unitary form based on the test report form (TRF) specific to each IEC standard of the CB Scheme. This test report is reviewed by the NCB to which the CBTL belongs, and a CB test certificate is issued to the product's manufacturer. CB test certificates are valid as long as the certified products continue to conform with the initial certification, unless canceled on the licensee's request. According to the IECEE rules, CB test certificates should not be used in any form of advertising or sales promotion. To obtain national certification in a target country, the manufacturer then submits a sample of the product, along with the CB test report and the CB test certificate to NCBs in that targeted country for certification. This certification confirms that the product conforms with national technical requirements, allowing legal access to that market.

Some conclusions regarding the CB Scheme follow:

- In some situations, it saves time and money and minimizes the risk of product recalls and reputation harm.

- It offers a higher degree of confidence in the production line, due to the auditing services that are involved during manufacturing of the accepted product.

- It brings a higher level of mutual confidence in the manufacturer's ability to place a product on the market using a more stringent method than a self-declaration from the point of view of the regulatory approvals.

2.5   Product Certification Marks

The entrance to a specific market is sometimes conditional on the presence of the certification mark on the product (e.g., CE for EU). It is very important for the global market access to identify for which categories of products the certification mark is mandatory and for which categories of products the marking is voluntary. This delimitation is designated by laws and regulations in each country; unfortunately, this information and the changes that may occur in time locally are not available accurately to manufacturers or supplies. These changes may generate delays in the process of receiving import approvals.

Generally, the certification bodies endorse manufacturers, at the end of the product certification or product qualification process, with a mark as a proof of fulfilling the tests and the qualification criteria stipulated in contracts, regulations, or specification. This certification is often mistakenly referred to as an "approval," which is often not true in terms of accessing a market. Certification marks are not globally recognized. (Some countries recognizeg them, but others do not.)

Issuance of a certification mark is at the discretion of the individual product certifier. When certification marks are issued and used on products, they are usually easy to see in the label of the product and enable users to track down the certification status to determine the criteria that the product meets and whether or not the listing is still active.

Also, certification marks are evidence of the existence of follow-up agreements between manufacturers and nationally accredited testing and certification organizations. A product which bears a Mark is inspected periodically, once a year, a half-year or a quarter, by the follow-up inspection conducted on site at the manufacturing location. The follow-up inspection verifies whether the product continues to comply with the criteria for which the product receives the right to bear the certification mark. Aspects related to the quality management system (QMS), critical components used, and correctness of the production line tests are a few of the inspected points during the follow-up visits.

There is a distinction between trademarks and certification marks. Trademarks are a badge of origin, whereas certification marks indicate that products are certified as having a particular quality or characteristic.

Table 2.1 summarizes a few examples of the usual certification marks for electrical and electronic equipment [1–3].

2.6 ISO Registration Process

The importance of quality (defined as totality of features and characteristics of a product to satisfy fitness for use, including safety and performance) is well recognized by all parties that do businesses. Regulators request that all steps of the design and manufacturing of a product be done in organizations that work based on ISO 9000 guidelines. According to ISO data, over one million companies and organizations in over 170 countries are certified to ISO 9001.

ISO 9000 is a quality management standard family that presents guidelines intended to ensure realization of a product that meets all relevant customer needs and expectations and complies with all relevant regulatory and statutory requirements.

The goal of ISO 9000 is to implement a quality management system within an organization, increasing productivity, reducing costs, and ensuring quality of processes and products. Table 2.2 summarizes the ISO 9000 family of standards (quality) and other management system standards (environmental, occupational health and safety, and energy).

Table 2.1
Examples of Certification Marks

Country	Mark	Notes
Australia		RCM Mark. Safety & EMC - Mandatory
Belgium		CEBEC Mark - Voluntary
Brazil		TÜV SÜD* Inmetro Mark – Mandatory – under Inmetro *Also, other Certification Bodies can provide the mandatory mark requested by Inmetro
Canada and US		CSA Mark for Canada and US – voluntary – under SCC and OSHA (NRTL) specifications.
Canada and US		QPS Mark for Canada and US – voluntary – under SCC and OSHA (NRTL) specifications.
Canada and US		LabTest Mark for Canada and US – voluntary – under SCC and OSHA specifications.
Czech Republic		EZU Mark Voluntary
EuroAsian Customs Union (CU): Russia, Belarus, Kazakhstan, Kyrgyz Republic and Armenia		Safety & EMC – Mandatory on all electrical products covered by EuroAsian Union Low Voltage and EMC Technical Regulations

Table 2.1 (continued)

Country	Mark	Notes
European Union		CE Mark Mandatory according with product specific EU Directives
European Union		Intertek S Mark – Voluntary Products bearing this Mark demonstrate compliance with legal European electrical safety requirements via third-party testing.
France		NF Mark - Voluntary
Germany		VDE (Verband der Elektrotechnik Elektronik Informationstechnik e.V.). Voluntary Indicates conformity with the VDE standards or European or internationally harmonized standards. The VDE mark stands for the safety of the product with respect to electrical, mechanical, thermal, toxic, radiological and other hazards.
Germany		VDE EMC Mark Voluntary Conformity of a product with applicable standards for electromagnetic compatibility
Germany	◁VDE▷ ◁HAR▷	VDE HARmonization Marking for cables and insulated cords according to harmonized certification procedures. Voluntary

Table 2.1 (continued)

Country	Mark	Notes
Germany		VDE Registration Number Voluntary Compliance with applicable sections of VDE standards if a fully applicable VDE standard does not exist for the product. This also applies to products which deviate from specific regulations, but can be tested in accordance with existing standards (e.g. special constructions, non-standardized cables and cords).
Germany		TÜV SÜD Mark – voluntary – under TÜV SÜD certification programs. Visit TÜV SÜD certification mark database under www.tuv-sud.com/ps-cert for variations of the mark for different products and standards etc.
Germany		TÜV SÜD* GS (Geprüfte Sicherheit = tested safety) Mark – voluntary – under ZLS *Also, other Certification Bodies can provide the GS mark.
Israel		Standards Institution of Israel (SII) Mark Voluntary Safety & EMC - Mandatory only for products for which the Commissioner of Standardization has decided that there is a requirement for surveillance.
Israel		Israel Testing Laboratories (ITL) Mark Voluntary Safety & EMC – For products or services whose specific Israeli official regulations so establish
Mexico		NOM (Norma Official Mexicana Mark) – ANCE Voluntary Safety & EMC – Mandatory for products or services whose specific Mexican official regulations so establish

Table 2.1 (continued)

Country	Mark	Notes
Norway		Nemko N-Mark - Voluntary
Poland		SEP-BBJ Mark - Voluntary
Poland		PCBC Mark - Voluntary
Russia		ROSSTANDART Mark Safety & EMC – Mandatory for products or services whose specific Russian official regulations so establish
Singapore		Safety - Mandatory EMC - Voluntary
Slovenia		SIQ Mark Voluntary
Spain		AENOR Mark.- Voluntary

Table 2.1 (continued)

Country	Mark	Notes
Switzerland		Swiss Safety Mark - Voluntary
The Netherlands		KEMA – KEUR Mark Powered by DEKRA.- Voluntary
US		UL Certified Mark Voluntary Product met UL's safety requirements
US and Canada		UL Listing Mark for US and Canada – voluntary – under OSHA (NRTL) and SCC specifications.
US and Canada		UL Recognized Component Mark Voluntary - Used on components certified by UL to both Canadian and U.S. requirements.
US and Canada		Intertek ETL Mark for US and Canada – voluntary – under OSHA (NRTL) and SCC specifications.
US and Canada		SGS Mark for US and Canada – voluntary – under OSHA (NRTL) and SCC specifications.
US and Canada		TÜV SÜD mark for US and Canada – voluntary – under OSHA (NRTL) and SCC specifications.

Table 2.2
ISO 9000 Family of Standards (Quality) and Other Management System Standards
(Environmental, Occupational Health and Safety, and Energy)

Standard	Title	Notes
AS9101:2000	Quality Management Systems Audit Requirements for Aviation, Space, and Defense Organizations	
ISO 9000:2015	Quality Management Systems—Fundamentals and Vocabulary	Covers the basic concepts and language
ISO 9001:2008 + Corrigendum 1:2009	Quality Management Systems—Requirements (will be withdrawn September 15, 2018)	Sets out the requirements of a quality management system
ISO 9001:2015	Quality Management Systems—Requirements	Sets out the requirements of a quality management system
ISO 9004:2009	Managing for the Sustained Success of an Organization—A Quality Management Approach	Focuses on how to make a quality management system more efficient and effective
ISO 10002:2014	Quality Management—Customer Satisfaction—Guidelines for Complaint Handling in Organizations	
ISO 10003:2007	Quality Management—Customer Satisfaction—Guidelines for Dispute Resolution External to Organizations	
ISO 10004:2012	Quality Management—Customer Satisfaction—Guidelines for Monitoring and Measuring	
ISO 10005:2005	Quality Management—Guidelines for Quality Plans	
ISO 10006:2003	Quality Management—Guidelines for Quality in Project Management	
ISO 10007:2003	Quality Management—Guidelines for Configuration Management	
ISO 10008:2013	Quality Management—Customer Satisfaction—Guidelines for Business-to-Consumer Electronic Commerce Transactions	
ISO 10012:2003	Measurement Management Systems—Requirements for Measurement Processes and Measuring Equipment	
ISO/TR 10013:2001	Guidelines for Developing Quality Management System Documentation	
ISO 10014:2006 + Corrigendum 1:2007	Guidelines for Realizing Financial and Economic Benefits	

Table 2.2 (continued)

Standard	Title	Notes
ISO 10015:1999	Quality Management—Guidelines for Training	
ISO 10017:2003	Guidance on Statistical Techniques for ISO 9001	
ISO 10018:2012	Guidelines on People Involvement and Competence	
ISO 10019:2005	Guidelines for the Selection of Quality Management System Consultants and Use of Their Services	
ISO 13485:2016	Medical Devices—Quality Management Systems—Requirements for Regulatory Purposes	
ISO 14001:2015	Environmental Management Systems— Requirements with Guidance for Use	
ISO 14004:2004	Environmental Management Systems— General Guidelines on Principles, Systems and Supporting Techniques	
ISO 14005:2010	Environmental Management Systems— Guidelines for the Phased Implementation of an Environmental Management System, Including the Use of Environmental Performance Evaluation	
ISO 14006:2011	Environmental Management Systems— Guidelines for Incorporating Eco Design	
ISO 14015:2001	Environmental Management—Environment Assessment of Sites and Organizations (EASO)	
ISO 14031:2013	Environmental Management—Environmental Performance Evaluation—Guidelines	
ISO 14971:2007	Medical Devices—Application of Risk Management to Medical Devices	
ISO 15378:2015	Primary Packaging Materials for Medicinal Products —Particular Requirements for the Application of ISO 9001, with Reference to Good Manufacturing Practice (GMP)	
ISO/TS 16949:2009	Quality Management Systems—Particular Requirements for the Application of ISO 9001 for Automotive Production and Relevant Service Part Organizations	
ISO 19011:2011	Guidelines for Auditing Management Systems	Sets out guidance on internal and external audits of quality management systems.
ISO 28000:2007	Specification for Security Management Systems for the Supply Chain	

Table 2.2 (continued)

Standard	Title	Notes
ISO 30001:2009	Risk Management —Principles and Guidelines	
ISO 50001:2011	Energy Management Systems—Requirements with Guidance for Use	
ISO/IEC 20000-1:2011	Information Technology—Service Management—Part 1: Service Management System Requirements	
ISO/IEC 20000-2:2012	Information Technology—Service Management—Part 2: Guidance on the Application of Service Management Systems	
ISO/IEC 20000-3: 2012	Information Technology—Service Management—Part 3: Guidance on Scope Definition and Applicability of ISO/IEC 20000-1	
ISO/IEC 27000:2012	Information Technology—Security Techniques—Information Security Management Systems—Overview and Vocabulary	
ISO/IEC 27001:2013	Information Technology—Security Techniques—Information Security Management Systems—Requirements	
ISO/IEC 27003:2010	Information Technology—Security Techniques—Information Security Management System Implementation Guidance	
ISO/IEC 27013:2015	Information Technology—Security Techniques—Guidance on the Integrated Implementation of ISO/IEC 27001 and ISO/IEC 20000-1	
ISO/IEC 90003:2014	Software Engineering—Guidelines for the Application of ISO 9001 to Computer Software	
ISO/IEC TR 90005:2008	Systems Engineering—Guidelines for the Application of ISO 9001 to System Life Cycle Processes	
ISO/IEC TR 90006:2013	Information Technology—Guidelines for the Application of ISO 9001 to IT Service Management and Its Integration with ISO/IEC 20000-1:2011	
OHSAS 18001:2007	Occupational Health and Safety Management Systems—Requirements	Sometimes incorrectly identified as ISO 18000
OHSAS 18002:2008	Occupational Health and Safety Management Systems—Guidelines for the Implementation of OHSAS 18001	

The ISO 9000 standard is applicable to businesses and organizations from every sector and provides guidelines for a company to establish, maintain, and improve the QMS.

A QMS is a set of interrelated and/or interacting elements (e.g., organizational structure, responsibilities, procedures, and resources) that organizations use to formulate quality policies and quality objectives and to establish the processes that are needed to ensure that these policies are followed in the right way and that objectives are achieved with acceptable risks.

ISO 9000 uses a process-oriented approach that allows manufacturers to understand how the processes interact and can be integrated with one another, as well as, which are the most important aspects of products and services intended to be supplied.

Once this process-oriented approach is implemented, audits need to be done to check he effectiveness of the QMS. Companies are registered with ISO 9000 through a third-party audit. In this case, an independent certification body (a registrar that meets the requirements of the ISO accreditation bodies) comes into an organization and evaluates it in terms of the ISO 9000 recommendations. If an organization meets the requirements of the standard, it becomes certified according to the ISO 9000 standard. To remain certified, the organization must continue to pass the on-site audit at regular intervals.

The registration process consists of the following steps:

- Application to registrar;
- Documents (e.g., quality manual, procedures, forms, and records) reviewed by registrar;
- On-site audit (including subcontractors) conducted by registrar (with a preaudit sometimes conducted as well);
- Responses from the organization to the findings (nonconformities) identified by registrar during the audit;
- Issuance of the registration certificate by registrar;
- Surveillance conducted by registrar on regular intervals (e.g., annual and biannual) depending on the registrar's policy.

It is important to know that evaluating the quality system and documentation to meet ISO requirements is allowed, but registrars cannot provide guidance on how to implement a quality system.

References

[1] Occupational Safety and Health Administration (OSHA), Registered Certification Marks, www.OSHA.gov.

[2] IECEE, "IEC System for Conformity Assessment Schemes for Electrotechnical Equipment and Components," Geneva, www.iecee.org.

[3] TRaC, "Component acceptability for CE product Safety," Technical Note 37, Worcestershire, U.K, 1999.

Selected Bibliography

Anderson, S. W., J. D. Daley, and M. F. Johnson, "Why Firms Seek ISO 9000 Certification: Regulatory Compliance or Competitive Advantage," *Production and Operations Management 8,* 1999, pp.28–43.

Australian Consumer Law, "Product Safety Guide for Business," 2012.

Electrical and Mechanical Services Department (EMSD) Hong Kong, "Guidance Notes for the Electrical Products (Safety) Regulation," 2007.

European Union, "Council Directive 93/68/EEC," Brussels, Belgium, 22 July 1993.

Harris, K., and C. Bolintineanu, "Electrical Safety Design Practices Guide," Tyco Safety Products Canada Ltd, Rev 12, March 14, 2016.

Higson, G. R., *Medical Device Safety: The Regulation of Medical Devices for Public Health and Safety,* Philadelphia, PA: Institute of Physics Publishing, 2002.

Pelnik, T. M., editor, *Supplement to the Quality System Compendium,* Association for the Advancement of Medical Instrumentation (AAMI), 2004.

Sroufe, R., and S. Curkovic, "An Examination of ISO 9000:2000 and Supply Chain Quality Assurance," *Journal of Operations Management 26,* 2008, pp.503–520.

U.S. Federal Register, *CFR Title 47 Telecommunication,* 2013.

U.K. Government Department for Business, Energy & Industrial Strategy, *Product Liability and Safety Law,* 2012.

3

Product Safety Standards

3.1 Introduction

This chapter is intended to make the products safety practitioner knowledge-able about the standards and the standardization environment in which a product must exist. It does not attempt to repeat the information in the standards themselves.

3.2 Product Safety and Standardization

In today's increasingly complex modern life and competitive circumstances, safety has become a top management challenge for compliance with demanding regulations. The increase in the quantity and complexity of products means an increase in potential hazards that can endanger people or property, when installed, maintained, and used for their intended purpose. "Manufacturing safer products" has become a catch phrase, affecting and influencing the minds of many designers and manufacturers. Building a safe and secure product requires that organizations have well-defined processes and methods for planning, designing, developing, testing, implementing, and decommissioning.

In such circumstances, manufacturers have a responsibility to produce products that satisfy the safety expectations of society and accordingly, allocate a large amount of investment to this end. These expectations are often incorporated in specifications. Technical specifications, however, may not in themselves guarantee that requirements will be consistently met if there are deficiencies in the specifications or in the organizational systems used to design and manufacture products. This possible mismatch has led to the development of standards and guidelines that complement relevant product requirements given in technical specifications [1].

Safety has become a special concern to regulatory authorities. In many fields, evidences is demanded to prove compliance with appropriate safety standards.

3.3   What Is a Standard?

A standard is an agreed upon and repeatable way of doing something. The global accepted definition for standard is the following:

> Document that provides requirements, specifications, guidelines, or characteristics that can be used consistently to ensure that materials, products, processes and services are fit for their purpose.

A standard is created for a particular material, product, process, or service and is done within independent, accredited, and recognized standards development organizations (SDOs). Standards are designed for voluntary use and do not generally impose regulations, but some laws and regulations may refer to standards and even make compliance with them compulsory.

Enforced by a government or trade association, regulations specify mandatory requirements that must be met under specific laws in order to legally operate and engage in business activity [2]. Some standards are written for certification and known as "technical specifications" or "requirements documents," giving presumption of conformity to local, regional, or global legislation.

The standardization process [3] can be characterized as follows:

- It is voluntary;
- It is evolutionary;
- It is collectively managed;
- It is a consensus-driven activity;
- It is carried out by and for the all relevant entities interested in the outcome, based on openness and transparency.

Standards should meet the following criteria:

- They should be fit for purpose;
- They should have a high degree of acceptability;
- They should be coherent with each other;

- They should be easy to apply;
- They should be based on sound scientific research;
- They should be updated and revised regularly at specified intervals;
- They should be hazards- and/or performance-based;
- They should allow for technological innovation and competition;
- They should consist of best practices and guidelines;
- They should adopt a system approach to effectively address changing technological, economic, and societal trends;
- They should bring together the expertise and experience of all interested parties, such as manufacturers, sellers, buyers, users, and regulators;
- They should help stimulate industry competition and market leadership;
- They should ensure consistency in product/service delivery and protect stakeholders;
- They should set the scene and create a level playing field for fair competition;
- They should ensure a common understanding and secure the interoperability of products and services;
- They should facilitate the spread of innovative products and/or technologies and services to the market.

Standards provide the following:

- Consideration of health, safety, and environmental matters;
- Performance and quality requirements;
- Measurement methods;
- A means to clearly indicate the rating on the product's packaging;
- Conditions, guidelines, or characteristics for products or related processes;
- Production methods;
- Related management systems practices.

3.4 Structure of the Product Safety Standard

Table 3.1 displays the general structure of a product safety standard [4].

Additional information can be included in a product safety standard including classification of components; delineation of procedures; specification

Table 3.1
Structure of a Product Safety Standard

Scope, object
Normative references
Terminology and definition, symbols and abbreviated terms definition, symbols and
General requirements
Classification
Identification, marking and documents
Protection against significant hazards
Safety requirements and/or protective measures
Construction of the equipment
Annexes (i.e., rationale)
In European Union CEN/CENELEC standards—Annexes Z [appropriate letter]—about the relationship between the standard and the essential requirements of the relevant EU Directive
Bibliography
Index of terms
Index of figures
Index of tables

of dimensions, materials, performance, designs, or operations; measurement of quality and quantity in describing materials, processes, products, systems, or practices; test methods and sampling procedures; and descriptions of fit and measurements of size or strength.

3.5 Conformity to Product Safety Standards

Conformity assessment refers to any activity that helps determine if a product, system, or service corresponds to the requirements that are contained in a specification. A specification, often a standard, is a technical description of the characteristics that need to be fulfilled. The activity itself can be executed by an individual, a company, or a test laboratory.

Standards are drafted by following the "neutrality principle," which means that the content of the standard shall not state a preference for a form or one type of assessment over another. In other words, the standard must be written so that it can be applied by any of the following:

- A manufacturer or supplier (first party);
- A user or purchaser (second party);
- An independent body (third party).

Accordingly, product safety standards specify the limits of parameters for the characteristics (i.e., values for leakage currents) that need to be evaluated and the test methods used to do this evaluation. For a specified characteristic, the test methods can be identical or it can differ from one product to another (i.e., for measuring leakage currents, different measuring devices are used for medical equipment and for information technology equipment, but for conducting temperature measurements the same test methods are used). Sometimes the test methods can be referenced to other existing standards (i.e., the test methods described in EMC basic standards).

Products that comply with standards often have a strong competitive advantage, as buyers will use that compliance to choose between comparable suppliers.

Standards can frequently lighten the regulatory burden that government regulations impose on businesses, since they offer a more flexible and business-oriented approach that helps to maintain market relevance.

In addition, standards open doors on a global scale as standardization promotes interoperability along the supply chain and gives the competitive edge necessary for effective worldwide trading.

A company has no legal obligation to comply with a standard. However, formal compliance does add an indirect legal aspect to standardization that must be considered.

A standards body may publish a standard, but it cannot claim authoritative regulatory powers over those standards. Any organization can become a conformity assessment body as a testing house or a certification body for specific standards.

To become a conformity assessment body (testing house or a certification body), the organization needs to be accredited by an accreditation body. For testing and calibration activities, accreditation to ISO 17025 standard is requested; for certification activities, accreditation to ISO 17065 standard is needed.

The bodies that provide accreditations apply the standard ISO/IEC 17011: "Conformity Assessment. General Requirements for Accreditation Bodies Accrediting Conformity Assessment Bodies."

3.5.1 Self-Assessment

In self-assessment, a company evaluates the criteria of a standard and declares that it meets the requirements of this standard (conformity). This can leave the company open to legal challenges should it be proven to be noncompliant. There are self-assessment tools available, designed by third parties, to help companies mitigate such risk.

3.5.2   Testing

One-off testing (verification of conformity), where all or a sample of products are laboratory-tested to meet a standard's specifications, presents a number of issues.

There are varying levels of test laboratories, ranging from a manufacturer's own facility to a fully accredited laboratory, and copies of a test report should be requested to evaluate the competence of the testing facility as well as the validity of the claim.

In all these cases, testing is a snapshot in time. A sample may meet the requirements of a standard during the testing phase; however, small changes of materials and components, staff rotation, and deterioration of manufacturing equipment may lead to products produced later that are lower-quality or even unsafe.

In addition, test samples, could be susceptible to *golden sampling*, where a company will choose examples that are certain to pass the tests for the process. To try and prevent this, reports or certificates gained through testing are usually very specific, stating, for example, "The sample submitted conformed to the requirements of [standard number]."

There is a degree of overlap between testing, calibration, and metrology. For the purposes of conformity assessment—demonstration that an object conforms to specified requirements—calibration and other aspects of metrology would fall outside this concept.

However, the confidence in the measurements made during testing (and inspection) depends on the national measurement system and the traceability to international measurement standards through calibration.

3.5.3   System Certification

To help achieve consistent production quality, management systems such as ISO 9001 can be implemented by the manufacturer. Based on the *plan, do check, act method,* a well-implemented management system will set out clear plans to assess and evaluate the manufacturing process from beginning to end. As with testing there are varying degrees of implementation, and the most robust and reliable method is to seek third-party certification of the system by an accredited body.

3.5.4   Product Certification

Product certification (attestation of conformity) is the most stringent form of product evaluation and as such provides the highest form of due diligence available today. Product certification schemes (see Chapter 2) allow a dedicated mark to be affixed on a product, proving its compliance with a specific standard and supervision of the production by the follow-up inspection process.

In order to achieve a mark for a product, a CB will assess the QMS at the factory and test the finished product to the appropriate standard. After issuing a mark certificate, the CB will then inspect the factory on an ongoing basis and audit test randomly selected products to ensure that there has been no reduction in quality and safety.

Two very important aspects of the product certification process should be clarified:

- The product testing and certification businesses simply assess a product against a set of objective criteria. This does not mean that the product it is "good," "high-quality," or necessarily fit for the purpose to which someone might wish to put it; the conformity of a product with a standard simply signifies that it meets or fails to meet the requirements stipulated in a standard.

- If an organization were to declare compliance and a product or service was proven to not conform to the standard, then the company making the declaration becomes legally culpable.

3.6 Types of Product Safety Standards

Based on geographic levels, standards are classified as follows:

- International;
- Regional;
- National.

The document "International Classification for Standards" (ICS) published in 2005 provides worldwide consistency in indexing product safety standards and serves as a structure for the classification of international, regional, and national standards and other normative documents. It may also be used for classifying standards and normative documents in resources such as databases and libraries.

In ICS, the general term *standard* is applied to all international, regional, and national normative documents, such as standards, technical reports, standardized profiles, technical specifications, technical regulations, guides, codes of practice, technology trends, and assessments and the in th drafts of such documents. For safety, ICS specifies the indexing listed in Table 3.2.

Table 3.2
The International Classification for Safety Standards

01.040.13	Safety • Environment. health protection. safety (vocabularies)
13	Safety • Environment. Health protection. Safety
13.100	Safety • Occupational safety Industrial hygiene
13.110	Safety • Safety of machinery
13.120	Safety • Domestic safety
13.220.01	Safety • Including fire safety
13.240	Safety • Including safety valves and bursting disc devices
13.340.50	Safety • Including safety boots and shoes
13.340.60	Safety • Including safety ropes, harnesses, and fall arrestors
27.120.20	Safety • Nuclear power plants Safety
29.020	Safety • Including voltages, general electrical terminology, electrical documentation, electrical tables, safety, and fire hazard testing
43.040.80	Safety • Including airbags, safety belts, traffic accident issues, and safety-enhancement matters
67.020	Safety • Including food hygiene and food safety
91.160.10	Safety • Including workplace lighting and emergency and safety lighting
97.190	Safety • Including child safety requirements for other household equipment
97.200.50	Safety • Including safety of toys

There are many standards that are applicable to product safety, some specific to sectors such as information technology (IT), medical (MED), household, customer (e.g., audio and video), and industrial (e.g., machinery), and some that are specific to areas including environment, risk management, usability, and software. Table 3.3 describes the categories of product safety standards [5].

Table 3.4 lists documents that are considered to be standards or associated with standards [6].

3.6.1   Elaboration of a Standard

A requirement of a particular standard takes priority over the general standard

The steps in the process for the elaboration of a standard [6, 7] are described as follows:

- An idea for a standard is issued [*preliminary work item* (PWI)] based on an analysis of a specific necessity for standardization.
- A proposal of a new work item [*new proposal/new work item proposal* (NP/NWIP)] is made to a specific committee. This proposal comes from within the committee or a member of the public.

Table 3.3

Type of Product Safety Standards

General	Standard that specifies general requirements applicable to a well-defined group of equipment (i.e., IEC60335-1 Household and similar electrical appliances—Safety—Part 1: General requirements)
Collateral	Standard that specifies general requirements applicable to a subgroup of equipment (i.e. IEC 60601-1-3 Medical electrical equipment—Part 1–3: General requirements for basic safety and essential performance—Collateral Standard: Radiation protection in diagnostic X-ray equipment) or to a specific characteristic of all equipment not fully addressed in the general standard (i.e.,IEC 60601-1-6 Medical electrical equipment—Part 1–6: General requirements for basic safety and essential performance—Collateral standard: Usability)
Particular	Standard that specifies requirements applicable to particular equipment (i.e. IEC 61010-2-010 Safety requirements for electrical equipment for measurement, control and laboratory use—Part 2-010: Particular requirements for laboratory equipment for the heating of materials).
Basic	Standard giving basic concepts, principles for design, and general aspects that can be applied to all fields that may or may not be specific (i.e., IEC 61000 series for EMC measurement methods)
Generic	Standards with a wide application, not related to any particular product, and dealing with one particular safety aspect (i.e., safety distances, surface temperature, noise, and immunity); or one type of safeguard (interlocking devices, pressure sensitive devices, and guards) that can be used across a wide range of products. These standards apply when a product- specific standard does not exist.
Horizontal	Standards that cover characteristics that are common to many products from the same technological area (i.e., IEC 61511 Functional safety—Safety instrumented systems for the process industry sector)
Vertical	Standards that cover characteristics that are common to many technological areas (i.e., IEC 60990, Methods of measurement of touch current and protective conductor current)
Product- specific	Standard specifying all or part of the requirements to be fulfilled by a product to establish its fitness for purpose (i.e., IEC 60730-1 Automatic electrical controls—Part 1: General requirements)

- The proposal is entered into a formal acceptance process by the committee members.

- Upon acceptance [*approved new work item* (AWI),] the committee will create a *working group* (WG) or allocate the work to an existing working group.

- The WG elaborates a draft of the standard [*working draft* (WD)], which goes out for public comment to committee members. This stage ensures that every standard is transparent and accepted by the wider public.

- Committee members submit comments on the draft;

- The WG answers comments and implements into the draft [*committee draft* (CD) and *committee draft for voting* (CDV)] the accepted inputs.

Table 3.4
Documents Considered to be Standards or Associated with Standards

Document Category	Features
Specification	Detailed document outlining performance and/or design and/or service requirements that need wide consensus.
Method	Detailed document that focuses on the way products and materials are tested or the way they are specified.
Vocabulary	Referenced/indexed document defining terms used in a sector technology.
Code of practice	Guidance and recommended options, including a wide range of subjects from outline design to workmanship and safe practice.
Guide	Provides general guidance with recommendations and background information. Tends to be less specific and more discursive than a code of practice-giving rules, orientation, advice or recommendations relating to standardization.
	Note: A guide can represent a guidance to technical committees for the preparation of standards.
Technical report— TR—(e.g., ISO/IEC TR 62354:2014)	Additional information to that published in international standards (e.g., data collection), containing informative material not suitable to be published as a standard or a technical specification
	Note: A TR may include, for example, data obtained from a survey carried out amongst the SDO national members, data on work in other organizations, or data on "state-of-the-art" in relation to national standards on a particular subject.
Technical Specification - TS—Technical Specification (e.g., ISO/TS 16949:2009)	Document establishing a norm where there is insufficient support for a full standard or where the state-of-the-art is not stable. Cannot conflict with an existing international standard but may compete with other TS. This document is adopted for which there is the future possibility of agreement on a standard.
Corporate Technical Specifications (CTS)	Contain explicit sets of requirements that relevant materials, products, or services should conform to. The contents of these standards are easily controlled by the wishes of the company or the company's dedicated employees producing them.
Publicly Available Specification (PAS)	A consultative document based on the national formal, regional, or international standard model. They are standards that begin as sponsored projects by stakeholders wishing to drive the creation of a best-practice document.
International Standard (i.e., IEC and IS)	Is voluntary and that all or a majority (at least 75%) of participants agreed with the rules and specifications that are part of the standard; is representative of the needs of many countries.

Table 3.4 (continued)

Document Category	Features
Regional Standard [i.e., European Standard (EN)]	Standard adopted by regional organization and carrying with it an obligation of implementation as an identical national standard and withdrawal of conflicting standards.
Amendment	Ratified document to a standard already circulated, to be read in conjunction with that standard and that modifies and/or adds to previously agreed technical provisions in that standard.
Corrigendum	Supplementary document to a standard that corrects one or more errors or ambiguities inadvertently introduced in either drafting or printing and that could lead to incorrect or unsafe application of those versions.

- Once the public comments are considered final, following the iterative stages [*final committee draft* (FCD), *draft international standard* (DIS), and *final draft international standard* (FDIS)], approval for publication must be reached.

- The approval for publication of the standard [*international standard* (IS)] can only be done through consensus, using voting systems.

The above process of standard elaboration should be completed in five years. If, in a specific stage, the process is delayed for any reason (e.g., WG problems or lack of consensus) and a term of completion that exceeds the allowed time is projected, the work can be removed from the scheduled program of the SDO. Standards are subsequently reviewed at a specified interval (i.e., at least once every five years), to ensure that they remain relevant and that any industry innovations are accounted for. Between revision intervals, *amendments to standards* can be issued, based on the technological progress. If a significant error is identified after publication, a *corrigendum* is published.

3.7 Objectives for Products Safety Standards

According to ISO/IEC Guide 51, safety means: freedom of unacceptable risk that leads to other definitions such as risk, risk analysis, risk evaluation, residual risk, tolerable risk, risk control and finally risk management (gathering all the previous risk tasks) [8]. The new approach to Safety assessment is based on this definition..

A few standards include examples of hazards, hazardous situations, and hazardous events to clarify these concepts and assist the designer in the process of hazard identification. A function of the standards is therefore to define the maximum acceptable probability for each hazard. In developing the standard, a decision should be made about the severity level for each of the generic hazards for the specific kind of equipment.

When a product standard is elaborated, all the possible hazards need to be taken into consideration, and the acceptable risk for each needs to be specified.

In general, the costs of managing risks needs to be commensurate with the benefits obtained. The rationale for the risk reduction actions taken should be that the cost/benefit relationship differs from one piece of equipment to another and depends on the relevant technologies used.

3.8   Product Safety Standard Developers

Product safety standards are governed by different bodies at international, regional, and national levels. Product safety standards developed by the International Organization for Standardization (ISO) and International Electroechnical Commision (IEC) are voluntary. They become mandatory after adoption at the regional or national level.

3.8.1   International (Examples)

The ISO, a nongovernmental organization, is a federation of 165 national standards bodies, from all regions of the world, one per country, including developed and developing countries as well as countries with economies in transition. Each ISO member is the principal standards organization in its country. The members propose new standards, participate in their development, and provide support in collaboration with the ISO central secretariat for the 3,000 technical groups that actually develop the standards. The ISO has published more than 19,500 international standards covering almost every industry, from technology to food safety to agriculture and healthcare [7].

The IEC is a nonprofit, nongovernmental international standards organization that prepares and publishes international standards for all electrical, electronic and related technologies—collectively known as *electrotechnology.* The IEC embraces all electrotechnologies, including energy production and distribution, electronics, magnetics and electromagnetics, electroacoustics, multimedia, telecommunication, and medical technology, as well as associated general disciplines such as terminology and symbols, electromagnetic compatibility, measurement and performance, dependability, design and development, safety, and the environment [6].

3.8.2   Regional (Example: Europe)

European standards are developed through the platforms provided by the European standardization organizations (ESOs), listed as follows:

- The European Committee for Standardization (CEN);

- The European Committee for Electrotechnical Standardization (CEN-ELEC);

- The European Telecommunications Standards Institute (ETSI).

The ESOs are officially recognized standards bodies under European legislation, entrusted with the development of European standards that support European regulations and policies.

CEN and CENELEC are officially recognized organizations responsible for developing and defining standards on the European level either in English, French, or German original text or translated into one of the other languages of the CEN/CENELEC member countries.

The members of CEN and CENELEC are the national standards bodies and national electrotechnical committees of 33 European countries including all of the EU member states plus Iceland, Norway, Switzerland, the former Yugoslav republic of Macedonia, and Turkey [9].

European standards [or the European norm (EN)], approved by CEN and CENELEC in accordance with internal regulations, are accepted and recognized in all of these countries. European Standards are "regional standards" within the sense of the ISO/IEC definition. CEN/CENELEC and CEN/CEN-ELEC members are responsible for implementing and updating European standards and for interpreting their content.

CEN and CENELEC work to promote the international harmonization of standards in the framework of technical cooperation agreements with the ISO and IEC. The specific activities covered by CEN, CENELEC, and ETSI are described as follows.

- Specific CEN activities cover the following: Accessibility, air and space, bio-based products, chemistry, construction, consumer products, energy and utilities, environment, food, health and safety, healthcare, heating, ventilation and air conditioning (HVAC), information and communication technologies (ICTs), innovation, machinery safety, materials, measurement, nanotechnologies, pressure equipment, security and defense, services, transport, and packaging.

- Specific CENELEC activities cover electrotechnical standardization in sectors such as the following: electric vehicles, household appliances, ICTs, EMC, electrical engineering, fiber-optic communications, fuel cells, medical equipment, railways, smart grids, smart metering, and solar (photovoltaic) electricity systems.

- ETSI produces globally applicable standards, standards, specifications and reports for ICT, including fixed, mobile, radio, converged, broadcast, and internet technologies. ETSI is a not-for-profit organization with more than 750 ETSI member organizations drawn from 63 countries across five continents worldwide.

3.8.3 National (Example: United States

The American National Standards Institute (ANSI) is a private nonprofit organization that oversees the development of voluntary consensus standards for products, services, processes, systems, and personnel in the United States. The organization also coordinates U.S. standards with international standards so that American products can be used worldwide [10].

3.8.4 International and Regional Standards Organizations

For specific areas of applicability standards developers exist at international and regional levels. As was specified previously, the standards issued by these organizations are voluntary. The following is a list of the main international and regional standards developers.

- AAMI: Association for the Advancement of Medical Instrumentation;
- AAQG: America's Aerospace Quality Group;
- Accellera: Accellera Organization;
- ACCSQ: ASEAN Consultative Committee for Standards and Quality;
- AHRI: Air-Conditioning, Heating, and Refrigeration Institute;
- Image Management;
- AMN: MERCOSUR Standardization Association;
- APCO: Association of Public-Safety Communications Officials-International;
- ARSO: African Regional Organization for Standarization;
- ASME: The American Society of Mechanical Engineers;
- ASTM International: American Society for Testing and Materials;
- BIPM, CGPM, and CIPM: Bureau International des Poids et Mesures;
- CableLabs: Cable Television Laboratories;
- CE: Consumer Electronics Association;
- CEN: European Committee for Standardization;
- CENELEC: European Committee for Electrotechnical Standardization;
- CISPR: International Special Committee on Radio Interference;

- COPANT: Pan American Standards Commission;
- CROSQ: CARICOM Regional Organization for Standards and Quality;
- CSA: Canadian Standards Association;
- DCMI: Dublin Core Metadata Initiative;
- DMTF: Distributed Management Task Force;
- EASC: Euro-Asian Council for Standardization, Metrology and Certification;
- ECA-Electronic Components Association;
- Ecma International: Ecma International (previously called ECMA);
- EIA: Electronic Industries Alliance;
- EIAJ: Electronic Industries Alliance of Japan;
- ETSI: European Telecommunications Standards Institute;
- FAI: Fédération Aéronautique Internationale;
- FCC: Federal Communications Commission;
- FM: FM Approvals;
- GS1: Global supply chain standards;
- HGI: Home Gateway Initiative;
- IEC: International Electrotechnical Commission;
- IAU: International Arabic Union;
- IEEE-SA: Institute of Electrical and Electronics Engineers: IEEE Standards Association;
- IETF: Internet Engineering Task Force;
- IMAPS: International Microelectronics and Packaging Society;
- IPC: Association Connecting Electronics Industries: Institute for Interconnecting and Packaging Electronic Circuits;
- IPTC: International Press Telecommunications Council;
- IRMM: Institute for Reference Materials and Measurements;
- ISEA: International Safety Equipment Association;
- ISO: International Organization for Standardization;
- ITI (INCITS): InterNational Committee for Information Technology Standards;
- ITU: The International Telecommunication Union;
- ITU-R: ITU Radiocommunications Sector (formerly known as CCIR);

- ITU-T: ITU Telecommunications Sector (formerly known as CCITT);
- ITU-D: ITU Telecom Development (formerly known as BDT);
- JEDEC: Joint Electronic Devices Engineering Council of Solid State Technology Association;
- LIA: Laser Institute of America;
- Liberty Alliance: Liberty Alliance;
- Media Grid: Media Grid Standards Organization;
- MSS: Manufacturers Standardization Society;
- NASPO: North American Security Products Organization;
- NEMA: National Electrical Manufacturers Association;
- NERC: North American Electric Reliability Corporation;
- NETA: InterNational Electrical Testing Association;
- NFPA: National Fire Protection Association;
- NIST/ITL: National Institute of Standards and Technology/Information Technology Laboratory;
- OASIS: Organization for the Advancement of Structured Information Standards
- OEOSC: Optics and Electro-Optics Standards Council;
- OGF: Open Grid Forum [merger of Global Grid Forum (GGF) and Enterprise Grid Alliance (EGA)];
- PASC: Pacific Area Standards Congress;
- PEARL: Professional Electrical Apparatus Recyclers League;
- RESNA: Rehabilitation Engineering and Assistive Technology Society;
- RIA: Robotic Industries Association;
- SADCSTAN: Southern African Development Community (SADC) Cooperation in Standardization;
- SCTE: Society of Cable Telecommunications Engineers;
- SDA: Secure digital association;
- SES: The Society for Standards Professionals;
- SMPTE: Society of Motion Picture and Television Engineers;
- SSDA: Solid State Drive Alliance;
- SSPC: The Society for Protective Coatings;
- TIA: Telecommunications Industry Association;
- TM Forum: Telemanagement Forum;

- UL: Underwriters Laboratories;
- URS: United Registrar of Systems;
- W3C: World Wide Web Consortium;
- WHO: World Health Organization, standards body;
- XSF: XMPP Standards Foundation.

3.8.5 National Standards Organizations

Generally speaking, each country has its own standardization body that is responsible for issuing national standards. These standards can be specific to a country or represent adapted international or regional standards, and include national variations (if applicable) within the country that issued the standard. The following organizations are presented within the list of the worldwide national standards developers [6, 7].

- Algeria: IANOR: Institut algérien de normalisation;
- Argentina: IRAM: Instituto Argentino de Normalización;
- Armenia: SARM: National Institute of Standards and Quality;
- Australia: SA: Standards Australia;
- Austria: ASI: Austrian Standards Institute;
- Bangladesh: BSTI: Bangladesh Standards and Bangladesh Standards and Testing Institution;
- Barbados: BNSI: ;Barbados National Standards Institution;
- Belarus: BELST: Committee for Standardization, Metrology and Certification of Belarus;
- Belgium: NBN: Bureau voor Normalisatie/Bureau de Normalisation (formerly: IBN/BIN);
- Belgium: BEC/CEB: The Belgian Electrotechnical Committee: Belgisch Elektrotechnisch Comité: Comité Electrotechnique Belge;
- Bolivia: IBNORCA: Instituto Boliviano de Normalización y Calidad;
- Bosnia and Herzegovina: BASMP: Institute for Standards, Metrology and Intellectual Property of Bosnia and Herzegovina;
- Brazil: ABNT: Associação Brasileira de Normas Técnicas;
- Brunei Darussalam: CPRU: Construction Planning and Research Unit, Ministry of Development;
- Bulgaria: BDS: Bulgarian Institute for Standardization;
- Canada: SCC: Standards Council of Canada;

- Chile: INN: Instituto Nacional de Normalizacion;
- China: SAC: Standardization Administration of China;
- China: CSSN: China Standards Information Center;
- Colombia: ICONTEC: Instituto Colombiano de Normas Tecnicas y Certificación;
- Costa Rica: INTECO: Instituto de Normas Técnicas de Costa Rica;
- Croatia: DZNM: State Office for Standardization and Metrology;
- Cuba: NC: Oficina Nacional de Normalización;
- Czech Republic: CSNI: Czech Standards Institute;
- Denmark: DS: Dansk Standard;
- Ecuador: INEN: Instituto Ecuatoriano de Normalización;
- Egypt: EO: Egyptian Organization for Standardization and Quality Control;
- El Salvador: CONACYT: Consejo Nacional de Ciencia y Tecnología;
- Estonia: EVS: Eesti Standardikeskus;
- Ethiopia: QSAE: Quality and Standards Authority of Ethiopia;
- Finland: SFS: Finnish Standards Association;
- France: AFNOR: Association française de normalisation;
- Germany: DIN: Deutsches Institut für Normung and Deutsches Institut für Bautechnik;
- Georgia: GEOSTM: Georgian National Agency for Standards, Technical Regulations and Metrology;
- Greece: ELOT: Hellenic Organization for Standardization;
- Grenada: GDBS: Grenada Bureau of Standards;
- Guatemala: COGUANOR: Comisión Guatemalteca de Normas;
- Guyana: GNBS: Guyana National Bureau of Standards;
- Hong Kong: ITCHKSAR: Innovation and Technology Commission;
- Hungary: MSZT: Magyar Szabványügyi Testület;
- Iceland: IST: Icelandic Council for Standardization;
- India: BIS: Bureau of Indian Standards
- Indonesia: BSN: Badan Standardisasi Nasional;
- Iran: ISIRI: Institute of Standards and Industrial Research of Iran;
- Ireland: NSAI: National Standards Authority of Ireland;
- Israel: SII: The Standards Institution of Israel;

- Italy: UNI: Ente Nazionale Italiano di Unificazione;
- Jamaica: BSJ: Bureau of Standards, Jamaica
- Japan: JISC: Japan Industrial Standards Committee;
- Jordan: JISM: Jordan Institution for Standards and Metrology;
- Kazakstan: KAZMEMST: Committee for Standardization, Metrology and Certification;
- Kenya: KEBS: Kenya Bureau of Standards;
- Republic of Korea: KATS: Korean Agency for Technology and Standards;
- Kuwait: KOWSMD: Public Authority for Industry, Standards and Industrial Services Affairs;
- Kyrgyzstan: KYRGYZST: State Inspection for Standardization and Metrology;
- Latvia: LVS: Latvian Standard;
- Lebanon: LIBNOR: Lebanese Standards Institution;
- Lithuania: LST: Lithuanian Standards Board;
- Luxembourg: SEE: Service de l'Energie de l'Etat, Organisme Luxembourgeois de Normalisation;
- Luxembourg: ILNAS: Luxembourg Institute for Standardization, Accreditation, Security, and Quality of Products and Services;
- Malaysia: DSM: Department of Standards Malaysia;
- Malaysia: SIRIM: Standards and Industrial Research Institute of Malaysia;
- Malta: MSA: Malta Standards Authority;
- Mauritius: MSB: Mauritius Standards Bureau;
- Mexico: DGN: Dirección General de Normas;
- Moldova: MOLDST: Department of Standardization and Metrology;
- Morocco: SNIMA: Service de Normalisation Industrielle Marocaine;
- Netherlands: NEN: Nederlandse Norm, maintained by the Nederlands Normalisatie Instituut (NNI);
- New Zealand: SNZ: Standards New Zealand;
- Nicaragua: DTNM: Dirección de Tecnología, Normalización y Metrología;
- Nigeria: SON: Standards Organisation of Nigeria;
- Norway: SN: Standards Norway (Standard Norge);

- Oman: DGSM: Directorate General for Specifications and Measurements;
- Pakistan: PSQCA: Pakistan Standards and Quality Control Authority;
- Panama: COPANIT: Comisión Panameña de Normas Industriales y Técnicas;
- Papua New Guinea: NISIT: National Institute of Standards and Industrial Technology;
- Peru: INDECOPI: Instituto Nacional de Defensa de la Competencia y de la Protección de la Propiedad Intellectual
- Philippines: BPS: Bureau of Product Standards
- Poland: PKN: Polish Committee for Standardization;
- Portugal: IPQ: Instituto Português da Qualidade;
- Romania: ASRO: Asociatia de Standardizare din România;
- Russian Federation: Rostekhregulirovaniye: Federal Agency for Technical Regulation and Metrology;
- Russia: GOST: Euro-Asian Council for Standardization, Metrology and Certification;
- Saint Lucia: SLBS: Saint Lucia Bureau of Standards;
- Saudi Arabia: SASO: Saudi Arabian Standards Organization;
- Serbia and Montenegro: ISSM -Institution for Standardization of Serbia and Montenegro;
- Seychelles: SBS: Seychelles Bureau of Standards;
- Singapore: SPRING SG: Standards, Productivity and Innovation Board;
- Slovakia: SUTN: Slovak Standards Institute;
- Slovenia: SIST: Slovenian Institute for Standardization;
- South Africa: SABS: South African Bureau of Standards;
- Spain: AENOR: Asociación Española de Normalización y Certificación;
- Sri Lanka: SLSI: Sri Lanka Standards Institution;
- Sweden: SIS: Swedish Standards Institute;
- Switzerland: SNV: Swiss Association for Standardization;
- Syrian Arab Republic: SASMO: The Syrian Arab Organization for Standardization and Metrology;
- Taiwan (Republic of China): BSMI: The Bureau of Standards, Metrology and Inspection;
- Tanzania: TBS: Tanzania Bureau of Standards;

- Thailand: TISI: Thai Industrial Standards Institute;
- Trinidad and Tobago: TTBS: Trinidad and Tobago Bureau of Standards;
- Turkey: TSE: Türk Standardlari Enstitüsü;
- Uganda: UNBS: Uganda National Bureau of Standards;
- Ukraine: DSSU: State Committee for Technical Regulation and Consumer Policy of Ukraine;
- United Kingdom: BSI: British Standards Institution aka BSI Group;
- United States of America: ANSI: American National Standards Institute
- Uruguay: UNIT: Instituto Uruguayo de Normas Técnicas
- Venezuela: FONDONORMA: Fondo para la Normalización y Certificación de la Calidad;
- Vietnam: TCVN: Directorate for Standards and Quality.

References

[1]   South African Bureau of Standards (SABS), "Economic Benefit of Standards—Pilot Project South Africa," 2011.

[2]   British Standards Institute (BSI), "White Paper—Standardization as a Business Investment," Chiswick, United Kingdom,, 2005.

[3]   BSI, "A standard for standards– Part 1: Development of standards—Specification," Chiswick, United Kingdom: BSI, 2005.

[4]   BSI, "A Standard for Standards—Part 2: Structure and Drafting—Requirements and Guidance," Chiswick United Kingdom: BSI, 2005.

[5]   BSI, "A Standard for Standards—Part 5. What Are the Different Types of Sstandard?," Chiswick, United Kingdom: BSI, 2009.

[6]   International Electrotechnical Commission, "IEC Statutes and Rules of Procedure, Geneva, (2001–2016).

[7]   International Organization for Standardization (ISO), "ISO/IEC Directives—Procedures Specific to ISO," Geneva, 2007.

[8]   ISO/IEC Guide 51, "Safety Aspects—Guidelines for their Inclusion in Standards," 2014.

[9]   CEN, "Internal Regulations Part 2: Common Rules for Standardization Work," Brussels, Belgium, 2010.

[10] National Standards Institute, "ANSI Essential Requirements: Due Process Requirements for American National Standards," ANSI, New York, 2012.

Selected Bibliography

CEN, "Internal Regulations Part 3: Rules for the Structure and dDrafting of CEN/CENELEC Standards," Brussels, Belgium, 2009.

ISO, "Assessing Economic Benefits of Consensus-Based Standards: The ISO Methodology," ISO Focus+, International Standards Organization, 2010, pp. 10–16.

ITU, "Measuring and Reducing the Standards Gap" Geneva, 2010.

4

Electrical Products Safety Philosophy

4.1 Introduction

Today's technical infrastructure is highly dependent on the safety of products that have become ever more indispensable in our daily lives and business operations. This implies that extended product failure could severely affect our daily lives or business activities. Indeed, recent years have seen a series of serious accidents that threaten the safety and security of society.

Zero risk does not exist: All decisions and actions involve some degree of risk. Nothing is absolutely safe, and safety is not the only—nor rarely the primary—goal in the development of products and systems. Some *risk* will remain, defined as *residual risk*. Therefore, a product, process, or service can only be relatively safe. Most of the time, safety acts as a constraint on product design and may conflict with other design goals such as reliability, operational effectiveness, performance, ease of use, time, and cost. Product safety techniques and approaches focus on providing information for decision-making about risk management trade-offs.

Safety for electrical products focuses on physical hazards that arise from products and on functionality aspects defined by the products' intended use. Basic safety refers to freedom from unacceptable risk directly caused by physical hazards. Basic safety relates to product properties that are not specifically related to intended use; IEC basic safety standards contain requirements that address specific safety properties (characteristics) that are common to the majority of electrical equipment.

Functional safety and essential performance relate to product operation as intended without creating a hazard. A failure in this area can be due either to a lack of performance or incorrect performance that could result in unacceptable risk. A problem exists when the feature or function in question is either absent or its characteristics are degraded to a point that the product is no longer suitable for its intended use.

Product safety also involves many nontechnical issues (e.g., legal, political, and resource certification of workers) that are, nevertheless, important influences on the attainment of an acceptable level of risk. These nontechnical aspects of system safety cannot be ignored.

If serious accidents are inevitable, how can we respond to their impact and manage complexity in a timely manner, so as to assure an acceptable level of safety and security?

The basic philosophy of safety is that safety features must be incorporated into products from the design stage and continue through the manufacturing, shipping, installation, and operation of the product. How safe is safe enough? No one in technology can answer this question [1]! However, through analysis and the study of engineering failures and their mechanisms, modern engineering designers can learn what to avoid and how to create designs with a lower chance of failure and with fewer potential hazards. Accordingly, to reduce the potential for harm, they need to understand the interdependence between safety and risk management and to apply risk management as a global methodology to estimate and evaluate the level of risks.

4.2   Safety Versus Safe

"Safety is a state in which hazards and conditions leading to physical or material harm are controlled in order to preserve the health and well-being of individuals and the community" [2]. Safety is both subjective and objective as it deals with both perceptions of being safe and the status of the surrounding conditions.

Safe is the state of being protected from identified hazards that are likely to cause physical harm. There is no such thing as being absolutely safe; that is, completely without the risk of harm.

Safe products require the implementation of knowledge, adequate construction, and the correct selection of the components. Risky products may result from design and manufacturing personnel ignoring safety regulations in order to get a job done, the inclusion of components and materials that are forbidden, and the failure to follow construction procedures in order to carry out jobs quickly. As unsafe or risky products are the immediate cause of most accidents, companies strive for ways to promote safe product development and manufacturing. Often safety programs call for a change in attitudes: As attitudes change, so can product safety. Still, there are strong arguments that focusing directly on attitudes may, nevertheless, lead to unsafe products. Sometimes people have a tendency to optimize risk instead of minimizing it. The level of risk that people are willing to take is the level at which people believe they will maximize their gain—and this is a real danger. Applying risk management requires a clear understanding of what constitutes "unnecessary risk," when benefits actually outweigh costs.

Safety is achieved by reducing *risk* to an acceptable level. Risk acceptance is not as elementary a matter as it may first appear. An acceptable level of *risk* is constituted by an optimal balance between the ideal of absolute safety and the demands to be met by a product, process, or service and factors such as benefit to the user, suitability for purpose, cost effectiveness, and conventions of the society concerned. It follows that there is a need to review continually the acceptable level, in particular when developments, both in technology and in knowledge, can lead to economically feasible improvements to attain the risk compatible with the use of a product, process, or service.

The use of the words *safety* and *safe* as descriptive adjectives should be avoided because they convey no useful extra information. In addition, they are likely to be interpreted as an assurance of guaranteed freedom from *risk* [2].

The recommended approach is to replace, wherever possible, the words *safety* and *safe* with an indication of the objective (i.e., *protective impedance device* instead of *safety impedance*) [3].

Unlike all other engineering disciplines, safety engineering is consensus-driven, not research-driven. It is almost devoid of physical laws to guide its practitioners.

4.3 How Do Reliability Engineering and Product Safety Differ?

Reliability engineers often assume that reliability and safety are synonymous, but this assumption is true only in special cases. In general, safety has a broader scope than failures, and failures may not compromise safety in all situations. There is obviously an overlap between reliability and safety, but many accidents occur without any component failure—the individual components were operating exactly as specified or intended, that is, without failure. The opposite is also true—components may fail without a resulting accident.

Reliability engineering is concerned primarily with component failures and failure rate reduction. The reliability engineering approach to safety thus concentrates on failure as the cause of accidents.

Reliability engineering uses a variety of techniques to minimize component failures and thereby the failures of complex systems caused by component failure, including parallel redundancy, standby sparing, built-in safety factors and margins, derating, screening, and timed replacements.

While these techniques are often effective in increasing reliability, they do not necessarily increase safety. In fact, their use under some conditions may actually reduce safety.

Safety and reliability are not only different product characteristics; they are sometimes in conflict. Reliable products are not necessarily safe, and safe products do not have to be reliable. In some instances, increasing reliability can actually decrease safety (e.g., the product continues to do something even though that behavior is unsafe in the current environment, and vice versa; the safest behavior under certain conditions may be to stop operating and switch to some fail-safe mode). Most accidents are caused not by the product stopping to fulfill its intended use (reliability deficiency), but by it operating doing something unsafe (e.g., electrical shock, fire, or unwanted radiation). Serious accidents have occurred while system components were all functioning exactly as specified—that is, without failure. If failures only are considered in a safety analysis, many potential accidents will be missed. In addition, the engineering approaches to preventing failures (increasing reliability) and preventing hazards (increasing safety) are different and sometimes conflicting, because it is relatively easy to protect products against total failure, but it is much more difficult to protect them against unsafe operation.

Accidents may be caused by equipment operation outside the parameters and time limits upon which the reliability analyses are based. Therefore, a system may have high reliability and still have accidents. In addition, accidents are often not the result of a simple combination of component failures [2].

Safety is an emergent property that arises at the system level when components are operating together. The events leading to an accident may be a complex combination of equipment failure, faulty maintenance, instrumentation and control problems, human actions, and design errors. Reliability analysis considers only the possibility of accidents related to failures; it does not investigate potential damage that could result from successful operation of the individual components.

Reliability uses a bottom-up approach [e.g., failure mode effect analysis (FMEA)] to evaluate the effect of component failures on system function, while safety requires a top-down approach that evaluates how hazardous states can occur from a combination of both incorrect and correct component behavior, such as proper behavior of a component at an improper time or under the wrong environmental conditions.

Care needs to be taken when applying reliability assessment techniques to safety. Since accidents are not necessarily caused by events that can be measured this way, it should not be used as a measure of risk. Reliability assessment measures the probability of random failures—not the probability of hazards or accidents. Also, if a design error is found in a product, safety will be more effectively enhanced by removing the design error than by measuring it in order to convince someone that it will never cause an accident. High reliability numbers do not guarantee safety, and safety need not require ultra-high reliability.

4.4 Perception of Risk

From ancient history, the concept of *risk* has described the uncertainty about the outcome when making decisions about future actions or activities. Generally, the term *risk* is taken as producing *negative consequences* (*harm*) and is considered as a combination of the *probability of occurrence of harm* (as an *event*) and the *severity of that harm* (negative consequence of the event) [4].

Risk is also considered in situations that result in positive outcomes, in the optimization of potential opportunities (*positive* consequences of the events). The best examples of this can be found in economic, financial, political, and organizational areas.

Acknowledging that risks can be positive or negative, optimizing risks means finding a balance between negative risk and the benefit of the operation or activity and between risk reduction and effort applied.

The acceptability of risk is driven largely by the way a risk is perceived. Factors that influence perception include whether exposure to the risk seems to have any of the following characteristics [5]:

- It is involuntary;
- It is avoidable;
- It stems from a man-made source;
- It is due to negligence;
- It arises from a poorly understood cause;
- It is directed at a vulnerable group within society.

There are important moral differences between risk-taking (where someone voluntarily chooses to take a risk) and risk exposure (where others are placed at greater risk of harm through another's actions). Several points must be kept in mind, listed as follows.

- Hazards that generate risks are a fundamental reality.
- Quantifying risk alone does not ensure safety.
- Risk is a matter of perspective.

- Realistically, some risk must be accepted. How much is accepted, or not accepted, is the prerogative of the defined decision authority. That decision is affected by many inputs.

- Hazard analysis and risk assessment do not free us from reliance on good judgment; they improve it. It is more important to establish clear objectives and parameters for risk management than to find a "cookbook" approach and procedure. There is no "best solution." There are normally a variety of directions to go. Each of these directions may produce some degree of risk reduction.

The uncertainties related to risks are not only connected to the probabilities but also to the different types of consequences. In these situations, the issue is not only technical, but new guidance is needed to tackle the human, moral, and ethical aspects of risks: Methods for ethical analysis that can deal with probabilities are needed.

Any assessment of risk necessarily requires a decision of what level of risk is acceptable. This in itself is a significant ethical issue and can be regarded as a *limit of concern,* or a threshold that determines whether potential risks should influence our judgment. This limit is arbitrary and may differ between various risk assessors and regulators. It is important to recognize that the level of acceptable risk is not based solely on scientific evidence and will necessarily reflect political, social, and ethical beliefs about risk.

Societal resources are allocated arbitrarily between different risk-reducing areas leading to large variations in cost per statistical life saved. With more consistent risk management, the resources of society could be spent in a more efficient way and thus save more lives for the same amount of money.

4.5 Failure

The following definitions are useful for this paragraph [2]:

- *Failure:* The end of the ability of a part or assembly to perform its specified function;

- *Fault:* Generally, a device, assembly, component, or piece of software that fails to perform in a specified manner; may be in the components used in an assembly, as a result of the assembly process, as a result of a software problem, or as a result of a poor design in which interaction problems occur between components that individually meet specifications;

- *Fault coverage:* The percentage of overall faults/failures that a given test will correctly detect and identify.

In an electrical product, the faults present can be grouped into the following general categories:

- Component faults that are manifested by the following [2]:
  - Electrical/electronic performance deficiencies pending on the type of component (e.g., passive components not meeting their tolerance or temperature coefficient specifications; analog components not meeting the frequency response specifications; and digital devices not meeting the rise time specifications);
  - A "short circuit" or "open" in an electrical/electronic component;
  - Mechanical failures caused by such problems as package failures (e.g., cracked component bodies), moisture absorption failures, and corrosion and electrochemical failures.
- Manufacturing faults (e.g., solderability errors, component placement errors, incorrect thermal profiles, and assembly errors);
- Performance faults (e.g., design deficiencies, component faults, software errors, dynamic failures, or a combination of any or all of these that together cause performance degradation);
- Software faults, which may manifest themselves in a number of performance ways and which require their own test/verification considerations.

Accidents are rarely caused by one single fault or action. Instead they are the consequence of a multitude of faults that may have occurred during the lifetime of the product. It is important to understand that component failure is not a major factor in accidents. More accidents result from dangerous design characteristics and interactions among components.

The goal is for electrical products to remain within acceptable risk limits in the presence of failures with the following characteristics:

1. They are obvious to the operator, (e.g., by a signal or absence of a function);

2. They can be detected by regular inspection or maintenance carried out in accordance with the accompanying documents;

3. They cannot be observed by the operator or detected during routine maintenance, but can be detected or controlled by built-in safety measures.

However, electrical products should also remain within acceptable risk limits in the presence of undetectable failures.

There are two widely used failure analysis techniques: FMEA (IEC 60812) and fault-tree analysis (FTA) (IEC 61025). FMEA deals with single-point failures by taking a bottom-up approach; it is presented as a rule in the form of tables. In contrast, FTA analyzes combinations of failures in a top-down way, and it is visually presented as a logic diagram.

Both methodologies are mainly employed in the design phase. However, these methodologies are heavily dependent on personal experience and knowledge, and FTA in particular has a tendency to miss some failure modes in failure mode combinations, especially emergent failures. For details refer to Chapter 5.

4.6   Single-Fault Safe

With reference to faults, on specific products (e.g., medical electrical), the single-fault philosophy is applied [6]. The single-fault condition (SFC) is defined as the condition in which a single means of protection against a hazard is defective, or a single external abnormal condition is present [7].

Practically, in a product that is single-fault-safe, a lower limit is established on the probability of occurrence of harm from a hazard. If this probability is achieved, then the risk level for the specific hazard is acceptable. Additionally, the probability of the simultaneous occurrence of two single faults is considered small enough to be negligible.

The single-fault safe philosophy considers the following principles [7]:

1. In any of the specified "single-fault conditions," hazards should not arise.

2. All product parts relevant to safety should be reasonably reliable so that the probability of a "single fault" is low.

3. The probability of two "single faults" will then be very low, so it is acceptable for a multiple-fault condition to produce a hazard (i.e., a hazard can arise, but the risk level should be considered acceptable-tolerable).

4. Where one "single fault" directly causes others, the probability is the same as that of the first fault, and the product should remain safe.

5. Where two faults can result from a common cause, the probability of the two faults is the same as that of the common cause.

6. A "single fault" should be discovered by an unmistakable and clearly discernible signal that becomes obvious to the operator.

7. Where a "single fault" is discovered and remedied by periodic inspection and maintenance that is prescribed by the manufacturer, exists a finite probability (which has to be low for each fault) that a second fault can arise before the next scheduled inspection and maintenance cycle. This means that the frequency of inspection and maintenance has to be high compared to the expected probability of occurrence of the fault.

8. Where a "single fault" cannot be detected by practical maintenance procedures and is unlikely to be noticed by the operator because it does not affect product function, the high probability of the fault remaining undetected for an extensive period should be taken into account in developing safety requirements.

Should a failure in the product remain hidden, with the product not alerting the operator to the failure, and a further failure occur with a significant effect on safety of the product, then this is considered to be only a single failure. In this case, the effects of the second failure should be determined to ensure that, in combination with the first undetectable failure, they do not result in a more severe failure effect. If so, the first failure should be alarmed. It is therefore important that the product alerts the operator to failure, and a means of failure detection, such as audible and visual warning devices, automatic sensing devices, and sensing instrumentation, should be implemented in the product.

Depending on the severity of the failure mode the operator will take corrective action by manual means, or the product will automatically take corrective action. It is important to remember that the place where a failure is first detected may not be where it started.

Adding verification or validation controls (e.g., alarms on failure) can reduce the probability of a failure being undetected and having a greater effect on the product if a further failure occurs.

The effect of faults that may remain undetected can be prevented by adequate design and sufficient safety factors. The probability of two independent faults occurring at the same time is considered very small, and a protective system is possible in which any single fault can be detected before a second fault occurs.

In general, the basic electrical safety provision is by basic insulation. However, because this may be defective (may break down or may be bypassed), additional protection is required. One solution is the use of the protective earthing of the accessible parts. It is recognized that a protective earth connection may fail and that if it does fail, no hazard is allowed. However, it is assumed that there is a negligible probability of both the basic insulation and the protective earth connection failing at the same time (or more accurately, of one failing after the other has already failed but has not been repaired).

In fact, the probability of two "single-fault" conditions is not zero. In some industries in which the potential hazards are very severe, the probability has to be extremely low. Multiple protective means are therefore necessary, and the probabilities of double and even multiple failures are assessed and compared with a stated acceptable probability.

The single-fault philosophy implies that, in general, the product is expected to have two means of defense against each hazard. This is considered to yield a negligible risk, provided that the probabilities of failure of individual systems are low.

4.7 Redundancy

Redundancy can be defined as the duplication of components to protect against individual failures or the existence of more than one means for accomplishing a given function. The various means need not be identical. The two basic types of redundancy are defined as follows:

- *Active:* Redundancy in which all redundant items operate simultaneously;
- *Standby:* Redundancy in which some or all of the redundant items are not operating continuously but are activated only upon failure of the primary item performing the function(s).

It means implementing two protective measures, and then, if one fails, the other will still work. This assumes that the causes of failure are independent and that the probability of failure is small enough for each protective measure. The failure of the first means of protection can be indicated acoustically or visually, and one can replace the defective means of protection during regular maintenance.

4.8 Safety Factors

Limit values for certain device characteristics may be established by applying safety factors. However, this approach should only be adopted where there is an established threshold below which no adverse effect occurs. Where such a threshold can be established, the application of a safety factor determines the limit value.

Some standards define and use the term "safety factor" [7] in a very specific context related to stresses that can be borne by mechanically loaded parts. However, the concept of safety factors underlies, without reference, the allowable limits or *threshold limit values* (TLVs). The proper use of safety factors is complex, and it can only be done in the presence of data on the effects of the hazard on humans. Furthermore, the use of safety factors requires determining the acceptability of the risks.

In general, the proper use of safety factors in arriving at acceptable human exposure levels rests on the assumption that a threshold dose exists below which no adverse effects occur. Provided the phenomenon studied shows a threshold below which no adverse effects occur, the safety factor approach sets the TLV below this threshold. In risk estimation, hazardous processes may be stochastic or nonstochastic. The use of safety factors is inappropriate in dealing with stochastic processes, for which a threshold may not exist. Stochastic effects for which a threshold does not exist require other methods of risk estimation. Nonstochastic effects, such as electrically induced tetany, are more uniform in nature. They occur in a more predictable fashion following exposure to a certain critical level of the stimulus or toxicant under study. For nonstochastic effects, one approach to setting acceptable levels of human exposure or threshold limit values is to apply a suitable safety factor or uncertainty factor to the dose or exposure level at which no adverse effects occurred in controlled studies. Dividing the *no-observed effect level* (NOEL) in controlled tests by the *safety factor* (SF) gives a TLV for humans (TLV = NOEL/SF). One should choose a TLV for which nearly all persons will experience no adverse effects following repeated normal exposure. Where the NOEL has been established, the TLV often includes a hundredfold safety factor (SF = 100). This allows for a tenfold variation in susceptibility between animal and man as well as a tenfold variation of individual susceptibility within the human population. When there is no no-effect level, the safety factor can be applied to the *lowest observed effect level* (LOEL), with an additional factor of fivefold or tenfold incorporated to adjust for the absence of a no-effect level. Hazardous effects of greater severity may demand higher safety factors. In some cases, one can identify an acceptable level of risk and a corresponding exposure level. In such cases, the safety factor should be one (SF = 1).

Where limits are established using safety factors, the accompanying rationale should indicate the following:

1. How the safety factors affect the chosen limits;
2. The specific safety factor(s) used;
3. The data used to set the NOEL (the threshold below which there is an acceptably low effect);
4. The assumptions made about the acceptability of risks;
5. Any other assumptions made.

4.9   Work Safety Versus Product Safety

Industrial work, or occupational safety, has traditionally focused primarily on controlling injuries to employees who manufacture or use the products. Industrial safety engineering usually deals with a fixed manufacturing design and preexisting hazards, many of which are accepted as necessary for operations. More emphasis is often placed on teaching employees to work within this environment than on removing the hazards.

Occupational safety professionals together with manufacturers' postmarket surveillance experts (part of the product safety process) collect data during the operational life of the product to eliminate or control unacceptable hazards stemming from the product. This data represents feedback that is used by designers of the product when evaluating the practicality of and possibilities for mitigating risks of harm. When accidents occur, they are investigated, and action is taken to reduce the likelihood of a recurrence—either changing the production methodology or changing employee work rules and training.

Occupational safety reviews and audits are conducted by work safety divisions to ensure that unsafe conditions in the manufacturing plant or in the use sites are corrected and that employees are following the work rules specified in manuals and instructions. Over the years, lessons learned from accidents have been incorporated into occupational health and safety management standards, with an emphasis on the design of workplaces and work rules. Often, standards are enforced by the government through occupational safety and health legislation. One such standard is OHSAS 18001, *Occupation Health And Safety Assessment Series for Health and Safety Management Systems.* This standard aims to help organizations control occupational health and safety risks. It was developed in response to widespread demand for a recognized standard against which work places could be certified and assessed. Establishing an occupational health and safety management system contributes to eliminating or minimizing risk to employees and other interested parties who may be exposed to occupational health and safety risks associated with specific workplaces.

In summary, work (occupational) safety deals with safety in the workplace, explaining and providing tools for improving employees' safety with adequate occupational health and safety management. In contrast, product safety is concerned primarily with products. The concept of loss is treated much more broadly: Relevant losses may include injury to nonemployees; damage to products, property, or the environment; and loss of intended use.

Instead of making changes as a result of operational experience with the product and manufacturing process, product safety attempts to identify potential hazards before the product is designed, to define and incorporate safety design criteria, and to build safety into the design before the product becomes operational.

The assessment methodology of work safety is also based on the principles of risk management as applicable to product safety. It is important is to remove the confusion that sometime exists when work safety is mixed with product safety.

The standards used in work safety are usually process rather than product standards as used for product safety. Reliance on design or product standards is often inadequate for work safety, where more emphasis is placed on industrial safety problems, such as injuries to the inside and outside of the plant, pollution, and dangerous manufacturing processes.

In summary, industrial safety activities are designed to protect workers in an industrial environment; extensive standards are imposed by codes or regulations providing for a safe workplace. However, few, if any, of these codes or regulations apply also to the protection of the product being manufactured.

References

[1] Schwing, R. C., and W. A. Albers, *Societal Risk Assesment. How Safe is Safe Enough?,* New York: Plenum Press, 1980.

[2] U.S. Air Force Safety Agency, *System Safety Handbook, 2000.*

[3] ISO/IEC Guide 51," *Safety Aspects—Guidelines for Their Inclusion in Standards,"* Geneva, 2014.

[4] ISO/IEC Guide 73,"*Risk Management Vocabulary—Guidelines for Use in Standards,"* Geneva, 2002.

[5] Sjöberg, L., B.-E. Moen, and T. Rundmo, *Explaining Risk Perception. An Evaluation of the Psychometric Paradigm in Risk Perception Research,* Trondheim, Norway: Rotunde publikasjoner, 2004.

[6] Mellish, R. G., "The Single Fault Philosophy: How It Fits with Risk Management," *ACOS Workshop VI, Safety of Electromedical Equipment—An Integrated Approach through IEC Standards,* Toronto, May 6–7, 1998.

[7] IEC 60601-1, "*Medical Electrical Equipment—Part 1: General Requirements for Safety and Essential Performance,"* Geneva, (2005 + 2012).

Selected Bibliography

Fadier, E., and J. Ciccotelli, "How To Integrate Safety in Design: Methods and Models," *Journal of Human Factors and Ergonomics in Manufacturing 9,* 1999, pp.367–380.

Fadier, E., and C. De la Garza, "Safety Design : Towards a New Philosophy," *Safety Science 44,* 2006, pp. 55–73.

IEC TR 60513, "Fundamental Aspects of Safety Standards for Medical Electrical Equipment," Geneva, 1994.

IEC 60664-1, "Insulation Coordination for Equipment Within Low-Voltage Systems—Part 1: Principles, Requirements, and Tests," Geneva, 2007.

International Laboratory Accreditation Cooperation (ILAC), "Traceability of Measurement Results," P-10, 2002.

Leveson, N., "*Safeware: System Safety and Computers*," Reading, MA: Addison-Wesley, 1995.

Loznen, S., "Product-Safety Requirements for Medical Electrical Equipment," *Compliance Engineering,* Vol. XII, No. 3, 1995, pp.17–30.

Martin, P. L., *Electronic Failure Analysis Handbook,* New York: McGraw-Hill, 1999.

5

Methods for Failure Analysis

5.1 FMEA

5.1.1 Introduction

The definition of FMEA is "a procedure for the analysis of a system to identify the potential failure modes, their causes and effects on the system performance" [1]. FMEA is used to determine the effect of a failure on the operation of a product or system and to attempt to quantify it. Hence, FMEA is an analysis that attempts to understand the failure modes of a product during the development phase. This information allows for the development of a risk profile, and based on the risk profile, changes to the design that can be made.

The FMEA serves as input and support to other engineering design activities, all of which also directly influence new product development and the postproduct development process. These include the following:

- Safety *engineering*: FMEA can support safety engineering efforts in analysis (hazard identification and risk control), and the failure modes with their assigned criticality can be determined.

- Testability *engineering*: When the FMEA is developed, information is captured to provide details on the sequence of events leading to a failure mode and the failure modes detection as well as the isolation response of the system. Associated with safety, critical failure modes that would otherwise go undetected may be identified. However, this is a function of experience with the product and may in some cases be reactive.

73

- *Sustaining engineering:* As part of the maintainability of the product analysis, this information may facilitate and refine the overall *mean time to repair* (MTTR) calculations for the product.

- *Logistics engineering:* For each failure mode occurrence, a resulting corrective maintenance task may be implemented. Therefore, the occurrence and severity of failure modes should be determined, and mitigating efforts should be planned for.

- *Availability engineering:* If a system has to be available at all times, and failure is mitigated by backup and/or rescue systems, FMEA can be used to ensure that critical systems have backups and that single points of failure are minimized.

- *Design engineering:* The FMEA supports the design engineering effort to ensure that program design requirements are addressed (e.g., regulatory, reliability, and safety requirements). The design FMEA developed by Price [2], function-directed electrical design analysis, describes the practical method for using functional knowledge to interpret the qualitative simulation of electrical circuits at an appropriate level.

The FMEA can be implemented as a functional and/or physical analysis. Earlier in a design process a functional analysis approach would be taken and proved through a series of process-centric benchmarks throughout production. With better definition of the design and as more details during the design stages are firmed up, a stage in the development cycle may be reached where a physical analysis is implemented. The function of the FMEA is to make a product more reliable and safe when a failure occurs. Product failures can result from various cause categories, and the FMEA can be used in all the categories or in a combination of categories. Safety-related defects might occur within the product development and life cycle in the following areas:

- *Design defects:* A product designer may design a new product and unintentionally allow for a safety-related defect in the product design.

- *Manufacturing defects:* During manufacturing a safety-related defect might be introduced during the assembly of the product.

- *Discrete component defects:* A discrete component in the product may have a latent failure causing the product to cease functioning or partially function in a dangerous or unsafe manner.

- *Repair defects:* Latent defects due to intermitted faults that were not repaired, incomplete repairs and assembly, and inadequate repairs.

- *Undiscovered defects:* There is always the risk that the FMEA process will not detect a safety-related defect, which can continue to live in the product design event if the product has gone through the proper processes to ensure a safe product. Three factors may cause this to occur: (1) lack of historical field experience, (2) insufficient product safety due to inadequate manufacturing quality control, and (3) failure analysis that lacks technical depth and accuracy.

Without a formal process, the necessary knowledge and experience knowledge base anticipating what might go wrong with a product is a challenge. The challenge is that the general FMEA should capture a thought process that can be adjusted and tailored to develop a more focused implementation and compliance process that can be implemented to more specific products or processes. Anticipating every failure mode is always a challenge, and the effectiveness of FMEA may, among many factors, rely on the experience of the group implementing this methodology.

However, the industry has successfully adopted and implemented FMEA for many years now with great success. The continuous refinement of FMEA has helped to minimize product safety risk.

5.1.2 General Background

The FMEA process can be initiated in conjunction with the development of the product concept. The FMEA process should be updated during the development cycle of the product and associated planning and should be included as a checkpoint in each phase of the *new product development process* (NPDP).

The above implementation may be followed for the new product; the FMEA can serve as a living document throughout the product development cycle. Apart from learning, understanding, and improving the safety performance of a new product during the development phase, the lessons learned from FMEA may be documented and applied to ensure that they are applied in the next version or generation of the product.

During the product development cycle and throughout the NPDP process, changes and updates may be made to the product and process. These changes may be likely candidates for precipitating new failure modes. Hence, the FMEA can be updated when changes occur in any of the following:

- *Design:* Changes in the subsystems and components;
- *System:* Changes in the integrated system and its functions;
- *Process:* Manufacturing process changes;
- *Market:* Changes in the anticipated market in which the product or process is expected to function;
- *Regulatory:* The implementation of new regulations;

- *Field experience:* Customer feedback and failed product returns that reveal problems in the product.

Changes in the above categories should be investigated and the effect of the changes on the reliability of the design should be adequately evaluated. In order to understand FMEA and its process, it is necessary to understand certain terminology, described in Section 5.1.3.

5.1.3   General Definitions

The following definitions of terms were obtained from the ISO [3]:

- *Failure mode:* The manner in which a failure is observed to occur and its impact on the product's performance.
- *Failure mechanism or failure cause:* The physical or chemical process, design defect, quality defect, component misapplication, or other factors that are the basic reason for failure or that initiate the physical process by which deterioration proceeds to failure.
- *Compliance:* A judgment that a product or service meets the requirements of a specific standard. This standard can be internal and external to a company, and there may be process compliance requirements for safety and quality that are major strategies and efforts in companies striving to consistently attain high levels of manufacturing and service compliance.
- *Severity:* The level and consequences of a failure mode. Severity considers the worst potential consequences of a failure, determined by the degree of injury (harm).
- *Specifications:* Documented detailed requirements with which a product or service has to comply. Specifications may be found at all levels of the product from the systems level to the component level.
- *System:* The principal functioning entities comprising the product (e.g., hardware and software); also, an organized and disciplined approach to accomplishing a task (e.g., a failure-reporting system).
- *Testing:* The determination by technical or scientific means of the properties or elements of a product or its components, including functional operation, and involving the application of established scientific principles and procedures.
- *Traceability:* The ability to trace the history, application, or location of a product and, in some cases, service by means of recorded identifications.

Traceability may refer to a product or a calibration and its relationship to the measuring equipment and the national or international standards, primary standards, basic physical constants, properties, or reference materials. Traceability requirements can be specified for some stated period of history or to some point of origin.

- *Validation:* The state of being confirmed by examination and provision of objective evidence that the particular requirements for a specific intended use have been met. Validation may be performed on the final product under defined operating conditions and, when necessary, is performed in earlier production stages. Multiple validations may be carried out for different intended uses.

- *Verification:* Confirmation by examination and provision of objective evidence that specified requirements have been met. In design and development, verification involves the process of examining the results of a given activity to determine conformity with the input requirement for that activity.

- *Component:* Any discrete part of a consumer product (e.g., a resistor or handle).

- *Subsystem:* A system that is part of some larger system that is made up of subsystems to form the complete system or product (e.g., a battery system inside a product).

- *Product components:* Defined as the most basic components into which a product can nondestructively be disassembled.

- *Subblock:* The most basic unique functionality block within a subsystem that fulfills a dependent or independent unique function in the subsystem. It can consist of a single or multiple discrete components.

- *Root cause:* An identified reason for the presence of a defect or problem; the most basic reason for failure, which, if eliminated, may prevent recurrence; the source or origin of an event.

- *FMEA* [4]: The process of identifying potential weaknesses through the review of information such as that provided by schematics, engineering drawings, and testing to identify basic faults at the part/material level and determine their effect at finished or subassembly level on safety and effectiveness.

- *Methodology* [5]: A set or system of methods, principles, and rules for regulating a given discipline, as in the arts or sciences.

5.1.4   Types of Failure Modes

Failure modes in products can be classified into two areas, predictable and unpredictable failure modes.

5.1.4.1   Predictable Failure Modes

Predictable failure modes are failure modes in products that are known and associated with a product or technology through field experience of research and the resulting accumulation of knowledge about a specific component, subsystem, subassembly, or entire product. Hence for a product or technology, these failure modes may be known to occur and thus may be predicted. Accordingly, designs can be firmed up and testing can validate whether these predictable failure modes have been mitigated. This knowledge base can be obtained through the following methods:

- *Experience:* Through past field experience and the accumulation of data points;
- *Literature reviews and secondary research:* Through the use of secondary research materials including failure analysis books, reports, studies, and the Internet;
- *Conferences:* Industry experts and their insights as delivered in papers on component and product failure analysis (with thought leadership specifically in these areas also presented at conferences);
- *Society meetings:* Institutional meetings such as those at the Institute of Electrical and Electronics Engineers (IEEE) Product Safety Engineering Society (PSES), which provide face-to-face access with fellow engineers

The above-proposed actions require diligence, the gathering of information, and, more importantly, the ability to associate and match the lessons learned to the current products' requirements and progression through the development process. This is a skill requirement, and it is necessary for an engineer or auditor to be able to take the lessons learned and adapt them to the new product technology.

5.1.4.2   Unpredictable Failure Modes

Unpredictable failure modes are failure modes in products that are either not publicly available or not known in the general industry (intellectual property of a company) or not known at all. The results of a test may validate the unpredictable nature of the failure. Further, a range of failure modes may result in an unpredictable failure mode, which makes their discovery all the more difficult. For instance, instead of a component failing a short circuit test, the fault could be a subtler dynamic low-resistance fault. The failure modes and effects of the component in these two cases may be different.

The implementation process and general methodology of an FMEA follow a logical path to ensure consistency in the implementation of the process. Four main stages are defined in IEC60821 [1] for the implementation of the FMEA, and these stages ensure that the FMEA becomes a useful document that lives alongside the product from the initial development stage of the product until the end of life of the product.

5.1.5 FMEA Ground Rules

The ground rules for the FMEA should be set prior to the implementation of the FMEA. There should be a clear definition of the purpose of the FMEA, how the FMEA will be supported, documentation control (for example revision), identification of the group experts responsible for the technical part of the FMEA, milestones and how action items and large risks will be mitigated. The FMEA severity, occurrence, and probability of detection ranking scales should be determined and agreed upon. The scale increments will be the same for all three categories, meaning that if severity is ranked from 1 to 5, then both occurrences and detection should also have a 5-incremented scale. IEC 60812 uses a scale of 1 to 10, with 1 representing no effect and 10 indicating a very severe effect affecting reliable system operation and safety without warning.

The FMEA presentation can follow a table format to document and present the information. Figure 5.1 shows a simplified table as an example of how the FMEA can be captured. The subsystem of the product is identified in the subsystem column. The next column is the component column, and the component in this column is identified. In the potential failure mode column, all the potential failure modes of the component can be listed, as well as the failure modes associated with the subsystem at systems level; there may be multiple line items. In a safety FMEA, it is common that only the extreme cases of the component failure are considered, but intermediate stages of failure should also

Sub-system	Component	Potential failure mode	Severity	Potential cause	Occurrence	Current design detection	Detection	RPN

Figure 5.1 A simplified FMEA table.

be considered because in these cases, the outcome may be unanticipated and true worst-case in terms of the failure mode.

The severity can then be determined based on the scale system adopted for this FMEA. The following column lists the potential causes for the listed component, subsystem, and system failures. An occurrence number based on the adopted scale can be assigned to each case. The ability of the system, subsystem, and component to detect and mitigate the failure can be evaluated for each identified failure mode. A detection value can then be populated in the detection column.

When the FMEA implementation process is complete, the FMEA can be executed in parallel with the new product development cycle and product life.

5.1.6   FMEA Execution

The FMEA can be executed once the technical team has been assembled and the product details are provided. Executing the FMEA from the start of the product development cycle is desirable. The FMEA can be executed in many ways, but the basic execution steps are summarized as follows:

- The product or process under consideration should be clearly articulated and characterized. The type of product, design, technology risks, and manufacturing, among many other factors related both to process and product development, should be considered. It is important to consider intended known applicable uses of the product.
- A block diagram of the product or process (e.g., manufacturing or service) can be created to define system relationships. This block diagram can display major components or process steps as blocks in a block diagram, connected by lines showing how the components or steps are interrelated or interconnected. A database should be created, and the following information may be included:
  - Product/system;
  - Subsystem or subassembly or component;
  - Component;
  - Design lead;
  - Prepared by;
  - Date;
  - Revision;
  - Revision date.
- The functions of the items in the database can be listed.

- The failure modes, including the following, can now be identified; for example:
  - System failure;
  - Intermittent performance;
  - Failure to charge a battery;
  - Defective keyboard.
- Time-dependent failure mechanisms resulting in the failure modes may not immediately be identified, such as the following:
  - Corrosion;
  - Contamination;
  - Aging;
  - Electrical failure;
  - Deformation;
  - Degradation.
- A failure in one component can serve as the cause for a failure mode in another component. This is often referred to as cascading failures. Failure modes should be listed for functions of each component or process step. The failure mode should be identified whether or not the failure is likely to occur.

- Research for similar products or processes and the failures that have been documented for them is an excellent starting point. However, this type of information outside the company or organization may be challenging to obtain.

- The effects of failure modes should be detailed. A failure effect is defined as the result of a failure mode on the function of the product or process. Effects should be described in terms of what the customer might see or experience should the identified failure mode occur. Examples of failure effects may include the following:
  - Risk of injury to the user or others;
  - Inoperability of the product or process;
  - Improper appearance of the product or process;
  - Odors;
  - Heat;
  - Fire;
  - Degraded performance;
  - Noise and vibration and other disturbances.
- A numerical ranking for the severity of the failure mode effect should be established based on the ranking criteria for the FMEA. The ranking ef-

fort enables the FMEA team to prioritize the failures and address the top issues. The severity can be characterized according to the scale proposed in IEC60821.

All of the failure causes or root causes for a specific failure mode can be identified. Potential causes could include the following:

- Improper operating conditions;
- Contamination;
- Erroneous algorithms;
- Improper alignment;
- Excessive loading;
- Excessive voltage.

- A probability factor can now be generated for the failure modes. This is the second part of the FMEA. The probability factor is a numerical weight assigned to each identified failure, because that indicates how likely that failure cause is (the probability of the cause occurring). The probability of the event occurring can be characterized according to the scale proposed in IEC60821.

- Control systems (design or process) can be identified. The control systems (design or process) may be the mechanisms that prevent the cause of a failure from occurring or detect the failure before it reaches the customer. The FMEA team should now identify testing, analysis, monitoring, and other techniques that can be or have been used on the same or similar products or processes to detect failures. The ability of the system to detect and react to the failure can be characterized according to the scale proposed in IEC60821, defining detection.

- Once the severity, probability, and detection have been characterized in alphanumerical numbers, the *risk priority number* (RPN) can be determined. The RPN is a mathematical product of the numerical severity, probability, and detection ratings [1]:

RPN = (Severity) x (Probability) x (Detection)

The RPN can now be used to prioritize failures that are of concern. It should be noted that severe events with low RPN numbers should also be considered in certain circumstances and that just relying on prioritizing by RPN number may not always be sufficient. For example, a specific failure mode in a space suit may have a high severity number but a low probability of failure and the detection by the user of the failure immediate. This failure event may yield a low RPN number but may result in a severe event. Therefore, high-severity events should also be considered and evaluated in conjunction with high-RPN events. This can be addressed in the FMECA.

- A recommended action(s) list is generated to evaluate the course of action to address potential failures that have a high RPN or identified with a high severity for further evaluation in the FMECA.

5.1.7 FMEA Summary and Corrective Actions

A summary of the FMEA analysis at the end of each review should be documented and tracked to help ensure that all the identified issues are addressed and that the product safety risk is in line with expectations. The corrective action can be implemented. Each corrective action can be assigned to a person with a completion date for the action(s). Progress should be tracked and the FMEA updated. Lessons learned can be noted for future products design consideration. FMEA is a useful tool for the risk management process, but it is not a substitute for the process itself.

5.1.8 Failure Mode Effects Criticality Analysis (FMECA)

The identified failure modes of concern in the FMEA may have been sufficiently investigated. However, depending on the nature of the FMEA, identified safety-related failure modes may be further investigated and characterized using a FMECA, which is described in IEC60821 [1]. MIL-STD-1629 [6]; other standards also provide guidance on the implementation of a FMECA. Thus, the FMECA can be seen as an extension of the FMEA.

The FMECA is a bottom-up analysis, based on a qualitative approach, while the FMECA takes a quantitative approach. As an extension of the FMEA, a criticality and probability of occurrence for each given failure mode is assigned. This would include the identification of the cause of the failure and its effect on the operational capabilities (functions) of an end item component, subsystem, or system.

5.1.8.1 FMECA Column Definitions

Typical definitions for a sample of columns used in an FMECA are provided as follows:

- *Sequence number:* A reference designation identification number for each identifed failure mode.
- *Item name and function:* A description of the hardware.

- *Failure modes:* All known failure modes for this hardware. The failure modes describe the way in which the failure manifested itself.
- *Failure effects:* The consequences of each identified failure mode on item operation, function, or status. The failure effects can be sorted by the following:
  - Local effects: Normally limited to the component.
  - Expanded effects: The effects of the failure at the subsystem level.
  - Final effects: Evaluation and definition of the total failure effect at the system level.
- *Severity classification:* A severity classification category is assigned to each failure mode depending upon its effects on the system. This is an effort that requires experience and knowledge of failure modes. If this information is lacking, then it can be supplemented with research or testing or both.
- The severity classifications are discussed in IEC60821 [1], MIL-STD-1629 [6], and MIL-STD-882 [7] and are listed as follows:
  - Category I—Catastrophic: A failure that may cause death or critical system malfunction;
  - Category II—Critical: A failure that may result in severe injury, or major property damage;
  - Category III—Marginal: A failure that may result in minor injury, or minor property damage;
  - Category IV—Minor: A failure not serious enough to cause injury, but is perhaps reliability related;
- *Failure detection method:* A description of the methods by which the failure mode is detected.
- *Failure isolation:* A description of the procedure that would allow the operator to isolate the malfunction or failure.
- *Remarks:* Any comments or recommendations to be incorporated into the FMECA report.

5.1.8.2   Criticality Analysis Implementation Process

The purpose of the criticality analysis is to rank each failure mode as identified in the FMEA. This action is performed according to each failure mode's severity classification and its probability of occurrence.

The result of the criticality analysis leads to the development of a criticality matrix. The failure mode criticality number (Cm) for each specific failure mode is calculated. The weights applied in the calculation are a subjective number often based on experience. In a military application, this works well due to the long life of products and the long period of time and data from field experience. However, commercial products have a significantly shorter life and, therefore, data is limited. In MIL 1629 [6], the failure mode Cm for each specific failure mode is calculated as follows:

$$C_m = \beta \times \alpha \times \lambda p \times \tau$$

where:

C_m: Failure mode criticality number;

β: Conditional probability of the failure;

α: Failure mode ratio;

λp: Part failure rate per million hours;

τ: Expected operational life in hours or operating cycles.

The criticality number of each component, subassembly, and assembly (or system) is calculated for each severity category. This criticality number is the sum of the specific failure mode criticality numbers related to the particular severity category [6]:

$$C_r = \sum_{n-1}^{j} (\beta \times \alpha \times \lambda p \times \tau) n$$

where:

C_r: Item criticality number;

n: Failure modes in the items that fall under a particular criticality classification;

j: Last failure mode in the item under the criticality classification.

For β =1.00 = Actual loss

>0.1 to 1.00 = Probable loss

>0 to = 0.10 = Possible loss

0 = No effect

The resulting FMECA analysis will enable a criticality matrix to be constructed. The criticality matrix displays the distribution of all the failure mode criticality numbers according to the severity category and referring to the criticality scale. According to MIL-STD-1629 [6] the scale is divided into five levels:

- Level A (high): High probability is defined as a probability equal to or greater than 0.2 of the overall probability of failure.
- Level B (moderate): Reasonable (moderate) probability is defined as more than 0.1 but less than 0.2 of the overall system probability of failure during the defined mission period.
- Level C (occasional): Occasional probability is defined as a probability more than 0.01 but less than 0.1 of the overall probability of failure.
- Level D (remote): Remote probability is defined as a probability more than 0.001 but less than 0.01 of the overall probability of failure.
- Level E (extremely unlikely): Extremely unlikely probability is defined as probability less than 0.001.

Once the FMEA is complete, the information generated can be presented in a way that will assist with a risk and safety assessment of the product design.

5.1.8.3   Criticality Matrix

The criticality matrix is a matrix that helps to place identified failure modes into perspective. The failure mode is the way in which the product will fail and is a description of risk and safety.

The scales in this matrix will follow the format of the scales to be used in the FMEA. In Figure 5.2, the scales are plotted on the X- and the Y-axes. Severity is plotted on the X-axis, and likelihood and probability are plotted on the Y-axis. The criticality table listed in IEC 60812 is shown in Figure 5.3.

Once the probability of the occurrence is calculated, the criticality number can be assigned. The failure modes can be plotted in the table using the X-axis and Y-axis coordinates. The risk of the specific failure mode can then be evaluated.

5.1.8.4   Risk Acceptability Assessment

In Figure 5.4, the arrow represents a simplified risk example profile that may be acceptable. This line can be adjusted based on the level of acceptance of risk. However, such an approach should be applied very carefully with the same consideration as mentioned in the FMEA with regard to prioritizing RPN numbers and severity. Here too, in certain failure modes, even an improbable risk may be too high and may not be acceptable, although it may fall below the line of acceptable risk.

Therefore, during the risk assessment, not just items above the acceptable line need to be reviewed, but also failure modes with a high severity number.

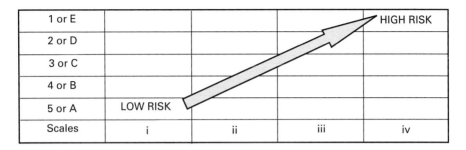

	i	ii	iii	iv
1 or E				HIGH RISK
2 or D				
3 or C				
4 or B				
5 or A	LOW RISK			
Scales	i	ii	iii	iv

Figure 5.2 An example of a criticality matrix as shown in IEC60812 showing the direction of increased risk.

Criticality number 1 or E	Improbable	Probability of occurrence: $0 \leq Pi \leq 0.001$
Criticality number 2 or D	Remote	Probability of occurrence: $0 \leq Pi \leq 0.001$
Criticality number 3 or C	Occasional	Probability of occurrence: $0 \leq Pi \leq 0.001$
Criticality number 4 or B	Probable	Probability of occurrence: $0 \leq Pi \leq 0.001$
Criticality number 5 or A	Frequent	Probability of occurrence: $0 \leq Pi \leq 0.001$

Figure 5.3 The criticality matrix described in IEC60812.

This will facilitate the risk assessment and take into account events that may have a low probability but a high severity number.

A risk matrix can also be represented in a table as show in IEC60812. The *X*-axis will consist of the severity levels shown in Figure 5.5.

A similar matric as in the risk assessment table can be generated. In this case the *X*-axis can be the frequency of occurrence and the *Y*-axis the severity levels.

IEC 60812 explains in detail alternative methods on how to perform the critical analysis based on the FMEA results with more detail and ranking with greater granularity. However, this may require more experience in the process, and perhaps starting out the criticality analysis in a more simplified manner may facilitate building confidence and experience until more sophisticated approaches can be mastered.

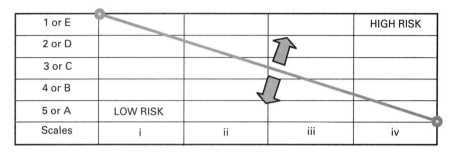

1 or E				HIGH RISK
2 or D				
3 or C				
4 or B				
5 or A	LOW RISK			
Scales	i	ii	iii	iv

Figure 5.4   The matrix showing an example risk line.

Severity number	Severity description
1	Insignificant
2	Marginal
3	Critical
4	Catastrophic

Figure 5.5   An example shown in IEC60812 for severity levels.

5.2   FTA

5.2.1   Introduction

Failures can be as simple as a light bulb going out or as complex as a computer motherboard failure. When a room experiences a lighting failure and turns dark, understanding the failure mode sounds simple, but it can be quite complex as there can be many reasons why the failure occurred. For example, somebody turned the light OFF; or there is a power outage, or a wiring defect or a switch failure, or a light connector failure; or the breaker to the light circuit tripped; or the light bulb failed. So perhaps what appears to be a simple failure may not be so simple, and there may be many causes for a specific failure mode. For more complex failure modes, the list can be much longer.

How can all the potential causes be captured to describe a specific failure mode? In addition, if failure modes are identified for a product, how can these failure events or failure modes be represented?

A popular solution is to use a FTA as shown in IEC61025 [8], where the global view of a single failure is captured in the fault tree. Many single-failure fault stresses can be broken down to form an interconnected fault tree comprised of many conditions precipitating from a failure mode. In a final step, the direct relationships between an event causing a failure, the component, and the product failure outcome are established using fault-propagation logic. Therefore, the interaction between systems and subsystems or components can be evaluated and displayed graphically.

5.2.2   Active and Passive Redundancy

There are various ways in which the FTA can be constructed. Active and passive redundancy assumes failure characteristics for active dependency to remain the same, independent of how many inputs are present. Passive redundancy is also referred to as standby redundancy and only considers the number of components required when operation is active.

5.2.3   Conditional Probability Repeated Events and Transfer-Out Events

Conditional probability events are events that will provide an output based on certain conditions. These conditions are referred to as binary gates. These binary conditions can consist of AND, OR, NAND, NOR, and other binary gates to describe the interaction of the component failures on the final product failure mode. For example, if the AND function is used, then it means that two or more component failures will have to occur for the observed failure mode to occur. If the OR function is used, then it implies that any one of the component failures in the FTA can result in the identified failure mode. IEC61025 provides a description of the gates in Annex A.

5.2.4   Fault Tree Construction and Application

The FTA structure only includes the relevant events. The FTA starts with the failure mode at the top, and all the events that may lead to this failure mode will be listed at the bottom of the FTA. In between the top of the FTA and the bottom, the sequence of events leading from the event to the final failure mode will be displayed.

The events that are considered are all events that may lead to the same failure mode. Some of the events may have a short sequence of events, and others may have a longer sequence. In addition, interdependencies may be added that will add to the complexity of the display structure. Therefore, all events in the FMEA should be considered, but only the events that will lead to the selected failure mode will be included in the FTA.

The structure of the fault tree consists of symbols, each of which has a functional meaning; these symbols are listed in IEC61025 [8]. The structure of the FTA is a bottom-up structure or a top-down structure depending on how the failure tree is displayed. In IEC61025 the failure tree starts with the failure mode at the top and the events initializing the failure mechanism at the bottom (see Figure 5.6).

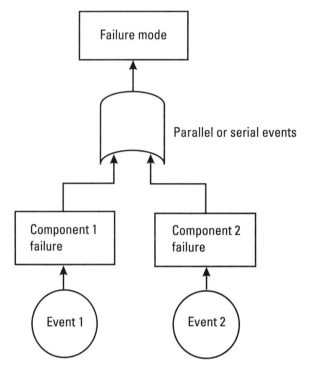

Figure 5.6   A simplified example of a FTA.

The events will involve components that are expected to fail in the observed failure mode. Below the failure mode block is a binary decision-maker function. This function determines whether the component failures have to happen in parallel or serial or whether there is a unique binary sequence of component failures that cause the observed failure mode.

Submulticonditional events can also form part of the FTA (see the dotted lined block in Figure 5.7). In this case, a failure of component 1 will result in the identified failure mode, but component 2 AND component 3 will have to fail to result in the identified failure mode.

The construction of the FTA will follow an analytical logic flow. The FTA needs information to be constructed, and this information can be obtained from an in-depth technical review of the product and it functions. This in-depth review will include the software (firmware), hardware design, and knowledge about discrete component failure modes and how failure can propagate in the architecture of the product.

Using the FMEA as the basis for the FTA is useful. If not, then information that is needed may include, drawing, schematics, control system state diagrams, functional diagrams, software commands, and user profiles. This in-

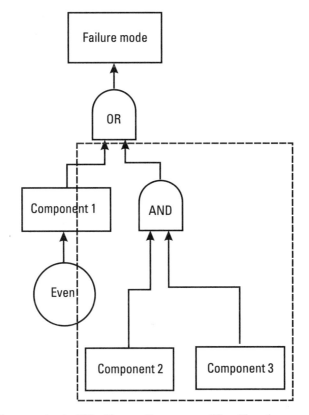

Figure 5.7   An example of a FTA with more than one conditional function.

formation can then all be compiled and the analysis performed to determine which causes are relevant as well as their interdependencies.

The analysis of the FTA shows the events and then follows the events down the fault tree to the cause. If a system failure cause is investigated and the events in the cause result in the system failure, a cause and sequence of events are identified, and only then can the failure mode be mitigated.

IEC61025 provides guidance on the Boolean simplification of the fault tree. The standard discusses the Esary-Proschan method [8] and provides guidance on how to manage and calculate rare events and represent the rare events in the FTA [8]. Disjointing in the FTA helps to prevent common branches in the FTA from being included in calculations [8].

In addition to being used to present probability, the FTA can be used for the analysis of failure rates. IEC61025 suggests that a Poisson distribution be used to characterize the occurrence of events. This makes it possible to develop a FTA that will characterize failure rates as well as failure probabilities.

IEC61025 suggests converting the failure rates to their respective probabilities of occurrence and applying the standard FTA principals.

5.2.5   FTA Reporting

IEC 61025 provides guidance on reporting and lists basic and supplementary items. The supplementary items are there to help clarify complex issues and thereby minimize interpretation that my result in inaccurate assumptions.

The basic reporting items include the objective, scope, system description, design, and operation. Boundaries of the evaluation need to be declared in the report to ensure that the FTA work boundaries are explained to the report reviewer. The FTA team and their experience and backgrounds need to be documented. The FTA report needs to include the basis for the evaluated cases as well as probabilities, to show the data, and to provide the results, conclusions, and recommendations.

Supplementary information can include all the technical information, relevant data that was relied upon, and the FMEA and FMECA analysis for follow-up activities.

5.3   Hazard and Operability Study (HAZOP)

5.3.1   Introduction

A HAZOP is a focused study with boundaries set to evaluate only conditions that represent a risk to animals, personnel, buildings, or equipment. HAZOP studies are not focused on general reliability but rather on safety-related issues.

The technique in IEC61882 [9] is based on the process of breaking a complex design into smaller blocks and then evaluating the blocks or nodes individually. The HAZOP is a qualitative technique that requires insight from the team to evaluate the product and identify the potential hazards and operability issues.

In the standards, the requirements for the team's experience are well-documented. Although the requirements are subjective, the HAZOP study—like the FMEA and FTA—requires experience and knowledge to correctly identify and understand the potential hazards and their outcomes.

The HAZOP process was initially developed to analyze major chemical processes but has diversified and can now be found in many other areas from power generation to software development in critical systems.

5.3.2   Implementation of the HAZOP Study

The HAZOP study can be applied to processes where sufficient information is available. The HAZOP analysis will review conditions that have been accounted for in the process but evaluate whether there are additional conditions that are not accounted for or whether the general conditions or scenarios set are sufficient to mitigate a hazardous outcome.

Each node in the system is evaluated by the HAZOP team. When evaluating the node, the team will use standardized terminology and process parameters to identify any deviations from the design intent.

For each deviation, the causes and consequences can be identified and documented. The mitigating measures to prevent a hazardous cause or consequences should be evaluated to be not present, sufficient, or lacking in effectiveness. If a hazard is identified due to an insufficient mitigating action, then an action must be identified. This action will provide direction as to how to eliminate the hazard. Therefore, the system can be studied, and all identifiable the hazards should be identified and characterized.

The hazard analysis may be performed as a single meeting or as many meetings based on the scope of the analysis. A trained HAZOP facilitator will help to document the process and ensure the quality and effectiveness of the HAZOP study.

5.3.3 Reporting

The report should include all the potential hazards that were identified as well as the evaluation for each hazard showing whether an action was necessary. Report recommendations need to focus on the actions. The actions need to be explained by describing the causes and consequences. Furthermore, recommendations for mitigating the action should be provided.

5.4 Action Error Analysis (AEA)

5.4.1 Introduction

AEA [10] focuses on the interactions between machines and humans. The AEA is an analysis that studies potential human error in task execution and the consequences. It is very similar to the FMEA. However, where the FMEA focuses on a product or system response to a system-related failure, the AEA is focused on the human interaction with the product or system. The automated interface between human and automated processes can be evaluated. For example, a pilot of a plane and its interaction between the cockpits controls displays and other equipment interactions.

The AEA is a decision-making process. It was designed to facilitate making decisions where the answers may not be intuitive in a binary manner. The situation is typically very complex and the answers require the critical assessment of many factors , which are then distilled down to a single answer.

The principal implementation philosophy is to find a decision that is based on the problem perceptions, analyze the problem perceptions, and present them in a means that can quantify and compare them, weighing different actions and alternatives against one other.

5.4.2   Implementation

The main objective of the AEA is to identify potential human errors in critical procedures. These critical errors are then evaluated and mitigating actions put in place to reduce risk to acceptable levels.

The process for the preparation of the AEA analysis is very much the same as for the FMEA and can also be divided into defined activities: preparation for the AEA, documentation and product familiarization and review, performance of the analysis, review of the analysis, and then identification of the necessary action items. The methodology of implementation is the same as that of the FMEA. Also, the risk can be valuated using the same method as that in the FMECA.

A worksheet can be generated to identify and track the following:

- *Action error:* What human machine error could occur;
- *Cause:* What may cause this error to occur;
- *Consequence:* What is the consequence of the error or event that occurred;
- *Risk:* What is the risk (which can be the failure rate and severity);
- *Suggested mitigating action:* Mitigating or minimizing the action from occurring, through action such as design changes, training, and improved documentation;

Representation of the work performed can also follow the methodology of the FTA but in an AEA context. Since the process of the evaluation follows the same methodology as the FMEA and FMECA, the team credentials and experience cannot be the same. The team will not just consist of technical members but will also consist of members familiar with the interfaces and human factors experts. The combined multidisciplinary team will then be able to identify, characterize, and rationalize the action errors, consequences, risks, and mitigating actions.

5.4.3   Reporting

The reporting of the work performed can follow the same guidelines as the FMEA and FMECA, but there may not be a *detection* column. Hence the risk may be a function of occurrence and severity. Since the evaluation and reporting will be from a human-to-machine interaction perspective, these high-risk items will be addressed in the report as recommendations and action items.

As discussed previously, in FMEA, a low-occurrence, high-risk event should be individually evaluated and excluded due to a risk number being low and falling below a risk-acceptable value. Therefore, in the reporting the high-severity items may have to be individually addressed, and action may be evaluated and motivated on a case-by-case basis.

5.5 Event Tree Analysis (ETA)

5.5.1 Introduction

ETA was successfully introduced in the early 1970s to simplify nuclear safety studies made complex by the sheer size of fault trees. The ETA is a forward-looking and bottom-up technique that describes both the success of an event as well as the failure on an event. When an initiating event occurs, the event tree will analyze a failed system response as well as a functioning systems response. Similar to the FMEA, the event tree can be constructed early on in the design to determine where the issues may be and where focus on the design may be necessary to mitigate risk. The Boolean logic that is used in the ETA helps to simplify the model. The ETA starts with a probabilistic risk assessment that identifies a set of initiating events that change the state of the system. The succession of events is identified and evaluated until the final outcome is identified. Figure 5.8 shows how this can be presented in the ETA. In Figure 5.8, the initiating event resulted in two succession events that led to three outcomes.

The three outcomes shown in Figure 5.8 can be presented as follows:

- Success of outcome A = (Initiating event) (event 1 success) (event 2 success);
- Failure of outcome B = (Initiating event) (event 1 success) (event 2 failure);
- Failure of outcome C = (Initiating event) (event 1 failure).
- Based on the outcomes, the corrective actions in the design can be decided upon and noted in the final report.

So, how does the ETA differ from the FTA? The answer lies in the way the tree is constructed. A FTA will start with an outcome or top event and work backward, following various events toward the initiating event or events. The ETA will begin with an initiating event and then follow subsequent events until

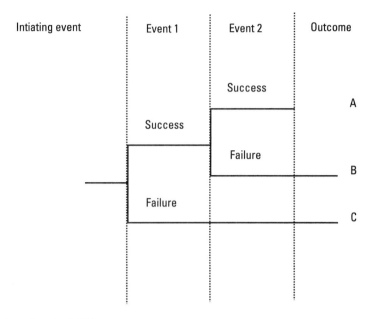

Figure 5.8 A typical ETA layout.

the outcome or the top event is reached. Hence the simplification is in the fact that a single initiating event is evaluated, whereas in a FTA, the outcome can be a result of many initiating events that are explored in the same diagram. The ETA can be successfully used in the FMEA to provide more details about very specific identified failure modes and to provide some degree of risk assessment.

5.5.2 Implementation

The implementation of the ETA follows a specific sequence of steps that are, to some extent, very similar to the FMEA, FTA, and other analysis systems. Teams need to be formed, the right knowledge base needs to be in the room, and the rules of the ETA need to be established. The typical steps associated with the ETA are described as follows:

1. Define the scope of work so that the ETA is manageable and does not spiral out of control.
2. Identify the hazards and accident scenarios that will be used to identify the initiating events.
3. Determine the identified initiating events. These events will form the ETA.
4. When each initiating event is identified, the resulting events for each should be identified.

5. Start to construct the ETA for each initiating event.

6. Determine the event failure probabilities. The failure probability of success may be determined by using 1 = probability of success – probability of failure.

7. Determine the outcomes of the identified initiating events and then, using the probabilities to determine the acceptability of the event.

8. Identify and propose corrective actions.

9. Ensure that the ETA and the whole process of the ETA is documented, dated, and updated as new information is made available.

The major advantage of the ETA is that it is a graphically presentable model focusing on the issues of concern and identified for complex systems, and this model can, thus, investigate sequences of events across system and subsystem boundaries.

References

[1]   IEC60812, "Analysis Techniques for System Reliability—Procedure for Failure Mode and Effects Analysis (FMEA)," Geneva, 2006.

[2]   Price, C. J., "Function-Directed Electrical Design Analysis," Department of Computer Science, University of Wales, Aberystwyth, Ceredifion, United Kingdom.

[3]   ISO Definitions, bizmanualz.com.

[4]   Merriam-Webster online, m-w.com.

[5]   Dictionary.com, 12/3/2006.

[6]   MIL-STD-1629A, "Procedures for Performing a Failure Mode, Effects and Criticality Analysis," U.S. Department of Defense, 1977.

[7]   MIL-STD-882, "Standard Practice for System Safety," U.S. Department of Defense, 2012.

[8]   IEC61025, "Fault Tree Analysis (FTA)," Geneva, 2006.

[9]   IEC61882, "Hazard and Operability Studies (HAZOP Studies)—Application Guide" Geneva, 2016.

[10] Bligard, L.-O., and A.-L. Osvalder, "Development of AEA, SHERPA, PHEA To Better Predict, Identify and Present Use Errors," *International Journal of Industrial Ergonomics,* 44, 2014, pp153–170.

6

Risk Management for Product Safety

6.1 Introduction

Risk management (RM) is defined as a continuous management process aiming to identify, analyze, and assess potential hazards in a product, system, or related to an activity, and to identify and introduce risk control measures to eliminate or reduce potential harm to people, the environment, or other assets [1]. By understanding the terminology, principles, and processes of risk management, one can obtain the tools to design and develop safe products.

All products include hazards and, therefore, some level of residual risk, so it is impractical to expect absolute safety in the use of electric and electronic products. Generally, it is accepted that no product can be completely fail-safe and that any associated risk should be reduced to a tolerable level.

To reach this objective during the design phase of an electrical product, it is necessary to analyze the harm (injury or damage to the health of people, or damage to property or the environment), hazard (potential sources of harm), and risk (combination of the probability of occurrence of harm and the severity of that harm) associated with the product during its life cycle. The probability of occurrence of harm includes the exposure to a hazardous situation (circumstance in which people, property or the environment are exposed to one or more hazards), the occurrence of a hazardous event (event that can cause harm), and the possibility of avoiding or limiting the harm. Only the exposure to hazards can generate a hazardous situation. If exposure to hazard does not exist, harm is not generated. The realistic expectation must be that risks are kept as low as practical, taking into account the cost that would be incurred in further reducing risk and versus the benefits resulting from use of the product [2].

If drawn up and carried out correctly, a risk assessment (including the risk analysis and risk evaluation) should address all the risk associated with a product. The overall process for the risk assessment and control of risk is referred to as risk management (Figure 6.1).

The risk analysis process (see Figure 6.1) consists of the following steps [2, 3]:

- Defining the product's intended use and product safety characteristics;
- Identifying hazards and threats, individualizing hazardous events;
- Identifying hazardous situations, considering hazard exposure;
- Estimating the risks, associating each hazard or hazardous situation with a level of risk to generate harm by determining the probability of harm occurrence and the severity (consequences) of the harm.

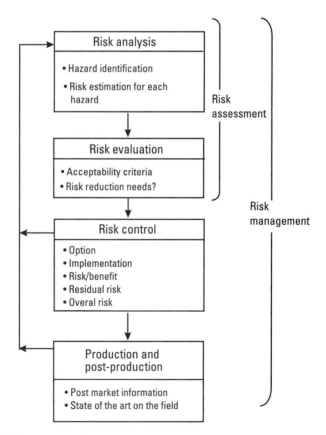

Figure 6.1   Risk management process .

Risk evaluation consists of the following steps.

- Evaluating the risks against risk acceptance criteria (established for each product and in each organization);
- Proposing risk-reducing measures, for intolerable risks;
- Assessing alternative risk-reducing measures.

Risk control consists of the following steps:

- Making decisions related to risk-reducing measures, conducting a risk/benefit analysis, and implementing measures;
- Conducting a residual risk evaluation;
- Monitoring the effects of the measures to not introduce new hazards

Postproduction information is described as follows.

- Collecting information from users that can contribute to product safety improvement;
- Analyzing the relevant product safety information from the market for technological developments in general and for similar products in particular;
- Reviewing the postproduction experience and implementing in the product the relevant product safety improvements.

The first step in the risk management process is the identification of the qualitative and quantitative product safety characteristics of the product or accessory under consideration. The following list includes some of the issues that could affect the safety of the evaluated product [3]:

- What is the intended use?
- Which are the safety-related materials and/or components used?
- Are product measurements made?
- Is the product interpretative?
- Is the product intended to control other equipment?
- Are there unwanted outputs of energy?
- Is the product susceptible to environmental influences?
- Is the product provided with accessories?
- Are maintenance and calibration required?

- Does the product contain software?
- Can the product be affected by longtime use or by delayed effects?
- To what mechanical forces will the product be subjected?
- What determines the lifetime of the equipment?

The answers to all these questions, and a supplementary functional description, provide a general view of the evaluated product.

6.2 Identifying Hazards

The second step of risk management process deals with the identification of hazards. The systematic identification of possible hazards, hazardous events, and hazardous situations during all phases of the product life cycle is essential. If a hazard is not identified, but exists, it cannot be controlled. No need to forget that some hazards are never known because the unidentified hazards haven't yet been determined.

A hazard can be defined as any real or potential condition that can cause degradation, injury, illness, or death to personnel or damage to or loss of product or property. Experience, common sense, and specific risk management tools help identify real or potential hazards.

Hazards, and factors that could generate hazards (e.g., component failure, abnormal use, human errors, and environmental effects), are identified based on the harm to be prevented and the definition of the intended use and product requirements. It is important in the hazards identification stage to consider all appropriate national rules and regulations, the standards applicable to the product, and the additional requirements for the intended markets. A hazard might have one, several, or many possible causes. Additionally, consider the cause of a hazard related to any set of events and/or circumstances, the combination of which might be expected to result in a hazardous event [4].

All the hazards analyzed should consider when the product is manufactured, installed, maintained, transported, in standby conditions, in normal operating conditions, or in foreseeable abnormal operating conditions and should include appropriate hazards that affect the operator, service personnel, bystanders, or the environment.

There are many ways to identify hazards. One of the best is through a group process involving representatives directly related to the product (e.g., manufacturers, users, and outside experts). Therefore, a multidisciplinary brainstorming process with a facilitator is recommended.

Hazard identification should begin with the examination of existing databases or any available historical and hazard information regarding similar products. Specific tools have been developed to identify hazards, hazardous events, and hazardous situations and to model the cause-consequence scenarios. Tools used for hazard identification include the following [5]:

- Action-error analysis (AEA);
- Consequence analysis;
- Energy trace and barrier analysis (ETBA);
- ETA;
- FMEA;
- FTA;
- Hazard analysis and critical control point (HAACCP);
- HAZOP;
- Interface analysis;
- Safety analysis of user system interaction (SUSI);
- "What-if" analysis.

It is up to the manufacturer to select the appropriate tool or combination of tools and the extent of effort to expend on each. Since there are generally no right or wrong selections, knowledge and experience will help in making the choice.

The hazards associated with the safety of electrical products are designated according to their characteristics and discussed in Sections 6.2.1–6.2.9. They are listed as follows:

- Electric shock hazard;
- Mechanical hazards;
- Heat, fire, and tracking hazards;
- Chemical hazards;
- Radiation hazards;
- Biological hazards;
- Human factors and ergonomic hazards;
- Functional (operational) hazards;
- Informational hazards;
- Aging of materials hazards.

Note: Some standards and publications related to risk management include as part of risk analysis the "identification of risks" rather than the "identification of hazards." This can generate misunderstandings that sometimes can pull down the whole risk management process. What is identified? The risks, the hazards, or both? The risk, as a combination of the probability of occurrence of harm and the severity of that harm, cannot be identified but it, can be estimated, evaluated. Only the hazard that causes the harm can be identified. While this seems to be a semantic issue, it is a more complex clue to the significance of the terms "hazard" and "risk." It is important to remember that hazard is different than risk. A risk is a chance of something happening, and it can be measured and evaluated, but it cannot be identified. We assess a process in which we identify the presence of hazards and evaluate as tolerable (acceptable) or intolerable (unacceptable) the risk of a harm occurrence caused by the identified hazards. We can be confronted with a mechanical (i.e., cutting) hazard that can produce harm (physical injury) with a small (low), average (medium), or great (high) risk (depending on the probability of occurrence and on the severity of the harm), but here we do not have a mechanical risk. Maybe the process to find, list, and characterize the elements of risk (probability, event, severity, and consequences), sometime defined as risk "identification" are better referred to as risk "characterization" or risk "specification." In conclusion, it is very important to avoid confusing the terms "hazard" and "risk."

6.2.1   Electric Shock

Electric shock is a hazard that is manifested as an electric current passing through the human body producing different levels of harm (e.g., body injury or death). Electric shock can be produced by the following:

- Unsafe access to hazardous voltages;
- Inadequate insulation;
- Inadequate grounding;
- High level of leakage current;
- High stored charges;
- Arcs;
- Incorrect connection to and interruption from a power supply.

It should be identified whether the accessible parts of a product can become hazardous when live or a source of discharge energy at a level that can produce electric shock.

Factors that influence the body's susceptibility to electric shock are as listed as follows [4]:

- Impedance of the human body (e.g., wetness of the skin and internal resistance of human body);
- The pathway of current through the human body (with the heart, the neck, and the head being the most dangerous pathways for the current);
- The duration and intensity of the current;
- The frequency of the current.

6.2.2 Mechanical Hazards

Mechanical hazards can be caused by the product or by the effect of expected external forces acting on the product. When mechanical hazards are identified, one should consider kinetic (moving mass and dynamic events) and potential (nonmoving mass and static events) energies and pressure (e.g., air, water, sound, and ultrasound)

Mechanical hazards include crushing, shearing, cutting or severing, entanglement, trapping, stabbing or puncturing, friction or abrasion, high-pressure fluid ejection, falling (drop), instability, impact, shock, vibration, and noise hazards. The category of mechanical hazards can also include explosion and implosion, hazards generated in products that incorporate components under pressure or under high vacuum [4].

A mechanical hazard can be produced by factors that include the following:

- Inadequate stability;
- Inadequate mechanical strength;
- Inadequate guards for moving parts;
- Inadequate finishing of the accessible parts of the enclosure;
- Inadequate lifting and carrying means;
- Inadequate handling in normal use;
- Expelled parts.

6.2.3 Heat, Fire, and Tracking Hazards

Heat hazards, which can produce different levels of burns, are generated by excessive temperature of materials ejected or accessible on product surfaces likely to be touched.

Fire hazards can be initiated by the electrical product itself or by substances produced, emitted, or used by the electrical product. One needs to identify the areas and components for which any excess heating can cause a hazard of fire within a product in normal and in single-fault conditions and can cause fire to spread outside the product. The fire hazard is a very complex phenomenon. Fire can produce, in a chain reaction, other types of hazards such as electric shock, mechanical hazards, and toxicity. When considering fire hazards, it is also necessary to take into account the additional factors of power dissipation, maximum admissible temperature, and the necessary energy to start the ignition, among others.

One needs to identify whether the selection and application of the components and materials was done so as to minimize the possibility of ignition and the spread of flame (i.e., components working at high temperatures need to have adequate clearance to effectively prevent overheating of their surroundings and need to be mounted on materials with the proper flammability class). The flammability of materials and tracking properties must be taken into consideration according to each type of product [4].

The possible damage caused by the use of flame retarders must be balanced with the damage caused by ignition of the electrical product.

Products that incorporate batteries present significate heat and fire hazards. Batteries should not cause explosions or produce a fire hazard as a result of leaking or ventilation, excessive charge or discharge, or installation with an incorrect polarity. Special attention must be paid to primary and secondary lithium batteries.

6.2.4   Chemical Hazards

Chemical hazards consist of emissions, production, and/or use of hazardous substances (e.g., toxicity produced by gases, liquids, dusts, mists, vapors, and moisture). Toxic substances can damage living tissues by their interaction.

Chemical hazards can stem from the following situations with products:

- Liquids with continuous contact (e.g., liquid pumps and containers);
- Liquids with occasional contact (e.g., cleaning fluids and liquids having accidental contact);
- Liquids in the area surrounding the product.

Where cleaning or decontamination is specified by the manufacturer, this should not cause an electrical shock hazard, nor a hazard resulting from corrosion. Special attention must be given to such possibilities as spillage, overflow, and leakage of liquids on the vessel connections.

6.2.5   Radiation Hazards

Radiation hazards need to be considered from nonionizing sources (e.g., ultraviolet, lasers, microwaves, infrared, and electromagnetic) and ionizing sources (e.g., nuclear radiation and x-rays).

The hazards presented by radiation depend on a number of factors including distance from the body, level of radiation, and time of exposure. Harmful consequences can result from constant exposure, even if the human body is subjected to low-level radiation. It is extremely important to control all types of radiation to which operators, service personnel, patients, and others may be exposed.

Special attention must be paid to high-power radiation sources that have the potential ability to change the shape of materials by heating and/or to penetrate the walls of protective housing by melting or vaporizing the materials of the enclosure. These effects depend on the type of radiation, exposure time, environmental factors, and the thermomechanical properties of the material irradiated.

6.2.6   Biological Hazards

Biological hazards are organic substances that pose a threat to the health of humans and other living organisms. Biological hazards include pathogenic microorganisms, bacteria, viruses, toxins (from biological sources), spores, fungi, and bioactive substances. Biological hazards can also include biological vectors or transmitters of disease.

For products that have parts in contact with the human body during normal use or foreseen abnormal conditions (intentional or unintentional), it is necessary to consider the biological hazards caused by the material of these parts (biocompatibility characteristics), caused by or due to poor hygiene.

Sources of biological hazards can cause a variety of health effects ranging from skin irritation and allergies to infections. Exposure to biological hazards is most common in electrical products used in the health services, agriculture, forestry, and fishing industries [3].

6.2.7   Human Factor and Ergonomics Hazards

Human factor hazards can be regarded as errors or violations generating a sequence of actions or decisions, leading to unintended immediate or delayed harm. The primary error types are slip, lapse, and mistake, and they occur in the use of the product. Human error may also be categorized based on action: omission, intrusion, repetition, wrong object, disordering, mistiming, and blends.

When the human factor fails, there is a whole chain of small errors that, had they occurred individually, would have generated harm. We can say that the human error is an action or a decision that is not planned and leads to an undesirable result.

In industrial processes, possible causes of errors and failure of the human factor include the following:

- Errors in communications;
- Insufficient or incorrect knowledgeability of the employees,
- Insufficient qualifications;
- Insufficient experience (lack of training) or practice;
- Personality and health assumptions about employees;
- Failure to maintain working procedures;
- Unsuitable working conditions and environment;
- Inattentiveness (momentary) of the employees;
- Inadequate product accessories;
- Misinterpretation of decisions;
- Erroneous data transfer.

In preventing ergonomics hazards it is important to identify, by use of ergonomic principles, the possibility of errors and thus hazards in designing or arranging workplaces, products, and systems to fit the people who use them. Refer to Chapter 13 for additional information on human factors and ergonomics hazards.

6.2.8   Functional (Operational) Hazards

Functional hazards are induced by the relationships between functions and hazards. To identify such hazards, it is necessary to determine the safety-significant functions (SSFs) of the product as well as the hazards associated with that functionality [6].

One should identify the hazards arising from malfunctioning, due to the following problems:

- Expected environmental conditions, including electric, magnetic, and electromagnetic disturbances considered as relevant in the product or generic EMC standard;
- Errors in hardware and accessories;
- Logic errors in software;

- Interruptions or normally expected fluctuations in the power supply;
- Unexpected starting or stopping of operation;
- Failure to stop or to start the product.

The analysis of the product behavior, the design of the circuits, and the mechanical design should provide the necessary information regarding the hazards that can arise during abnormal operation and single-fault conditions of the product.

If the product is intended for use in combination with other products, each product should be evaluated to determine combinations of the products that do not create hazards or to identify the hazards generated by such combinations. Section 6.6 provides further information on functional safety.

6.2.9 Informational Hazards

The failure to transfer the correct and needed information to a product user can lead to hazards. Contributing factors are listed as follows:

- Unavailable user instructions;
- Inadequate operating instructions;
- Overcomplicated instructions;
- Instructions inconsistent or too difficult to follow;
- Inadequate warning of potential hazards;
- Unclear use of symbols;
- Inadequate specification of the accessories to be used with the product;
- Inadequate specification of preuse checks;
- Inadequate description of performance characteristics;
- Inadequate specification of intended use;
- Inadequate disclosure of limitations;
- Inadequate information about service and maintenance.

Fortunately, proper instructions and training can eliminate many informational hazards.

6.2.10 Aging of Materials Hazards

Aging of materials hazards are due to the gradual process in which the properties of a material change (for worse), over time or with use, due to biological, chemical, or physical agents; corrosion; obsolescence; and weathering. Every endeavor is made to prevent or retard the natural aging, deterioration, and degradation of materials and to take adequate measures to maintain the quality of products.

Consider the environmental impact of the aging and deterioration of organic and inorganic matter and the proof of resistance of organic materials against biological degradation. The results of a highly accelerated life test (HALT) can also be considered.

6.2.11   Identification of Hazards Output

The output of the identification phase is a listing of hazards or hazardous situations and the harm that could result. Associated with the identification of hazards should be the initiating causes, which include operator error, component failure, software error, integration error, and environmental impact. A list of the causes associated with each hazard based on the tools used to identify the hazards (e.g., FTA and FMEA) is very useful.

A hazard may have multiple causes related to management, product, human factors, environment and intended use. (See Table 6.1 for a sample list of identified hazards.) In each case, try to identify the root cause (the first link in the chain of events leading to intended use degradation, personnel injury, death, or property damage). Risk controls can be only effectively applied to root causes.

6.3   Estimation of the Risk

The third step of the risk management process is the estimation of the risk, the application of quantitative, semiquantitative, or qualitative measures to deter-

Table 6.1
Sample List of Identified Hazards

Number	Hazard	Conditions •Normal use (NU) •Incorrect use (IU) • Single-fault (SFC)	Harm to: •Operator •Service personnel •Bystanders Environment	Hazard Rating Number (HRN)	Counter-measures (Risk control): •Safe design (SD) •Protection measures (PMs) •Informing user (IU)	New Hazard Rating Number (NHRN)

Note: This table also refers to other aspects (hazard rating number and countermeasures) of risk management, which will be presented later.

mine the level of risk associated with a specific hazard. This process defines the occurrence probability and severity of the harm that could result from hazards based upon the exposure of personnel or assets to that hazard.

Risk estimation is the process that associates "hazards" with "risks," referring to the various impacts a hazard may have on possible harm and an estimate of how likely it is to occur [5].

A risk can only be assessed and managed once a hazardous situation has been identified. Documenting the reasonably foreseeable sequences of events that can transform a hazard into a hazardous situation allows this to be done systematically. The difficulty of this step is that estimation of risk is different for every hazardous situation that is under investigation as well as for every product.

Because hazards can occur both when the product functions normally and when it malfunctions, it is necessary to look closely at both situations. In practice, both components of risk, probability and severity (consequence), should be analyzed separately.

Another aspect of risk estimation is the prioritizing of risks. To rank associated risks of harm, one must make the best possible estimate of the probability, severity, and exposure of a hazard compared to the other hazards that have been identified.

Probability is the estimate of the likelihood that a hazard will cause harm. Some hazards produce losses frequently; others almost never do. Using deductive analysis can estimate the frequency of the hazardous event and situations based on experience, data, and/or past/expected incident occurrence rates, derived from such information as historical data or simulations, results of failure analysis, and expert opinion. Based on these results we can establish the likelihood of the harm occurrence. The probability of occurrence of harm is calculated by estimating exposure to the hazard and the occurrence of hazardous events and determining whether the harm may be avoided or limited.

The likelihood of harm occurrence can be categorized in several ways, described as follows[5]:

- Frequent (likely to occur frequently);
- Probable (occurring several times in the life of the product);
- Occasional (likely to occur sometime in the life of the product);
- Remote (unlikely but can reasonably be expected to occur in the life of the product);
- Improbable (very unlikely to occur, allowing for the assumption that occurrence may not be expected).

The severity of harm consists of an estimate of the magnitude of injuries: how many are harmed and how severe are their injuries. Here, an inductive analysis is carried out to identify all potential sequences of events that can emerge from the hazardous event and situations to generate harm on different levels. To estimate the severity of the harm, consider the range of potential consequences and how likely those consequences are to occur.

The severity of harm can be categorized as follows [5]:

- Catastrophic (has the potential to result in multiple deaths or serious injuries);
- Critical or major (has the potential to result in death or serious injury);
- Marginal or moderate (has the potential to result in injury);
- Negligible or minor (has little or no potential to result in injury).

The third key aspect is exposure, which is the number of personnel or resources affected by a given event or, over time, by repeated events. Repeated exposure to a hazard increases the probability of harm occurring. Understanding the exposure level may serve as a guide for devising control measures to limit exposure to a specific hazard.

After estimating for each hazard, it is necessary to determine the following:

- The e consequence (severity of harm) level due to hazard exposure;
- The likelihood of harm occurrence due to the exposure level and to the hazard situations leading to harm;

This data is combined to obtain an estimated level of risk to attribute to each hazard. This can be an HRN (refer to Table 6.1) or a qualitative designation [3]:

$$\text{risk level} = \text{severity} \times \text{likelihood of harm}$$

The risk level, can be expressed in quantitative, qualitative, or semiqualitative terms, described as follows:

- Quantitative analysis estimates realistic values (HRNs) for consequences and their likelihood and produces values of risk in specific units defined in the context.
- Qualitative assessment defines consequence, probability, and risk with words such as high, medium, and low. Such assessment may combine consequence and probability using a matrix method and evaluate the resultant level of risk against qualitative criteria.

• Semiquantitative methods use numerical rating scales for probability and consequence and combine them using a formula. Scales may be linear or logarithmic or have some other relationship, and formulae used can also vary.

Uncertainty and its influence is significant in the process of risk estimation, and it applies especially when assessing the risk from the quantitative point of view. The variance of the results is caused in great part by different approaches to assessing and presenting the risk.

Along with hazard identification, the attribution of the HRN is the most difficult stage of the risk management process, requiring a great deal of experience and special skills from an assessor. Additional data can be obtained from sources such as scientific data, field data from similar equipment, reported incidents, and relevant standards.

To better estimate risks, their components (severity of harm and probability of harm occurrence) should be analyzed if they occur in the absence of a failure, in failure mode, or only in a multiple-failure condition (see Tables 6.2 and 6.3). Data used to calculate risk levels should be appropriate for the particular application. Where possible, such data should be based on the specific circumstances under analysis.

It is known that the results of any risk estimation are inevitably uncertain to some degree. Because of inevitable limitations in the risk assessment approach it must be acknowledged that true risks could be higher or lower than estimated.

Note: On the stage of risk estimation, confusion is sometimes caused by the use of the FMEA method as a risk management method, by applying the estimation parameters of FMEA (probability, severity, and detectability of the failure). The problem here is the mix between failure and harm, by including the detectability of failure as part of the risk level

Table 6.2

Example of Qualitative Severity Levels

Severity of Harm	Description
Catastrophic	Results in patient death
Major (critical)	Results in permanent impairment or life-threatening injury
Moderate (serious)	Results in injury or impairment requiring professional medical intervention
Minor (negligible)	Inconvenience or temporary discomfort, injury, or impairment not requiring professional medical intervention

Table 6.3
Example of Semiqualitative Probability Levels

Probability Levels of Harm Occurrence	Examples of Probability Range
Frequent	$> 10^{-3}$
Probable	$<10^{-3}$ and $>10^{-4}$
Occasional	$<10^{-4}$ and $>10^{-5}$
Remote	$<10^{-5}$ and $>10^{-6}$
Improbable	$<10^{-6}$

estimation. FMEA in general only analyzes failure effects based on a single failure in the product (failure of components), process (manufacturing and assembling of components), or application (during the use or misuse of the product by the end user). The failure can be a source of hazard, but to estimate the risk of harm occurring, it is necessary to be consider also other parameters as hazard exposure, hazardous situations, additional factors that can contribute to harm for a specific failure (e.g., environment conditions), and the different levels of harm severity. These aspects are not identified by FMEA or FMECA; such inclusion of the third factor, detectability, on the estimation of the risk level is not useful. The detection of failure can be a recommended intrinsic risk control (evaluating the contribution of detection-type controls to the mitigation of a risk associated with the hazard induced by the failure) attribute, but not a parameter that estimates the risk level. It is not correct to confer detectability with an equal weight for probability of harm occurrence and severity of harm, during risk estimation. Detection is an assessment of the likelihood that the mechanisms provided to prevent the cause of the failure from occurring will detect the cause of the failure or the failure itself. Accordingly, detectability can be considered also when the probability of harm occurrence is estimated. In risk management methodology when estimating the probability of occurrence of harm (detection seems to be an integral part of this probability), we factor the detection of the error at that point. Then if we also include detectability as an independent factor, we're "double-counting" that impact. In consideration of these factors, we need to be careful with the use of FMEA parameters and risk management parameters as well.

6.4   Risk Evaluation

Risk evaluation is the fourth step of the risk management process where the acceptance of the assessed risk is evaluated by comparing estimated levels of risk against the preestablished criteria. If the levels of risk established are low, then risks may fall into an acceptable category and treatment may not be required.

The phase of stating the risk acceptability is important from the point of view of further control. In most cases the criteria of acceptability are stated already in the preparatory phase of the risk assessment and included in the risk management plan.

In general, there is an acceptability matrix specific for each organization and each product. Risk evaluation is a value- and morality-based task, and the acceptability matrix reflects management priorities.

Decisions about the acceptability, or unacceptability, of risks are based on the two following levels:

- The acceptable (negligible) level of risk: This represents a socially acceptable level of the risk in which the probability of occurrence of an adverse effect (harm) is small. It means that this level of risk does not require any regulation or other measures for its reduction.

- The unacceptable level of risk: This requires the inevitable exercise of regulatory measures or other specific measures for its reduction.

Establishing the acceptability level of safety required and obtaining agreement on acceptable risk levels is a political and social activity involving a wide range of interests. Every individual as well as every society has values for risk acceptability that are a compromise in many cases or sometimes a consensus reflecting their real "cultural," technological, or operational maturity—in technical practice, this is often designated as the hazard-based culture.

The specific risk level for each hazard identified can be categorized as one of the following [5]:

- *Acceptable:* Risk that is so small it is negligible;
- *Tolerable:* Risk that can be tolerated in a given context based on the current values of society;
- *Undesirable:* Risk that can be deemed, with reasonably certainty, to give rise to harm;
- *Intolerable:* Risk that cannot be tolerated due the significant danger posed by its consequences.

Table 6.4 qualitatively outlines an example of the relationship between risk level, the likelihood of a harm occurring, and the resulting harm severity were the harm to occur.

Table 6.4
Risk Level, Likelihood of Harm Occurrence, and Harm Severity

	Minor (Negligible)	Moderate (Serious)	Major (Critical)	Catastrophic
Frequent	Undesirable	Intolerable	Intolerable	Intolerable
Probable (likely)	Tolerable	Undesirable	Intolerable	Intolerable
Occasional	Tolerable	Tolerable	Undesirable	Intolerable
Remote (seldom)	Acceptable	Tolerable	Tolerable	Undesirable
Improbable (unlikely)	Acceptable	Acceptable	Acceptable	Undesirable

There are at least two dimensions of subjectivity involved in the use of the acceptability matrix. The first is in the interpretation of the matrix categories—consider that your interpretation of the term "critical" may be quite different from mine. The second is in the interpretation of the hazard. This subjectivity naturally leads to some inconsistency.

Intolerable and undesirable risks should be reduced (using risk control measures) by reducing the harm severity and/or the likelihood of the harm occurrence to the point at which the resulting risk level is acceptable or tolerable.

Practically, the reduction of harm severity is very difficult to achieve. For this reason, the most commonly used way to reduce the risk level is to reduce the likelihood of harm occurrence.

6.5   Risk Control

The reduction of the severity and/or the likelihood of the hazards will bring us to the fifth step of risk management process: risk control.

In order to treat risks, decision makers have to select which countermeasures to implement to mitigate the risks. However, investment decisions are complicated. An organization needs the best possible information on risks and countermeasures to determine the best investment. The countermeasure expenditure, together with its ability to mitigate risks, are factors that affect the selection. Inappropriate and overexpensive countermeasures represent money lost. Usually, the risk is acceptable if the resulting outcome is valuable.

Accordingly, decision makers need to investigate specific strategies and tools that reduce, mitigate, or eliminate the risk of harm. Risk should be controlled so that the estimated risk of each identified hazard is made acceptable.

Risk control serves to outline the procedures applied to reduce any possible risk, and it refers to a solution for reducing the likelihood or potential severity of a hazard, or both. These solutions should be directed at the cause of the hazard or should introduce protective measures that operate when the cause of the hazard is present, specifying safety requirements to eliminate or minimize hazards and to achieve an acceptable risk level.

Applying the following three methods will ensure that the residual risk (the risk remaining after implementation of risk control means) has been adequately reduced in order to answer the question: Is this product safe? [3]

1. Eliminating the hazard or reducing the risk, for instance, by design, by the substitution of less hazardous materials and substances, or by the application of ergonomic principles;

2. Reducing the risk with the application of technical protective measures (e.g., devices and alarms) that adequately reduce risk for the intended use and that are appropriate for the application;

3. When the application of safeguarding or other protective measures is not practicable, turning to information for use, which must not be regarded as a substitute for the correct application of 1) and 2). In applying this method, decision makers should take notice of any residual risk that may exist. Accordingly, among other safeguards, it is necessary to ensure that the following are true:

   • That the operating procedures for the use of the product are consistent with the ability of personnel who use the product or other persons who can be exposed to the hazards associated with the product;
   • That the recommended safe working practices for the use of the product requirements have been adequately described;
   • That users are sufficiently informed about the residual risks in the different phases of the life of the product.

Products with excessive warning labels mean that design solutions or other protection means were not successful and resulted in only the labeling (informing the user) as the applicable method for risk control. This is a clear indication that the product is not safe enough.

RM is an ongoing process throughout the life cycle of the product. Postproduction information about the product and similar products should be systematically reviewed for possible relevance to product safety.

Note: Countermeasures provided by design and protective measures are preferable and more effective than those of informing the user. Indications about whether products can be considered safe may be derived from positive answers to the following questions:

- Have all operating conditions and all intervention procedures been taken into account?

- Have hazards been eliminated or risks been adequately reduced?

- Is it certain that the measures taken do not generate new hazards?

- Are the users sufficiently informed and warned about the residual risks?

- Are the users' working conditions and the usability of the product not jeopardized by the protective measures taken?

- Are the protective measures taken compatible with each other?

- Has sufficient consideration been given to the consequences that can arise from the use of a designed for professional/industrial use when it is used in a nonprofessional/nonindustrial context?

- Is it certain that the measures taken do not excessively reduce the ability of the product to perform its function?

6.6 Functional Safety

Before we discuss the evaluation of equipment from the perspective of functional safety, let's try to understand its meaning.

In order to fully understand the "Functional Safety of Electrical/Electronic/Programmable Electronic Safety-Related Systems" (as the title of the 61508 series of standards [7] refers to it), we will first postulate that functional safety should be regarded more like a concept and not as a measurable parameter of the equipment. The words from which this expression is comprised will allows us to understand the correct meaning and to arrive at a detailed explanation for this concept.

We consider first, as specified in Chapter 1, the meaning of the word safety: the freedom from unacceptable risk, (ISO/IEC Guide 51, definition 3.1). Second, we expand this phrase, freedom from unacceptable risk, and expand it to a more detailed form: freedom from the unacceptable risk of suffering a physical injury by persons, and/or, of the damage to the health of people, and/or, of the damage of the property, and/or, of a damage of the environment, directly, or indirectly, as a result of the functioning and using of an electrical product.

At the same time, considering the expression unacceptable risk, we consider the definition of the antonym expression, designated within the standards as tolerable risk, or "risk which is accepted in a given context based on the current values of society" [8].

When the electrical product in discussion is performing (along with the task for which it was designed), a safety function (e.g., in process plants, the emergency shutdown of facilities, chemical plants, and refineries; in machinery, the safety-related control systems for all types of machines used in factories; in power generation, including nuclear plants, boiler systems, gas turbines, and wind turbines; in the automotive industry, in-car safety systems such as automatic steering and braking systems; in the aerospace industry, in fly-by-wire systems and electronic throttle control units; and/or even in medical/patient testing systems, including MRI and X-ray machines), the evaluation of the ability of these systems to perform properly their safety function within a tolerable risk, should be evaluated.

According to the ISO definition, the objective of keeping pace with the current values of the society should be regarded as a continuous duty, because the safety of the people should be regarded continuously as paramount.

These conditions resulted in the request for developing standards to establish, in full accordance with the values of the society, a framework in which tolerable risk is defined as well as methods to evaluate its acceptance.

The IEC 61508 and, generally speaking, the standards that are used for the evaluation of functional safety, apply to safety-related systems that incorporate electrical and/or electronic and/or programmable electronic (E/E/PE) devices. This concept of functional safety has absolutely no applicability to passive components [7].

This concept and type of evaluation is fairly new. It appeared in 1998 as a necessity, a result of the evolution of technology over the preceding two decades: equipment in the aforementioned fields of industrial applications with programmable electronic systems able to perform safety functions and computer system technology developed to be effectively and safely exploited. It is vital that all the elements responsible for making decisions within a process have necessary and sufficient control of all the involved safety aspects of that process as well.

Functional safety is the part of the overall safety that depends on a system or product functioning correctly in response to its inputs. Functional safety comes to complete the evaluation of a system by identifying the potentially dangerous conditions resulting in the activation of a protective, or corrective, device or mechanism to prevent foreseeable hazardous events, or, at least, it will provide the assurance that a mitigation of the consequence of any hazardous event will be in place in case of a foreseeable functioning failure.

When discussing functional safety, the first step is it to understand whether this type of evaluation (based on the concept presented within the Standard IEC61508 or equivalent) is applicable to the product in question. We need to determine whether the characteristics of the product (or component) fall under the scope of the intended-to-be-applied standard.

The following are examples of test objects from the point of view of functional safety:

- Safeguards and critical safety components in machinery;
- Programmable or configurable controllers with safety functions;
- Drive systems with safety functions;
- Bus systems or devices with safety-related bus communication;
- Furnaces and plant controls and safeguards;
- Safety-related modules and components (e.g., relays with forcibly guided contacts, position switches, valves, and ASICs);
- Software products (compilers, or programs that process statements written in a particular programming language and translate them into machine language or "code" that a computer's processor uses programming).

In almost each and every electrical system that is programmable (or that uses software) within an area of a function that is related to safety, the functional safety of that system should be evaluated.

We use the term should (recommended) and not shall (mandatory), in order to avoid applying excessive stress on manufacturers. At the end of the day, each manufacturer will understand when it shall or should evaluate the functional safety of the products that leave their warehouses.

It is not an easy task to exclude any programmable electrical products from this type of evaluation (although, of course, products whose safety function do not depend on software decision may be excluded).

Due to the complexity of the work involved in a functional safety evaluation, we know that many software specialists will try to combat the following point of view: It is the duty of the manufacturer to prove to the testing house that the software it uses is fail-safe.

We strongly advocate the idea that software or firmware should only be allowed and included as a protection against hazards when the software or firmware is completely separate from any other system software (stand-alone) within the hardware architecture, so that it cannot be corrupted and will have only that one dedicated function. The hardware people will be in the position to fight for their right to remain silent when the software department drops the task of functional safety into the hardware department's list of responsibilities.

Today, companies developing product have started to understand the interdependence between software and hardware and compliance with applicable requirements as a whole and complex process. In our engineering judgement, management needs to be aware of and understand the definition of tolerable risk and the fact that it is a continuous process that defines with each step new requirements in full accordance with the current values of society. This is one of the reasons that manufacturers need to be actively involved in the process of developing and elaborating standards for products.

Since not all of the involved specialists subscribe to this belief, the compliance engineers—mainly electrical safety specialists—should consider at least the following tips:

- Never trust any software types, not even a single one. It is a mode of survival!

- Learn how to read code like a book (which means you will need to understand the language's basic syntax and structural characteristics) to be fully aware of the steps that the software is trying to accomplish.

- Learn how to run code in an emulator that can run under fully static clock conditions.

In our experience, testing houses assume that software fails 100% of the time from a safety point of view (and we agree with this view). Manufacturers need to prove to the testing laboratories that the software is fail-safe, which is probably not an easy task for the designers, and, most of the time, may not be possible from a practical point of view. It is a 100% correct and necessary decision to consider the safety evaluation of an electrical product in conjunction with the function of the subject product. For many years, the function of the product (even if safety-related) was neglected but we have never heard anyone state that some aspects may be neglected because they were not directly safety-related. In our opinion, directly or indirectly, all aspects of the product should be considered with the utmost attention.

Functional safety is part of the active systems only. The following are examples of functional safety that should be evaluated:

- The detection of smoke by sensors and the ensuring automatic activation of a fire suppression system;

- The activation of a switch in a medical X-ray system that limits a potentially dangerous level that has been reached to prevent further irradiation of the patient.

Safety achieved by measures, equipment, or components that rely on passive systems does not fall under the concept of functional safety. Consider this example:

A fire-resistant door or insulation to withstand high temperatures is a measure that is passive in nature and can protect against the same hazards as those controlled by functional safety concepts (detection with smoke detectors and automatic activation of a sprinkler system), but, this passive component—the fire door—does not meet functional safety concept ideas.

Functional safety covers possible hazards caused by failure of the safety functions to be performed by the E/E/PE safety-related systems and are distinct from hazards arising from the E/E/PE product's electrical safety characteristics (e.g., electric shock, radiation hazards, and risk of fire). It represents a part of the overall safety, which depends on the correct functioning of the product, as a response to its inputs.

The range of E/E/PE safety-related systems to which IEC 61508 and the rest of equivalent standards can be applied includes the following [7]:

- Emergency shut-down systems;
- Fire and gas systems;
- Turbine control;
- Gas burner management;
- Crane automatic safe-load indicators;
- Guard-interlocking and emergency-stopping systems for machinery;
- Medical devices;
- Dynamic positioning;
- Railway signaling systems;
- Variable speed motor drives used to restrict speed as a means of protection;
- Remote monitoring, operation, or programming of a network-enabled process plant;
- Any information-based decision-support tool, where erroneous results may affect safety.
- Examples of components that implement safety functions include the following:
- Electromechanical relays (i.e., electrical);
- Nonprogrammable solid-state electronics;
- Programmable controllers, microprocessors, application-specific integrated circuits (ASICs), or other programmable devices (e.g., sensors, transmitters, and actuators).

The applicable requirements of the standard apply to the entire E/E/PE safety-related system (e.g., from sensor, through control logic and communication systems, to the final actuator, including any safety critical actions of a human operator interaction). It is important to treat the system as a whole and to consider the interaction of all the components implied in the chain of action.

A risk assessment process should be performed before the functional safety evaluation. It will determine if functional safety is necessary. A risk assessment will define what actions of the product are safety-relevant and what actions are not considered safety-relevant; from the risk assessment, the product will be defined as having a list of safety functions, and a list of consequences of failures will be drawn. These lists will generate the fundamental engineering judgment on the functional safety approach.

The main goal of the functional safety assessment is to ensure that each function mentioned within the risk assessment is safety-related and relevant and that it carries out the intended function with a reliability level commensurate to the level of the criticality of the function if it will fail to perform.

"The safety integrity level (SIL) of a safety function defines the required reliability level for a safety function in the product. SIL is defined in four classes, from SIL 1 (the lowest required reliability level for a safety function) to SIL 4 (the highest required reliability level for a safety function). For safety functions with a relatively low criticality, SIL 1 may be appropriate. Safety functions with a high degree of criticality may require a SIL 3 or SIL 4 designation" [7].

Lower-level SIL targets allow the manufacturer to do a self-assessment; it should be performed when the company has internally a certified expert for functional safety. Higher-level SIL targets require a third-party assessment.

Companies that are seeking to certify their own experts may contact several certification agencies. The certification is provided according to the profile in which the expert will perform the activity. (e.g., automotive safety application, automation cybersecurity, machinery safety, process safety application, safety hardware development, and safety software development).

A functional safety assessment normally is broken down into several assessments:

- Review of safety requirements specification and audit of safety design management system;
- Review of hardware, software requirements specification, and verification and validation testing plan;
- Review of hardware and software design;
- Witness testing of hardware and software verification testing;
- Witness testing of validation testing and results;
- Review of user documentation and instructions;

• Review of complete technical file and all life-cycle documents.

In order to achieve the required functional safety of a system, there are several objectives; amongst them, we consider that these are the most important:

1. Any system that performs a safety function should use reliable components.
2. The faults should be diagnosed, and once detected, the system should be taken to a safe state.
3. When diagnosis is not possible, redundancy should be considered.

6.7 Standards for Risk Management

Table 6.5 lists the most significant risk management and functional safety standards.

Table 6.5
Risk Management and Functional Safety Standards

Standard	Name of the Standard	Notes
ANSI B11 TR3	Risk Assessment and Risk Reduction—A Guideline to Estimate, Evaluate, and Reduce Risks Associated with Machine Tools	
ANSI/RIA R 15.06	Industrial Robots and Robot Systems—Safety Requirements	
AS/NZS HB 203	Environmental Risk Management—Principles and Process	
AS/NZS HB 221	Business Continuity Management	
AS/NZS HB 240	Guidelines for Managing Risk in Outsourcing	
AS/NZS HB 436	Risk Management Guidelines Companion to AS/NZS 4360	
AS/NZS 4360	Risk Management	
BS 6079-3	Project Management. Guide to the Management of Business Related Project Risk	
CSA Q 850	Risk Management: Guideline for Decision Makers	
CAN/CSA Z434	Industrial Robots and Robot Systems—General Safety Requirements	
EN ISO 13849-1	"Safety of machinery—Safety-Related Parts of Control Systems"	
IEC 61508	Functional Safety of Electrical/Electronic/Programmable Electronic Safety-Related Systems	

Table 6.5 (continued)

IEC 61511	Functional Safety—Safety Instrumented Systems for the Process Industry Sector
IEC 62061	"Safety of Machinery—Functional Safety of Safety-Related Electrical, Electronic and Programmable Electronic Control Systems"
IEC 62198	Managing Risk in Projects—Application Guidelines
ISO/IEC 14971	Application of Risk Management to Medical Devices
ISO/IEC Guide 51	Safety Aspects—Guidelines For Their Inclusion In Standards
IEC/ISO 31010	Risk management—Risk assessment techniques
IEEE 1540	IEEE Standard for Software Life Cycle Processes—Risk Management
ISO 10218	Robots And Robotic Devices—Safety Requirements for Industrial Robots
ISO 12100	Safety of Machinery. General Principles for Design. Risk Assessment and Risk Reduction
ISO 14121	Safety of Machinery -- Risk Assessment
ISO 15743	Practical Aspects of Management of Risk—Risk Assessment and Management for Cold Workplaces
ISO 31000	Risk Management—Principles and Guidelines
ISO/TS 14798	Lifts (Elevators), Escalators and Moving Walks—Risk Assessment and Reduction Methodology
MIL-STD-882E	Military System Safety—Environment, Safety, and Occupational Health Risk Management Methodology for Systems Engineering
ONR 49000	Risk Management in Organizations and systems In German
PAS 56	Guide to Business Continuity Management
PD 6668	Managing Risk for Corporate Governance
SEMI S10-1103	Safety Guideline for Risk Assessment and Risk Evaluation Process
SEMI S14-1103	Safety Guidelines for Fire Risk Assessment and Mitigation for Semiconductor Manufacturing Equipment
SNZ HB 8669	Guidelines for Managing Risk in Sport and Recreation
UL 991	Safety-Related Controls Employing Solid-State Devices
UL 1998	Software in Programmable Components

References

[1] ISO/IEC Guide 73, "Risk Management: Vocabulary Guidelines for Use in Standards," Geneva, 2002.

[2] IEC/ISO 31010, "Risk Management—Risk Assessment Techniques," Geneva, 2009.

[3] ISO/IEC 14971-1, "Medical Devices—Risk Management Part 1: Application of Risk Analysis," Second Edition, Geneva, 2007.

[4] Bolintineanu, C., and S. Loznen, "Product Safety and Third Party Certification," *The Electronic Packaging Handbook*, edited by G. R. Blackwell, Boca Raton, FL: CRC Press LLC, 2000.

[5] U.S. Air Force Safety Agency, "System Safety Handbook," 2000.

[6] Storey, N., *Safety Critical Computer Systems*, Harlow, United Kingdom: Pearson Education Limited, 1996.

[7] IEC 61508-1, "Functional Safety of Electrical/Electronic/Programmable Electronic Safety-Related Systems—Part 1: General Requirements," Geneva, 2010.

[8] ISO/IEC Guide 51, "Safety Aspects—Guidelines for Their Inclusion in Standards," Geneva, 2014.

Selected Bibliography

Aven, T., *Foundations of Risk Analysis*, Chichester, UK: John Wiley and Sons, 2002

Bedford, T., and R. Cooke, *Probabilistic Risk Analysis (Foundations and Methods)*, Cambridge, Great Britain: Cambridge University Press, 2001.

Bell, J., and J. Holroyd, *Review of Human Reliability Assessment Methods*, Norwich, UK: Health and Safety Laboratory, 2009.

Chopra, S., and M. S. Sodhi, "Managing Risk To Avoid Supply Chain Breakdown," *Sloan Management Review* 46, 2004, pp.53–62.

European Union website: http://ec.europa.eu/growth/single-market/goods/building-blocks/notified-bodies_en.

EU Directive 2006/42/EC of the European Parliament and of the Council of 17 May 2006 on Machinery, and Amending Directive 95/16/EC.

Haynl, M., "A Look at IEC 61508 The Standard Drives Functional Safety," *Control Design*, April 2010.

IEC/ACOS/387/DC, "Risk Management—Guidelines for Principles and Implementation of Risk Management," ISO TMB/WG, 2005.

IEC62061, "Safety of Machinery—Functional Safety of Safety-Related Electrical, *Electronic And Programmable Electronic Control Systems*," Geneva, 2005.

IEC TR 60513, "Fundamental Aspects of Safety Standards for Medical Electrical Equipment," Geneva, 1994.

Kumar, S., Schmitz, S., "Managing recalls in a consumer product supply chain – root cause analysis and measures to mitigate risk", *International Journal of Production Research* 49, 2011, pp.235–253.

MIL-STD-882- "Standard Practice for System Safety," U.S. Department of Defense, 2012.

Lewis, M.A., "Cause, Consequence and Control: Towards a Theoretical and

Practical Model of Operational Risk," Journal of Operations Management 21, 2003, pp. 205–224.

Loznen, S., "Make Safer Products by Standardization the Risks," Quality Assurance, Bucharest, Romania, 2016, pp. 8–10.

Lowrance, W. W., Of Acceptable Risk: Science and the Determination of Safety, Los Altos, CA: William Kaufman Inc., 1976.

Rexroth Bosch Group, "Rexroth IndraDrive Integrated Safety Technology as of MPx-1x," R911332634 Edition 04.

Riswadkar, A., and D. Jewell, "Strategies for Managing Risks from Imported Products," Professional Safety, 52 (11), 2007.

Vose, D., Risk Analysis—A Quantitative Guide, Chichester, UK: John Wiley and Sons Inc., 2008.

7

Electrical Product Safety Concepts

7.1 Means of Protection

The process of providing adequate *means of protection* (MOP) against hazards generating harm needs to identify all known and foreseeable hazards associated with the product in both normal and abnormal conditions. The process used to identify hazards is covered in Chapters 5 and 6. This section provides an overview of the MOP concept.

MOP[s] are designated also as *levels of protection* (LOP). The term MOP is replaced in some documents (i.e., the "Hazard-Based Standard," or IEC 62368-1) with the term "safeguards." A *safeguard* is a physical part or system or instruction specifically provided to reduce the likelihood of unacceptable risks of harm (pain, injury, death, or damage to property or the environment). Other standards (i.e., IEC 60601-1) define MOP as a means for reducing the unacceptable risk of harm due only to electric shock hazard [1].

MOP can be used for all types of separation between nonhazardous areas and hazardous areas for all hazard categories. Depending on the areas that need to be separated by the insulation, it should provide one means of protection or two means of protection.

MOP examples include the following:

- Reducing the levels, slowing the transfer rate, or changing the direction of a specific kind of energy that can cause a hazardous situation;
- Disconnecting, interrupting, or disabling the source of the hazardous situation;

- Interposing a barrier between the source of the hazardous situation and the humans or areas that need to be protected;
- Limiting access to the area of the source of the hazardous situation.

A MOP can be applied to the equipment, to the installation, or to a person, or it can be a learned or directed behavior intended to reduce the unacceptable risk of harm. A MOP may be a single element, or it may be a set of elements.

Total protection is never possible, and the best safety measures involve finding reasonable and well thought-out compromises in which priority is given to safeguarding people. The MOP provided by a part of the product can be estimated by compliance of the subject part with specified tests.

7.1.1 MOP(s) Against Electrical Shock

MOP(s) against electrical shock should be provided for direct contact with live parts and for indirect contact (failures of separation between live parts and accessible conductive parts). They consist of or are provided by solid insulation, spacing (air clearance and creepage distances) between hazardous and non-hazardous areas, protective earth connections, components (i.e., impedances, overcurrent protection devices, and safety interlocks), barriers and enclosures to prevent accessibility to hazardous areas, installation instructions, warning markings on hazardous areas, and protective equipment (glove-resistant to hazardous voltages).

From note [1]:

- Basic insulation (BI) is a spacing or a physical insulation barrier providing one MOP.
- Supplemental insulation (SI) is also a spacing or a physical insulation barrier providing one MOP.
- Double insulation (DI) is BI and SI and provides two MOP.
- Reinforced insulation (RI) is a single spacing or physical insulation barrier that provides two MOP(s).
- Protective impedance is a component (such as a resistor) that provides one MOP.
- Protective earth (PE) is a well-grounded part that provides one MOP.
- Class I equipment is defined as using PE as one MOP.
- Class II equipment (also known as double-insulated) is defined as not using PE as one MOP.
- Y1 capacitors provide two MOP(s).

- One layer of spirally wrapped tape or extruded layer of insulation provides one MOP.

- Two layers of spirally wrapped tape or extruded layers of insulation provide one MOP.

- Three layers of spirally wrapped tape or extruded layers of insulation provide two MOP(s).

- Solvent-based enamel in winding insulation under any circumstances is not considered to provide two MOP(s).

7.1.2 MOP(s) Against Mechanical Hazards

{text MOP(s) against mechanical hazards consist of barriers (guards), pressure-relief valves, safety catches and interlocks, rounding of sharp edges and corners, installation instructions, warning markings on access to dangerous areas, and protection equipment (e.g., impact resistant goggles and face shields and earplugs).

7.1.3 MOP(s) Against Radiation (Ionizing and NonIonizing) Hazards

MOP(s) against radiation consist of screening of radiation sources, components that provide limitation of radiation, safety interlocks to limit access to radiation areas, installation instructions, warnings on radiation areas, and protection equipment (safety spectacles).

Note: An opaque *enclosure* that meets part of or all relevant tests (steady force, enclosure impact, drop, stress relief, and glass fragmentation) is considered to provide two MOP(s).

7.1.4 MOP(s) Against Thermal (Heat and Fire) Hazards

MOP(s) against thermal hazards consist of insulation (separation) of the potential ignition sources (e.g., overload in windings, bad contacts, short-circuits, and arcing) from combustible parts, use of materials with appropriate flammability, components (e.g., overcurrent protection devices, thermal cutoff, and temperature-limiting devices), warning markings on the potential hot parts, installation instructions, and protection equipment (i.e., gloves and special clothing).

7.1.5 MOP(s) Against Biological Hazards

MOP(s) against biological hazards consist of biocompatible materials, per the ISO 10993 standard for parts in contact with the human body, warning markings on potential biological hazardous areas, and protection equipment (e.g., gloves and special clothing).

7.1.6   MOP(s) Against Chemical Hazards

MOP(s) against chemical hazards consist of separation and sealing of containers with dangerous substances, warning markings on access to dangerous areas, installation instructions, and protection equipment (e.g., gloves, special clothing, and chemical-resistant goggles and face shields).

> *Note:* A vessel that meets part of or all relevant tests (e.g., hydrostatic pressure, creep-resistance, tubing and fittings compatibility, vibration, thermal cycling, and force) is considered to comprise two MOP(s).

7.1.7   MOP(s) Against Informational Hazards

MOP(s) against informational hazards consist of all safety information provided by user manuals, information for use, and safety information.

> *Note:* Instructional safeguards (e.g., safety symbols and cautionary warnings) are considered to provide one MOP.

7.2   Insulation Diagrams

Insulation diagrams are a representation of how hazardous areas are insulated. Insulation separates hazardous areas by the use of a MOP to reduce or prevent the transmission of heat, electricity, radiation, or another form of energy available from the subject's hazardous area. In fact, forms of energy from hazardous areas that can generate unacceptable risks of harm (i.e., injuries, fire, or death) to humans or the environment are identified with the well-known physical hazards [e.g., electrical, mechanical, chemical, radiation, and thermal (heat and fire)].

The areas that are insulated are significantly different one from another one from the point of view of the danger that may arise. Insulation can fail due to mechanical damage, vibration, excessive heat or cold, dirt, oil, corrosive vapors, and moisture from processes or just humidity. Furthermore, pin holes or cracks can develop, and moisture and foreign matter can penetrate the surfaces of the insulation.

Note: The term *insulation* means "the action or means to isolate, detach, or separate," where the term "isolation" represents the "state of being isolated, detached, or separated." A part is "isolated" by "insulation" material or by grounding, as a MOP.

Thermal insulation is a general term used to describe MOP(s) that reduce heat loss or heat gain by providing a barrier between areas that are significantly different in temperature.

Acoustic insulation is normally found in parts providing separation between areas with dangerous levels of noise and areas that need to be protected from excessive noise. Specialized soundproofing materials are usually reserved for special applications.

Electrical circuitry that can be in galvanic contact with humans (in a non-hazardous area) needs to be isolated from an electrical hazardous area (where currents and voltages exceed the limits of danger). It permits the two parts of the circuit to be at different voltage levels, which means that one can be safe while the other side is at hazardous voltage levels. For electrical isolation to be safe, it needs to have two things: high-integrity insulation components (i.e., optocouplers, transformers, and capacitive couplers) and a safe insulator barrier. For example, this insulator can be a piece of plastic, a keep-out space (creepage distance) in a PCB, or an air gap (air clearance).

Good electrical insulation has high resistance; poor electrical insulation as relatively low resistance (resistance decreases with the temperature or moisture content of the insulation).

From the electrical safety perspective, a piece of equipment should implement two MOP(s) or LOPs or safeguards such that if a failure occurs within one area, a second mechanism provides insulation from electric shock hazards due to leakage currents passing through the body. Depending on how the protection against electrical shock is provided the electrical equipment is designated Class I or Class II. [It is important not to confuse these classes with classifications established by European directives (e.g., Class I, IIa, IIb, and III) or the FDA (e.g., Class I, II, and III).]

Class I

Class I products use BI in combination with PE. These products have a three-pronged power cord, and the ground blade is attached to any accessible metal on the product. Class I products have higher allowable leakage currents as the ground provides a level of protection for the operator and effectively drains off leakage current that a person might come in contact with. Leakage current limits for Class I products also vary depending upon whether the power cord is detachable or permanent. [1].

Class II

Products with a two-pronged power cord are Class II products. Class II products rely not only on basic insulation but also on double insulation or reinforced insulation. These products are often referred to as double-insulated products, as their protection from shock relies on two layers of insulation. Since there is no protective earth to drain off excess leakage current, the limits of acceptable leakage current for Class II products are lower than those for Class I products. (In Class II equipment, the human body that is in contact with the equipment will be the only way to conduct any current from the enclosure to the earth) [1].

> *Note:* There is a possibility that a Class II electrical product, with a MOP against electrical shock that is provided by a nonconductive enclosure (plastic), is using a three-pronged power cord. This plug is used for EMI reasons of power supply, but the connection to protective earthing does not provide a MOP against electrical shock.

The characterization of electrical insulation is done by specifying insulating materials (solid insulation), air clearances, and creepage distances, including the use of these materials in components. To assess the integrity and the efficiency of a solid insulation, a dielectric withstand test is used. If the electrical insulation does not meet both the dielectric and the spacing (air clearances and creepage distances) requirements, it cannot be considered as a LOP and can be shorted as a normal condition.

> *Note:* The two (or more) layers of insulation do not have to be the same type of material; one layer could be an air gap, and another layer could be tape (distance-through-insulation).

Insulation providing MOP functions are designated as follows [2]:

- *Functional (operational) insulation:* Insulation that is necessary only for the correct functioning of the equipment but that does not protect against electric shock. It may, however, reduce the likelihood of ignition and fire.
- *Basic insulation:* Insulation providing basic protection against electric shock.
- *Supplementary insulation:* Independent insulation applied in addition to basic insulation in order to provide protection against electric shock in the event of a failure of basic insulation.
- *Double insulation:* Insulation comprising both basic insulation and supplementary insulation;

• *Reinforced insulation:* A single insulation system that provides a degree of protection against electric shock equivalent to double insulation providing two MOP(s).

For a complete understanding of the insulation used in electrical equipment, an *insulation diagram* is the most practical and useful solution. An isolation diagram is a block diagram that can show insulation information about the product without extensive schematics. An isolation diagram indicates how a product is designed to isolate from the mains (hazardous areas) the secondary circuits (nonhazardous areas.)

In general, the insulation diagram is accompanied by a table that specifies the requested values for spacing (air clearance and creepage distance) for each type of insulation provided. A table defines the designation as basic, supplementary, or double (reinforced) or can be indicated by the numbers of MOP(s) corresponding to each type of insulation (one MOP for basic and supplementary and two for double—reinforced). Each product safety standard specifies what kind of insulation is required between the product parts.

7.2.1 Drawing an Insulation Diagram

Figure 7.1 is an example of an insulation diagram for a piece of medical electrical equipment that needs to comply with the standard IEC 60601-1. On this kind of equipment, the MOP(s) are divided into means of protection of operator (MOOP) and means of protection of patient (MOPP) categories [1].

Note: For drawing the insulation diagram for the example product in Figure 7.1, the requirements for the different insulation specified in IEC 60601-1 was applied [1].

The device in Figure 7.1 is a class II device without a protective earth connection. The internals are simplified to show only the isolation barriers. It is assumed that the device has to be able to be used up to an altitude of 2,000m. It is used in a hospital (pollution degree 2, overvoltage category II). The applied part is not defibrillator-proof, and the PCB material is standard rated for flammability.

For normal work conditions and for a single fault condition, the working voltages need to be calculated. This includes the voltage type (primary or secondary). Primary dominates over secondary. If both sides have different voltage types, the dominating type is used for calculation.

Peak working voltage is the sum of the peak voltages. DC working voltage is the sum of the DC voltage or 0 if not purely DC. RMS is the square root of the sum of the squares of the RMS values.

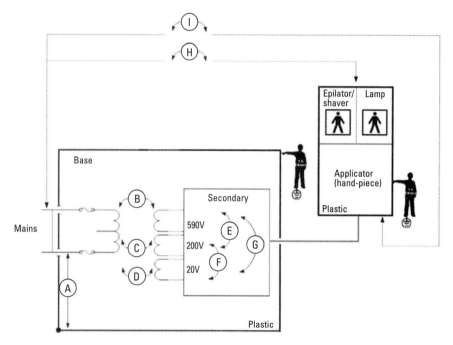

Figure 7.1 Example of an insulation program.

Based on the calculation of the working voltages for each insulation, select from the appropriate tables of the IEC 60601-1 the requested values for air clearance and creepage distances. For solid insulation, one should use the tables that specify the test voltage for dielectric withstand. Table 7.1 shows an example of the evaluation of spacings based on Figure 7.1.

The creepage distance is compared to the air clearance. If it is lower, then the air clearance is taken, because the creepage distance cannot be less than the air clearance.

7.3 Safe Current and Voltage limits

Electrical shock and its effects can be caused and influenced by several factors. The primary effect is the result of electrical current passing through the human body. Severity of the injury to the human body is directly affected by such variables as: the nature of the electrical voltage (AC, DC); environmental conditions (relative humidity and ambient temperature); the pathway through the human body; conductivity of the contact (wet or dry); the size and shape of the individual involved (i.e., the person's impedance); duration of the contact; and the size of the contact area.

Table 7.1

The Evaluation of Spacing as per the Insulation Diagram in Figure 7.1

Initial Conditions:

Pollution degree: 2

Overvoltage category: II

Altitude: Up to 2,000m

Additional details on parts considered as applied parts: □ None □ Areas _____

Area in Insulation Diagram	Number and type of MMOP: MOOP, MOPP	CTI (IIIb, unless known)	Working Voltage Vrms (VAC)	Vpk (VAC)	Required Creepage (mm)	Required Clearance (mm)	Measured Creepage (mm)	Measured Clearance (mm)	Remarks
A	2 MOPP	IIIb	240	340	8	5	Reinforced insulation is achieved by solid insulation (width 3 mm min.)		L+N to base plastic enclosure
B	2 MOPP	IIIb	590	---	12.6	10	28	28	Primary to secondary 590V
C	2 MOPP	IIIb	200	---	8	5	28	28	Primary to secondary 200V
D	2 MOPP	IIIb	20	---	8	5	8.2	8.2	Primary to SELV 20V
E	2 MOPP	IIIb	590	---	12.6	10	18.5	18.5	secondary 590V to secondary 200V
F	2 MOPP	IIIb	240	-	8	5	17	14.2	Secondary 200V to SELV 20V

Table 7.1 (continued)

F	2 MOPP	IIb	240	-	8	5	17	14.2	Secondary 200V to SELV 20V
G	2 MOPP	IIb	590	---	12.6	10	18.5	18.5	Secondary 590V to SELV 20V
H	2 MOPP	IIb	240	-	8	5	31.2	31.2	L+N to applied parts (metal part + electrodes)
I	2 MOPP	IIb	240	340	8	5	Reinforced insulation is achieved by solid insulation (width 1.6 mm min.)		L+N to Applicator plastic enclosure
J	1 MOOP	IIb	240	-	3	1.6	4.5	2.5	Operation insulation as basic insulation between L and N

The frequency in hertz (Hz) of the electrical source is also a determining factor in the subsequent effect and/or reaction of the human body when subjected to electrical current flow. Studies have shown that low-frequency voltages, such as AC power line voltage (50–60 Hz), have a more immediate and damaging effect than DC voltage when contact with the human body occurs. Therefore, it is important that electrical products be designed to protect the user from contact with AC line/primary voltage.

7.3.1 Safe Current Limits

A person typically perceives current flow through his or her body when it reaches approximately 1 mA. This amount of current will produce a slight tingling feeling through the fingertips. Current above the threshold can cause an uncontrolled muscular spasm or shock. Between 10 and 20 mA, the person experiences muscle contractions and finds it more difficult to release his or her hand from an electrode. An externally applied current of 50 mA causes pain, possibly fainting, and exhaustion. An increase to 100 mA will cause ventricular fibrillation. The risk of harm due to electrical shock is highest and approximately equal for frequencies in the 10–200-Hz range. It is lower, by a factor of nearly 5, at DC and by approximately 1.5 at 1 kHz. Beyond 1 kHz, the harm probability decreases rapidly. However, lower limits are needed for DC to prevent tissue necrosis with long-term application. Currents of low frequency flowing directly into or through the heart considerably increase the danger of ventricular fibrillation. For currents of medium- or high-frequency, the risk of harm due to electric shock is less or negligible, but the risk of harm due to burning remains.

> *Note:* Not surprisingly, these limits were determined by performing experiments on humans, experiments that determined a threshold of perception.

The experiments were conducted by Charles Dalziel, a former UC Berkley professor, in the late 1940s. He did very risky research on human body's reaction to electric shock hazards. Using volunteers in his experiments—and being assisted during the experiment by medical staff—he tested the human body's reaction to the passing of electric current through it; he found that the body reacts to different levels of electrical current in different ways. Dalziel conducted the tests only at low levels of current, and later, based on calculations derived from his experiments, it was determined that the human body may be considered to have an average resistance of 1,000 ohms hand-to-hand and/or hands-to-feet. During those experiments, it was also determined that the human body's answer to the applied current follows an exponential model. In order to be even safer, later on, a 500-ohm equivalent resistance was considered as acceptable as a representative impedance for the internal human body resistance (less the skin), and it is considered to serve as the current-feeling resistor in the measuring circuit of the touch current.

An equivalent circuit of the human body consists of an input resistance of 1,500 ohms shunted by a capacitance of 0.15 microfarads.

> *Note:* According to the IEC60990 standard, the elementary touch current network model considers as representative a network that comprises a three-component combination, a 500-ohm resistor in series with a parallel combination of a 1,500-ohm resistor and a capacitor of 0.22 μF. The 1,500-ohm resistor in parallel with the capacitor represents the combined impedance of the entry and exit skin contacts [3].

To provide a margin of protection, product safety standards usually require that a product exhibit leakage current of less than 500 μA in a single fault condition. The current density created at the heart by current entering the chest is 50 μA/mm^2 for 1A. Accordingly, the current density at the heart for 500 μA entering the chest is 0.025 μA/mm^2 [3]

Acceptable levels of leakage currents are specified for each particular type of product, but they are not very consistent.

In North America, some of the standards, set a maximum acceptable value for earth leakage and touch currents of 1 mA.

Other European and international standards that were adopted in North America impose a limit for the same kind of currents from 0.25 mA and up to 3.5 mA, depending on the class of equipment.

In *single-fault conditions,* an AC current up to 1 KHz exceeding 0.5 mA RMS (0.707 mA peak) or 2 mA DC, or when there is an AC current within the range 1 to 100 kHz exceeding 0.5 mA RMS multiplied with f (in kHz), and an AC current with f above 100kHz exceeding 50 mA RMS, is considered *hazardous current* [4].

In normal conditions, an AC current up to 1 KHz exceeding 5 mA RMS (7.07 mA peak) or 25 mA DC, or when there is an AC current within the range 1 to 100 kHz exceeding 5 mA RMS + 0.95 multiplied with f (in kHz), and an AC current with f above 100 kHz exceeding 100 mA RMS, is considered hazardous current [4].

> *Note:* RMS values are used only for sinusoidal current; the Peak values are used for nonsinusoidal current.

7.3.2   Safe Voltage Limits

Products should be designed to be safe at any supply voltage to which they are intended to be connected. If the product is intended for direct connection to an AC or DC mains supply, the tolerances of the rated voltage at which the tests are conducted should be considered as listed in Table 7.2. Protection is provided by the use of a nondangerous voltage supplied by a safety source.

In normal conditions, an AC voltage up to 1 KHz exceeding 30 V RMS (42.4 V peak) or 60 V DC, or when there is an AC voltage within the range 1 to 100 kHz exceeding 30 V RMS + 0.4 multiplied with f (in kHz), and an AC voltage with f above 100 kHz exceeding 70 V RMS, is considered hazardous voltage [4].

In single-fault condition,s an AC voltage up to 1 KHz exceeding 50 V RMS (70.7 V peak) or 120 V DC, or when there is an AC voltage within the range 1 to 100 kHz exceeding 50 V RMS + 0.9 multiplied with f (in kHz), and an AC voltage with f above 100 kHz exceeding 140 V RMS, is considered hazardous voltage [4].

Note: RMS values are used only for sinusoidal voltage; the peak values are used for nonsinusoidal voltage.

If the extra-low voltage (ELV) is not provided by a safety source (e.g., an autotransformer, electronic power supply, or variable control unit), the circuit concerned must be subject to protective measures other than ELV (generally the same as those of the LV supply circuit).

Safety ELV (SELV) can provide protection against direct contact and indirect contact at the same time. A SELV installation meets two criteria:

• All the live parts are separated from the live parts of all other installations, by double or reinforced insulation.

• The live parts are isolated from earth and from any protective conductors belonging to another installation.

• A protection ELV (PELV) installation also meets two criteria:

• Installation is in the ELV range.

Table 7.2
Tolerances on the Mains-Rated Voltage

Type of Mains Supply	Tolerance on Rated Voltage
AC	+6 % and −10 %
AC-rated voltage 230-V single-phase or 400-V three-phase	+10 % and −10 %
DC	+20 % and −15 %

- All the live parts are separated from the live parts of all other installations, by double or reinforced insulation.

7.3.3   Power Distribution Systems

According to IEC 60364-1, AC *power distribution systems* are classified TN, TT, and IT, depending on the arrangement of current-carrying conductors and the method of earthing. Table 7.3 details the classification of power distribution systems.

There are three types of TN power distribution systems, described as follows.

- *TN-S:* In which a separate protective conductor is used throughout the system;
- *TN-C-S:* In which neutral and protective functions are combined in a single conductor in part of the system;
- *TN-C:* In which neutral and protective functions are combined in a single conductor throughout the system.

Some TN power distribution systems are supplied from a secondary winding of a transformer that has an earthed center tap (neutral). Where the two-phase conductors and the neutral conductor are available, these systems are commonly known as "single-phase, three-wire power distribution systems."

Power distribution systems are also considered motor-driven generators and uninterruptible power supplies (UPS). Around the world, the following types of equipment connections are considered:

- Single-phase, two-wire;
- Single-phase, three-wire;
- Two-phase, three-wire;
- Three-phase, three-wire;
- Three-phase, four-wire;
- Three-phase, five-wire.

Some examples of single-phase systems are listed as follows:

1. Europe: 230V (L-N), 50 Hz;
2. North America (United States and Canada): 120V (L-N), 60 Hz;

Table 7.3

Classification of Power Distribution Systems

First Letter (Indicates the Relationship of the Power Distribution System to Earth)		
T	Direct connection of one pole to earth	
I	System isolated from earth, or one point connected to earth through an impedance	
Second Letter (Refers to the Earthing of the Equipment)		
T	direct electrical connection of the equipment to earth, independently of the earthing of any point of the power distribution system	
N	Direct electrical connection of the equipment to the earthed point of the power Distribution system (in AC systems, the earthed point of the power distribution system is normally the neutral point or, if a neutral point is not available, a phase conductor)	
Third Letter (If Used Specifies the Arrangement of Neutral and Protective Conductors)		
S	The protective function is provided by a conductor separate from the neutral or from the earthed line (or in AC systems, earthed phase) conductor	
C	The neutral and protective functions are combined in a single conductor (PEN conductor)	

3. Japan: 100V (L-N), 50 Hz in eastern Japan and 60 Hz in western Japan;

4. Australia: TN-S.

The following are examples of three-phase systems:

1. Europe: 400V (L-L), Y connection, 50 Hz;

2. North America (United States and Canada): 208V (L-L), Y connection, 60 Hz;

3. Japan: 200V (L-L), - connection, 50 Hz in eastern Japan and 60 Hz in western Japan.

7.4 Leakage Currents

Leakage currents or touch currents are mostly a generic term that expresses the unwanted (nonfunctional) currents present on the accessible parts of a piece of equipment due to an inadequate insulation or improper earthing of the internal supplies and the accessible (mainly conductive) parts of the equipment.

Leakage currents are classified as follows:

- Protective conductor current, or earth leakage current: Defined in the IEC 60601-1 standard as "current flowing from the mains parts through or across the insulation into the protective earth conductor or a functional earthed connection."
- Touch current, or enclosure leakage current: Defined in the IEC 60990 standard as "the electric current through a human body or through an animal body when it touches one or more accessible parts of an installation or of equipment."
- Patient leakage current (present in medical electrical equipment): Defined in the IEC 60601-1 standard as "current flowing from the patient connections via the patient to earth."

Leakage currents are defined in several ways, but their effects are always the same. Leakage currents should be considered a potential electric shock hazard generated by any electrical equipment operated from the mains that can be felt by any person (e.g., user, operator, or service provider) in contact with the equipment.

Leakage currents are ignored when the equipment is properly designed and earthed. They will not be felt by end user it in the majority of cases.

Excessive values of a leakage currents may result for several reasons:

- Improper earthing or installation of the equipment;
- Aging and deterioration of the insulation of the equipment;
- Damaged components.

Equipment with a leakage current higher than the acceptable values poses the risk of electric shock, which is the physiological result of current passing through the human body.

Leakage currents are, in fact, the normal result of the fact that any type of insulation has a certain impedance, which, when it is interposed between the mains and the accessible parts of an equipment, will conduct some current: The current will try to find the easiest path to the earth ground, and when the easiest path is offered by the human body (touching the enclosure of a piece of electrical equipment), that current will flow through the human body to an earth ground. If the value of the leakage current is above the limit of sensitivity of that body, it may cause an electric shock.

Talking about the sensitivity of a human body, or even an animal body, is itself a sensitive topic that needs to remain central to the field of the research. It reminds us that we have to measure the value of leakage currents and to keep them within the required limits.

In order to protect end users against shocks generated by the presence of leakage currents, in type tests (tests performed on electrical equipment during a complete safety evaluation), the touch current/protective earth current/leakage current test is performed using specific testers (with a specific measurement network for the model of the human body) for this type of measurement. The measurement of the leakage currents should be performed at the highest limit of the rated voltage and as well at the highest frequency at which the equipment is working. When choosing components that are directly involved in the variation of the earth and touch leakage currents (e.g., RF filters) the ratings of those components should be reviewed with caution: More than once we have found that some manufacturers are rating the components for a wide range of input voltage (e.g., 100–240-V AC) and within the specification the leakage current is given at 120-V applied voltage. It generates not only confusion: we observed that by erroneously interpreting the ratings, not once was it necessary to change the design due to a higher value of the leakage current that was developed within equipment with multiple power supplies.

The measuring network to determine the value of the leakage currents should be the one indicated within the product standard using an isolation transformer (which is not mandatory but strongly recommended); when the isolation transformer is not used, the equipment under test (EUT) should be tested on an insulated stand, following all of the precautions of not touching any conductive part nor the tester's leads or tips of the used instrument.

Special consideration should be given to multiple power supplies within an electrical installation in which the summation of the leakage currents occurs.

7.5 Spacing: Air Clearance and Creepage Distances

Spacing is a very complex subject in the field of electrical equipment safety. The spacing distance between components and conductive parts that is required to withstand a given voltage within specific environmental conditions using certain materials is specified in terms of air clearance and creepage distances.

The *air clearance* distance (Figure 7.2) is defined as the shortest distance between two conductive materials measured through air. A compliant air clearance distance prevents breakdown due to the ionization of the air space between conductive parts that are at different voltages, and it avoids any possible flashovers. The pollution degree, temperature, and relative humidity influence the tendency for a breakdown. Breakdown along an air clearance path is a fast

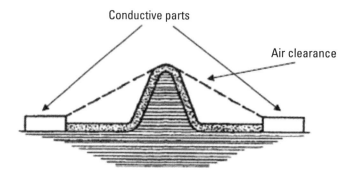

Figure 7.2   Air clearance [1].

phenomenon where damage can be caused by a very short duration impulse. Therefore, it is the maximum peak voltage, including transients, that is to be used to determine the required air clearance spacing.

To determine air clearance distances, several factors (described as follows) should be considered:

- Working voltage (the highest voltage to which the insulation under consideration is, or can be, subjected when the equipment is operating at its rated voltage;
- Mains supply voltage of the equipment;
- Type of the required insulation;
- Overvoltage category and values of transients;
- Pollution degree of the environment in which the equipment will work;
- Maximum altitude at which the equipment is intended to be installed.

Air clearances should be dimensioned so that the overvoltage transients that may enter the equipment and the peak voltages that may be generated within the equipment will not break down any clearance.

Creepage distance (Figure 7.3) is defined as the shortest path between two conductive parts measured along the surface of an isolator, which is in between. Providing the required creepage distance eliminates the risk of failures due to the tracking on surfaces between conductive parts over the lifetime of a piece of equipment. Due to the high voltage that it is applied during the lifetime of a piece of equipment, between the conductive parts along the insulated path on the surface—depending on the environment in which the equipment is used (e.g., temperature, humidity, presence of some pollution such as dust)—and the material characteristics of the insulation, the so-called comparative tracking index (CTI), tracking of the high voltages including breakdown of some

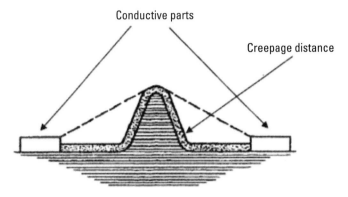

Figure 7.3 Creepage distance [1].

insulation may occur between conductive parts that are at different voltages [5]. The CTI characterizes the ability of an insulating material to track over the surface the voltage from a conductive part to another one.

In the determination of the creepage distance, several factors should be considered:

- Working voltage;
- Type of insulation that shall be provided;
- Pollution degree;
- Tracking characteristic (CTI class of the material) of the insulated material that is used (e.g., PCB material, plastic materials, or barriers);
- Type of circuit (e.g., primary, secondary, TNV, SELV, or ELV).

As a rule, the creepage distance cannot be less than the air clearance.

For each piece of equipment that falls within the scope of product safety standards the minimum air clearances and creepage distances for insulation in primary circuits and between primary and secondary circuits (expressed in millimeters) are defined within the applicable standard. There are installations, and even complex equipment, for which more than one standard is applicable. In such situations, we consider that the most severe conditions that are specified with the standards that may be used for that equipment should be applied from that stage of the design.

It is the manufacturer's goal to ensure that the equipment placed on the market is safe and reliable from the point of view of electrical safety as well as from the performance point of view.

It is not mandatory to have a piece of equipment certified/listed based on several standards at the same time. (This solution is often used to proof the level of the electrical safety of the equipment.) On the other hand, manufacturers are expected to supply equipment that meets all of the known requirements specified within the applicable standards; this should be the goal for any manufacturer. Moreover, in doing so, manufacturers drastically reduce their liability.

7.6   Earthing/Grounding

Both of these terms have the same meaning. [Such definitions depend upon on the authors of the standards, who decide to change and to adopt different terminology with or without including it within the international electrotechnical (IE) vocabulary.]

The earthing (a term mainly used within the European standards) of electrical equipment is required when it has within it hazardous voltages, and it contains parts, or it has an enclosure with conductive walls. (e.g., a metallic enclosure) (equipment with accessible conductive parts).

Earthing, which means intentionally creating a low-resistance path that connects the accessible conductive parts to the earth, is normally considered a secondary protective measure to protect against electric shock.

To protect against electric shocks, Class 1 equipment should have a connection to a protective conductor in the equipment, or a combination of conductive parts in the equipment, connecting a main protective earthing terminal to a part of the equipment that is required to be earthed for safety purposes.

For equipment that is intended to be installed before use, note that the protective conductor is not considered effective until the equipment is installed in the field.

In this situation, it is strongly recommended that manufacturers offer detailed installation instructions regarding this issue, in order to advise installers that it is part of their job to complete the implementation of this safety feature.

Grounding is used for several purposes, listed as follows:

• As a protection against electric shocks;
• As a feature for the correct functionality of the equipment;
• For electromagnetic interference (EMI) compliance;
• Since a reliable connection within the equipment of the protective earthing conductor is a must.

It is interesting to note that even if manufacturers perform routine tests in production (tests to which each individual device is subjected during or at the end of manufacture to detect manufacturing failures and unacceptable tolerances in manufacturing and materials) to verify the integrity of the protective earth connection, the effectiveness depends on the installation of the equipment in the field. This discrepancy highlights the role electrical inspectors play in preventing incorrect installations.

Separation of the circuits from the protective earth is specified within the applicable standard for the evaluated product.

While earthing/grounding may have initially been considered only as a safety guard against electric shocks (by eliminating the difference of potential), within today's electronics industry and technology, earthing/grounding has become an important measure for reducing and/or eliminating the "noise" that may drastically reduce the performance and even the functionality of electrical equipment. Proper earthing/grounding not only removes the undesirable "noise," but it can even make the overvoltage protection devices work more safely and efficiently.

7.7 Fire, Electrical, and Mechanical Enclosures

The *enclosure* is a part or component, that protects equipment from external influences in any direction and from direct contact with electrical equipment. It should also provide the following protections [6]:

1. Protections of persons against access to hazardous parts (electrical and/or mechanical) inside the enclosure [International Protection (IP) code];

2. Protection of the equipment inside the enclosure against ingress of solid foreign objects (IP code);

3. Protection of the equipment inside the enclosure against harmful effects due to the ingress of water (IP code);

4. Protection of electrical equipment against external mechanical impacts (IK code) (impact protection) or specified environmental conditions [National Electrical Manufacturers Association (NEMA) designation]. IK code provides a means of specifying the capacity of an enclosure to protect its contents from external mechanical impacts.

When the intended market is asking for a specific IP or IK degree of protection, access probes and tests are used to determine the acceptable degree of protection for enclosures.

An enclosure should be regarded as a part of the equipment providing one or more of the functions described as follows:

• *Electrical enclosure:* A part of the equipment intended to limit access to parts that may be at hazardous voltages or hazardous energy levels or TNV circuits.

- *Fire enclosure:* A part of the equipment intended to minimize the spread of fire or flames from within. Materials used for enclosures of equipment should be such that the risk of ignition and the spread of fire or flames are minimized. Metals, ceramic materials, and glass that are heat-resistant-tempered, wired, or laminated are considered to comply without testing. The following components require a fire enclosure:
    - Components with unenclosed arcing parts, such as open-switch and relay contacts and switches;
    - Components with windings, such as transformers, solenoids, and relays;
    - Wiring;
    - Semiconductor devices, such as transistors, diodes, and integrated circuits;
    - Resistors, capacitors, and inductors;
    - Components within a limited power source including overcurrent protective devices, limiting impedances, regulating networks, and wiring up to the point where the limited power source output criteria are met.
- *Mechanical enclosure:* A part of the equipment intended to prevent injury due to mechanical and other physical hazards (e.g., heat and fire, chemical, and radiation).

When mechanical or electrical enclosures also serve as fire enclosures, more stringent requirements for fire enclosure apply.

7.7.1 The IP Code

The IP codes are presented and explained within the IEC 60529 Standard.

The IP code consists of two characteristic numerals. Optional, additional, and supplementary letter(s) may be used.

If an enclosure provides different degrees of protection for different intended mounting arrangements, the relevant degrees of protection should be indicated by the manufacturer in the installation instructions.

The first characteristic numeral indicates the degree of protection against access to hazardous parts and against solid foreign objects; it may have values between 0 and 6. (e.g., zero means not protected). This value has two meanings: protection of equipment against ingress of solid objects and protection of persons against access to hazardous parts with different things (e.g., back of the hand, finger, toll, and wire).

The second characteristic numeral indicates the degree of protection against ingress of water with harmful effects; it may have values between 0 and

8. (with zero meaning not protected and 8 meaning protected against ingress of water with harmful effects during a continuous immersion in water).

The additional letter provides more detail regarding the protection of persons against access to hazardous parts something such as the back of hand or a finger, tool, or wire.

The supplementary letter gives supplementary information specific to a variety of a possibilities including the high-voltage apparatus, motion during a water test, and weather conditions.

It is important to be aware of the conditions with which the end user has to comply in regard to the enclosure. Outdoor enclosures should be designed by considering all possible negative effects, including the formation of ice. Details regarding mounting, assembling, and positioning should be provided within the equipment manuals. The standard IEC 60529 specifies all the applicable requirements regarding the IP degree of protection provided by enclosures.

> *Note:* The degree *of* protection provided by an enclosure is indicated by the IP code in the following way:
>
> IP N_1 N_2 L_1 L_2, where:
>
> IP: Code letters (IP);
>
> N_1: First characteristic numerals 0 to 6, or letter X—degrees of protection against access to hazardous parts or against solid foreign objects;
>
> N_2: Second characteristic numerals 0 to 8, or letter X—degrees of protection against ingress of water;
>
> L_1: Additional letters A, B, C, D (optional)—degrees of protection against access to hazardous parts
>
> L_2: Supplementary letters H, M, S, W (optional)—supplementary information related to specific equipment or tests.

Where a characteristic numeral is not required to be specified, it should be replaced by the letter "X" ("XX" if both numerals are not required).

IPN₁X

A coding system to indicate the degrees of protection provided by an enclosure against access of persons to equipment's hazardous parts and simultaneously the degrees of protection provided by an enclosure against the ingress of solid foreign objects. The degrees of protection provided by an enclosure against ingress of water are not specified.

The significance of N_1 is detailed as follows:

0: Nonprotected.

1: Protected against access of persons to hazardous parts with the back of a hand and against penetration of the equipment by solid foreign objects of 50 mm Ø and greater. The access probe, sphere of 50 mm Ø, should have adequate clearance from hazardous parts and should not pass through an opening of the enclosure.

2: Protected against access of persons to hazardous parts with a finger and against penetration of the equipment by solid foreign objects of 12.5 mm Ø and greater. The jointed test finger of 12 mm Ø, 80 mm length, should have adequate clearance from hazardous parts and the access probe, sphere of 12.5 mm Ø, should not pass through an opening of the enclosure.

3: Protected against access of persons to hazardous parts with a tool and against penetration of the equipment by solid foreign objects of 2.5 mm Ø and greater. The access probe of 2.5 mm Ø should not pass through an opening of the enclosure.

4: Protected against access of persons to hazardous parts with a wire and against penetration of the equipment by solid foreign objects of 1.0 mm Ø and greater. The access probe of 1.0 mm Ø should not pass through an opening of the enclosure.

5: Protected against access of persons to hazardous parts with a wire and against access of dust into equipment. The access probe of 1.0 mm Ø should not penetrate. The dust should not penetrate in a quantity to interfere with the satisfactory operation of the equipment or to generate unacceptable risks.

6: Protection against access of persons to hazardous parts with a wire and against access of dust into equipment. The access probe of 1.0 mm Ø should not penetrate, and any quantity of dust should not penetrate.

IPXN$_2$

A coding system to indicate the degrees of protection provided by an enclosure against ingress of water. The degrees of protection against access of persons to equipment's hazardous parts and the degrees of protection provided by an enclosure against the ingress of solid foreign objects are not specified.

The significance of N$_2$ is detailed as follows:

0: Nonprotected.

1: Protected against vertically falling water drops. Vertically falling drops should have no harmful effects.

2: Protected against vertically falling water drops when enclosure tilted up to 15°. Vertically falling drops should have no harmful effects when the enclosure is tilted at any angle up to 15° on either side of the vertical.

3: Protected against spraying water. Water sprayed at an angle up to 60° on either side of the vertical should have no harmful effects.

4: Protected against splashing water. Water splashed against the enclosure from any direction should have no harmful effects.

5: Protected against water jets. Water projected in jets against the enclosure from any direction should have no harmful effects.

6: Protected against powerful water jets. Water projected in powerful jets against the enclosure from any direction should have no harmful effects.

7: Protected against the effects of temporary immersion in water. Ingress of water in quantities causing harmful effects should not be possible when the enclosure is temporarily immersed in water under standardized conditions of pressure and time.

8: Protected against the effects of continuous immersion in water. Ingress of water in quantities causing harmful effects should not be possible when the enclosure is continuously immersed in water under conditions that should be agreed on between manufacturers and users but that are more severe than for 7).

$IPN_1X L_1$ ($IPXXL_1$)

An additional coding system to indicate the degrees of protection provided by an enclosure against access of persons to equipment hazardous parts when this kind of protection is higher than that indicated by N_1, or if only the protection against access of persons to hazardous parts is indicated, the first characteristic numeral N_1 being then replaced by an X.

The degrees of protection provided by an enclosure against ingress of water are not specified.

The significance of L_1 is detailed as follows:

A: Protected against access of persons to hazardous parts with the back of a hand. The access probe, sphere of 50 mm Ø, shall have adequate clearance from hazardous parts.

B: Protected against access of persons to hazardous parts with a finger. The jointed test finger of 12 mm Ø, 80 mm length, should have adequate clearance form hazardous parts.

C: Protected against access of persons to hazardous parts with a tool. The access probe of 2.5 mm Ø, 100 mm length should have adequate clearance from hazardous parts.

D: Protected against access of persons to hazardous parts with a wire. The access probe of 1.0 mm Ø, 100 mm length should have adequate clearance from hazardous parts.

$IPN_1N_2 L_2$ (IP $N_1N_2 L_1 L_2$)

An supplementary coding system related to the use of equipment with degrees of protection provided by the enclosure against access to the equipment's hazardous parts, ingress of solid foreign objects, and ingress of water.

The significance of L_2 is detailed as follows:

H: High-voltage apparatus;

M: Tested for harmful effects due to the ingress of water when the movable parts of the equipment (for example, the rotor of a rotating machine) are in motion;

S: Tested for harmful effects due to the ingress of water when the movable parts of the equipment (for example, the rotor of a rotating machine) are stationary;

W: Suitable for use under specified weather conditions and provided with additional protective features or processes

7.7.2   The IK Code

In regard to the IK code, the standard IEC 62262 specifies [7] the way enclosures should be mounted when tests are carried out, the atmospheric conditions that should prevail, the number of impacts and their (even) distribution, as well as the size, style, material, and dimensions of the various types of hammers, designed to produce the energy levels required (Table 7.4).

Table 7.4
IK Code and Impact Energy

IK Code	IK00	IK01	IK02	IK03	IK04	IK05	IK06	IK07	IK08	IK09	IK10
Impact Energy	*	0.14	0.2	0.35	0.5	0.7	1	2	5	10	20

7.7.3   NEMA Enclosure Type Number

The U.S. NEC specifies that equipment enclosures should be identified for use in certain operating environments. For nonhazardous locations, NEMA has established, in NEMA Standards Publication 250, a type designation for enclosures. This type designation is applicable on power distribution and control equipment enclosures such as cabinets and cutout boxes, enclosed panel boards or switchboards, meter sockets, enclosed circuit breakers or switches, industrial control, and other equipment. Outdoor enclosures are also suitable for use indoors. An enclosure that fulfills the requirements for more than one type may be marked with multiple designations [6]. Table 7.6 lists NEMA enclosure type numbers.

7.8   Ratings

When talking about ratings of electrical components and equipment, there are several aspects about which the manufacturer assigns specified operating conditions, representing in fact the capabilities of the equipment.

The ratings are in fact all the characteristics of the components and equipment that are set within the product definition document (PDD) and that are set to be achieved during the design stage and then the manufacturing of the equipment.

Electrical equipment ratings for normal load are listed as follows:

- Supply voltage or voltage range (e.g., 120V; 230V; 100-240 V; 120V/230V; 3/N AC 400V; 3/PEN AC 400V; 3/N/PE AC 400V);

Table 7.5
Impact Test Characteristics

IK Code	IK00	IK01 to IK05	IK06	IK07	IK08	IK09	IK10
Impact Energy (J)	*	<1	1	2	5	10	20
R (mm)	*	10	10	25	25	50	50
Material	*	polyamide	polyamide	steel	steel	steel	steel
Mass (kg)	*	0.2	0.5	0.5	1.7	5	5
Pendulum hammer	*	YES	YES	YES	YES	YES	YES
Spring hammer	*	YES	YES	YES	NO	NO	NO
Free fall hammer	*	NO	NO	YES	YES	YES	YES

Note: R is the radius of the striking element.

Table 7.6

NEMA Enclosures Type Number Depending on Environmental Conditions

Enclosures type number	Environmental conditions
1	Indoor use; marked "Indoor use only"
2	Indoor use, limited amounts of falling water; marked "Drip tight"
3	Outdoor use plus windblown dust, undamaged by the formation of ice on the enclosure; marked "Rain tight" and "Dust tight"
3R	Outdoor use, undamaged by the formation of ice on the enclosure; marked "Rainproof"
3RX	Outdoor use plus resists corrosion, undamaged by the formation of ice on the enclosure; marked "Rainproof" and "Corrosion resistant"
3S	Outdoor use plus windblown dust, undamaged by the formation of ice on the enclosure; external mechanisms remain operable while ice laden; marked "Rain tight" and "Dust tight"
3SX	Outdoor use plus windblown dust plus corrosion-resistant, undamaged by the formation of ice on the enclosure; external mechanisms remain operable while ice laden; marked "Rain tight" and "Corrosion resistant" and "Dust tight"
3X	Outdoor use plus windblown dust plus resists corrosion, undamaged by the formation of ice on the enclosure; marked "Rain tight" and "Corrosion resistant" and "Dust tight"
4	Outdoor use, splashing water, windblown dust, hose-directed water, undamaged by the formation of ice on the enclosure; ; marked "Rain tight" and "Watertight"
4X	Outdoor use, splashing water, windblown dust, hose-directed water plus resists corrosion, undamaged by the formation of ice on the enclosure; marked "Rain tight" and "Watertight" and "Corrosion resistant"
5	Indoor use to provide a degree of protection against settling airborne dust, falling dirt, and dripping noncorrosive liquids; marked "Drip tight" and "Dust tight"
6	Outdoor use, undamaged by the formation of ice on the enclosure plus entry of water during temporary submersion at a limited depth; marked "Rain tight" and "Watertight"
6P	Outdoor use, undamaged by the formation of ice on the enclosure plus entry of water during prolonged submersion at a limited depth; marked "Rain tight" and "Watertight" and "Corrosion resistant"
12, 12K	Indoor use, dust, dripping noncorrosive liquids; marked "Drip tight" and "Dust tight"
13	Indoor use, dust, spraying water, oil and noncorrosive coolants; marked "Drip tight" and "Dust tight"

- Frequency or frequency range (e.g., 50Hz; 60 Hz; 50/60 Hz; 50-60 Hz; 400 Hz);
- Current rating (in A);

- Power rating (in VA or in W for power factor > 0.9);
- Number of phases (when the number of phases is not specified, it is considered to be a single-phase circuit);
- Maximum output voltage and current range (applicable for outlets).
- Environmental ratings for equipment under normal operation are listed as follows:
- Maximum operating temperature;
- Storage temperature;
- Operating relative humidity;
- Storage relative humidity.
- Maximum altitude.
- Special ratings (if applicable) are listed as follows:
- IP, IK classification for enclosure;
- NEMA designation for enclosure;
- Level of output energy (e.g., RF or laser);
- Radiation wavelength (e.g., UV or laser);
- Fire-resistance;
- Load-restricted;
- Enclosure type;
- Safety integrity level;
- Performance level.

All of these *ratings* will be declared by the manufacturer in the user manual, and some of them are present in the markings on the equipment. During the testing the evaluation of the equipment is done for the specified ratings values.

For the ratings of the components used in electrical equipment see Chapter 8.

7.9 Types of Circuits

Depending of the terminology used by different standards the circuits found within electrical equipment can be classified in two main categories:

- *Primary circuits:* An internal circuit that is directly connected to an external supply mains or other equivalent source that supplies electric power;

- *Secondary circuits:* An internal circuit that has no direct connection to primary power circuit and derives its power from a transformer, converter, or equivalent isolation device or from a battery.

In turn, the primary circuits could be one of the following types:

- AC;
- DC.

The *primary circuits* include components such as all the means for connection to the AC mains supply, the primary windings of transformers, and motors.

The *secondary circuits* are categorized strictly based on the NECs and/or as per the applicable standards, depending on the current that flows through those circuits and on the power that can be developed within, as well based on the type of installation/application in which the circuits are used based on their functionality. In North America, specific rules are offered within the NEC and CEC for the wiring of these secondary circuits.

Relating the types of circuits to the limitations of voltages and currents in electrical products leads to the following circuits [2]:

- *Limited-current circuit:* A circuit that is designed and protected so that, under both normal operating conditions and single-fault conditions, the current that can be drawn is not hazardous.

- *SELV circuit:* A secondary circuit that is designed and protected so that under normal operating conditions and single-fault conditions, its voltages do not exceed a safe value.

- *TNV circuit:* A secondary circuit that is in the equipment and to which the accessible area of contact is limited; and that is designed and protected so that, under normal operating conditions and single-fault conditions, the voltages do not exceed specified limit values. TNV circuits, classified as TNV-1, TNV-2, and TNV-3 circuits, are described as follows.

  - *TNV-1:* A TNV circuit whose normal operating voltages *do not exceed* the limits for a SELV circuit under normal operating conditions, and on which overvoltages from telecommunication networks and cable distribution systems are possible.
  - *TNV-2:* A TNV circuit whose normal operating voltages *exceed* the limits for a SELV circuit under normal operating conditions; and that is <u>not</u> subject to overvoltages from telecommunication networks.

- *TNV-3:* A TNV circuit whose normal operating voltages *exceed* the limits for a SELV circuit under normal operating conditions; and on which overvoltages from telecommunication networks and cable distribution systems are possible

7.10 Normal Load

The *normal load* of any electrical equipment is represented by the system configuration, which represents the realistic maximum power consumption when the equipment operates and performs all of the functions for which it was designed to performed; this should be the mode of operation of a piece of equipment, approximating as closely as possible the most severe conditions of normal use of the equipment when it is operated in accordance with the manufacturer's installation and the user's manual instructions.

This parameter is very important during the evaluation of electrical equipment. It is used to perform the applicable tests according to the ratings of the equipment (input test, heating test, single-fault conditions) and is also used for rating the critical components used in conjunction with the equipment (power supply cords, switches, etc.).

Normal load is a value that the manufacturer declares for the equipment, and it should be respected during installation in the field. It is important that during the evaluation the normal load be accurate (as close as possible to the real value) and very precise (to be able to obtain repeatable values of it during the type tests that are performed).

7.11 Abnormal Operating Conditions

It is expected that during normal operation, electrical equipment will perform as intended. The questions to be raised are: What will happen with the equipment in case of a misuse or a failure of a component that will still allow the equipment to work? Which of the components are most likely to fail? How will the equipment behave in the case of such failure? The answers to these questions characterize the status of *abnormal operating conditions* of the equipment.

In the case of a component failure, nobody may expect that the equipment will continue to fully perform as intended, but absolutely everyone expects that the equipment will remain totally safe for the end user.

Here we are not discussing reliability issues or aspects. We are just trying to underline that the design team that worked hard to build electrical equipment should consider all of the foreseeable component failures (including the software) and ensure that in such cases, the safety of the equipment will not be compromised. The SFC is treated as the presence of a single abnormal operating condition. In other words, the SFC is the condition in which one means for protection against hazards is defective or one fault that could cause a hazard is present. Since there are no reliable verifiable requirements defined for the prevention of faults, all possible simultaneous faults should be considered. The worst cases of simultaneous faults are those that lead to the most dangerous results.

Recently, we found that defining this condition of abnormal operation generates more questions than answers. The IEC 62368-1 Standard defines it as a "temporary operating condition that is not a normal operating condition and is not a single fault condition of the equipment itself" [4].

In some respects, we cannot totally agree with this definition. An abnormal operating condition may be introduced by the equipment or by a person who is in contact with the equipment or who is trying to operate the equipment. Similarly, an abnormal operating condition may result in a failure of a component, a device, or a safeguard and may lead to a SFC. In our opinion, it is not possible to set a clear barrier between the abnormal operating conditions of a piece of equipment and SFCs within the equipment.

A good example of abnormal operation is a piece of equipment whose enclosure has ventilation openings and that contains a fan; end users could introduce an abnormal operation by covering the ventilation openings with an object, possibly forcing the equipment to work in more difficult conditions. However, the safeguards designed to prevent the unacceptable risk of harm due to fire should function when the internal temperature becomes hazardous. The SFC that may appear in this situation is that due to a foreign object, the fan was locked.

The presence of safeguards is mandatory, but at the same time, their activation should be designed so that they *do not operate* under normal conditions, which is sometimes called *nuisance tripping*. Otherwise, safe equipment can become dangerous for the end user; a good example is a recessed luminaire that, during a heating/temperature test, was found unsafe because the safeguard was activated less than six hours after the start of the test. We have to understand that a luminaire cannot turn off automatically before it performs its function of providing light for the user for as long as the user needs it. The evaluation of this luminaire concluded that even if it was safe from the point of view of electrical safety, it failed the test due to its inability to fully perform its function.

Similar examples exist in any industry. It is manufacturers' responsibility to ensure that equipment fully performs its functions and remains safe during normal operation under normal load and under abnormal operation and in SFCs when some of its components are failing. Only during abnormal operation and in SFCs, it is acceptable to activate the safeguards disregarding the functionality of the equipment. During abnormal operating conditions that lead to a SFC, supplemental safeguards designed and implemented to protect in such situations shall remain effective.

References

[1]   IEC 60601-1, "Medical Electrical Equipment—Part 1: General Requirements for Safety and Essential Performance," Geneva, (2005 + 2012).

[2]   IEC 60950-1+AMD1+AMD2 "Information Technology Equipment—Safety—Part 1: General Requirements," Geneva, 2005–2013.

[3]   IEC 60990, "Methods of Measurement of Touch Current and Protective Conductor Current," Geneva, 2016.

[4]   IEC 62368-1, "Audio/Video, Information and Communication Technology Equipment—Part 1: Safety Requirements," Geneva, 2014.

[5]   IEC 60664-1, "Insulation Coordination for Equipment Within Low-Voltage Systems—Part 1: Principles, Requirements and Tests," Geneva, 2007.

[6]   Hoffman Enclosures Inc., "*Standards,*" Anoka, USA, 2003.

[7]   BS EN 62262 +Amd.1, "Degrees of Protection Provided By Enclosures for Electrical Equipment Against External Mechanical Impacts IK Code," 2002.

Selected Bibliography

Bolintineanu, C., and S. Loznen, "Product Safety and Third Party Certification," *The Electronic Packaging Handbook,* edited by Glenn R. Blackwell, 1999, Boca Raton, FL: CRC Press.

ECMA-287 European Association for Standardizing Information and Communication Systems, "Safety of Electronic Equipment," Geneva, 2002.

IEC 61032, "Protection of Persons And Equipment by Enclosures—Probes for Verification," Geneva, 1997.

IEC 61557-4, "Electrical Safety In Low Voltage Distribution Systems up to 1 000 V a.c. and 1 500 V d.c.—Equipment for Testing, Measurement or Monitoring of Protective Measures—Part 4: Resistance of Earth Connection and Equipotential Bonding," Geneva, 2007.

ISO 13857, "Safety of Machinery—Safety Distances To Prevent Hazard Zones Being Reached by Upper And Lower Limbs," Geneva, 2008.

Pyke, D., and C. S. Tang, "How To Mitigate Product Safety Risks Proactively? Process, Challenges and Opportunities," *International Journal of Logistics Research and Applications,* 13, 2010, pp. 243–256.

U. S. Department of Energy, "LED Luminaire Lifetime," 2011.x

8

Selection of Components

8.1 Introduction

Once a product is defined and the design started, the hardware team will try to select the components that fully meet the requirements stated within the PDD.

We will not try to move people from one technology to a newer one using different components; we will just review some of the electrical safety aspects to get an understanding of some of the so-called safety-critical components from the beginning of the design and determine how those may be selected. In the process, we will list some of the factors that may determine the selection of components and consider what hardware design engineers may want to know when choosing such components.

Following the construction requirements, the selection of components represents the second of three aspects of compliance with any product safety standard, with the third being testing.

To achieve the safety of electrical equipment, the materials and components to be used in construction should selected and arranged so that they can be expected to perform in a reliable manner for the anticipated service life of the equipment. This means that the selected materials and components should remain within their manufacturers' ratings without creating a hazard during normal operating and fault conditions. When the components have not been previously investigated, the probability of failure is much higher and can generate unacceptable risks.

Components that are critical to the safety of equipment (meaning that their failure could result in a hazardous situation) are known as *safety critical components.*

Generally speaking, these are components intended to prevent (along with the design of the equipment along with installation/user's instructions) any injuries, or damages due to the applicable hazards that may arise during the manufacturing, packaging, transporting, installation, and use and/or service of a piece of electrical equipment.

In addition to these components, components with high-integrity characteristics are also used in electrical products. These are components where one or more characteristics [i.e., mean time between failures (MTBF)], ensures that its function is fault-free in relation to the safety requirements of a standard during the expected service life of the equipment and reasonably foreseeable misuse. It is recommended that manufacturers use components with high-integrity characteristics (i.e., Y1 capacitors and some integrated circuits) when a fault in a particular component can generate an unacceptable risk.

The safety-critical components, which include power supplies, transformers, supply cords, fuses in primary, power entry modules, mains capacitors, EMI filters, circuit breakers, power switches, DC-DC converters, relays, wiring material, motors, fans, thermoplastic material, EMC coating, optoisolators, batteries, PTCs, fuses in secondary, and interlock switches, must be *approved.* Such components have been evaluated against relevant national or international component standards and are provided with a third-party (NRTL or European) approvals like (e.g., a UL listing or recognition, CSA, or VDE). CE marking is not legally required for components. The approval status is documented by a copy of the approval certificate or by the license for the component. (The use of catalog data sheets it is not the right way to prove compliance.) Particular attention needs to be paid to conditions of acceptability in the end-use product for correct application and use of the components within their specified electrical ratings; these shall not be exceeded.

Recognized components are intended only for factory installation in end products or in equipment where the limitations of use are known to the end-product manufacturer and where their use is within such limitations as a third party evaluated them. The conditions of acceptability of the recognized components need to be compatible with the specific end-product application.

An approved component is normally marked with the "mark" of the third-party certification body. The recognized component mark is applicable to components that are incomplete in construction features or limited in performance capabilities.

In addition, there is a certificate detailing the ratings limits of the approval (e.g., voltage and temperature) and a full supporting test report. In some cases, the component may not be marked but is supported by a certificate or report.

In some situations, due to limitations on dimensions, the marking is done on the package.

Those components bearing the appropriate NRTL recognized component marking should be considered as being covered by NRTL's recognition and follow-up service.

It is possible to buy nonapproved components at a lower cost than that for approved components, but then it is necessary to pay the additional cost for testing these components.

Each test report form for product safety standards includes a table designated as *list of critical components* or *list of components and circuits relied on for safety*. This list of components must be kept for internal or external audit purposes and should be part of the quality system documentation for each piece of equipment.

The following information should be provided for each critical component:

1. Component name;
2. Manufacturer/trade mark;
3. Type/model;
4. Technical specifications;
5. Applicable standard;
6. Mark of conformity (approval status) [e.g., mark(s) of conformity from UL, CSA, TÜV, and VDE].

Technical specifications should be considered relevant technical information that may influence the safety features (e.g., flammability class, maximum operating temperature, voltage operating range, maximum current, breakdown voltage, insulation resistance, and dimensions; protection from electric shock and energy hazards; electrical insulation, resistance to fire, and mechanical strength).

Due to evolving technology, software is used to preserve the safety of equipment, as it stores data/code, and thus, it should also be considered a safety-critical component. The version of software used when the equipment is placed on the market should be specified.

The software subject is extremely vast, and it should be a part of an attentive investigation of the design team and as well as the manufacturer. Having a robust program for testing the electromagnetic susceptibility of any system that uses software for safety functions is necessary.

We may accept transient behavior in computers and other products but not when it is used for safety systems. Medical electrical equipment or equipment designed to coordinate traffic, for example, will likely require user action for recovery after a failure event. Accordingly, the hardware/software design team needs to prove during an evaluation that the system is fail-safe.

In any case, life-critical systems need to be, at least, redundant, with fail-safe shutdowns if the processes do not agree at timed checkpoints. They should also have hardware-based watchdog timers (sometimes built in to the microcontroller, itself) to guarantee continued function. Furthermore, it is also typical for software that runs on redundant processors to be written by different teams, so that an error in a program on one side is not duplicated in the other half or third of the redundant CPUs. It is important to note here that Windows licenses prohibit the use of Windows products in safety-critical applications.

How is an approval status defined? There are several ways to prove that a component that will be used as a safety-critical component may be accepted for use and that it will offer a high degree of confidence in its ability to safeguard the equipment. These include the following.

- Certification/listing/recognition;

- Evaluation of the product during the type tests;

- Tests to ensure compliance with the component standard;

- Acceptance based on other official documents (e.g., component-acceptance service announcement and special inspections).

All of the above may be used for equipment components, considering also the characteristics of the electrical equipment in which they are used, the applicable standard whether the equipment performs a safety function or not. When equipment performs a safety function, it is vital to use certified/listed components. Only such components benefit from surveillance programs over their manufacturing, (the so-called follow-up services, or programs assured by the involved certification body). For such applications, supplementary to the certification/listing characteristics of a component, special attention should be paid to the reliability verification. An example is included in Table 8.1 with a few real examples to understand how to complete the list of critical components.

Table 8.2 lists components with specific ratings and component standards (international and UL) [1]. For UL standards [2], specify also the UL category code number (CCN). The UL listing category is designated by four letters. For a recognized category to these letters, number 2 is added for the United States and 7 for Canada.]

8.2 Semiconductors

Electrical safety regulations of various countries recognize that semiconductor components that are incorporated within electrical equipment as safety-critical components protect users from electric shock and from secondary injuries asso-

Table 8.1

Sample of a List of Critical Components

Clause Number in Standard (e.g., 1.5.1 in IEC 60950-1; 8.10 in IEC 60601-1; and 24.1 in IEC 60335-1)			List of Critical Components		
Component/ Part Number	Manufacturer/ Trademark	Type/model	Technical Data	Standard (Edition or Year)	Mark(s) of Conformity[1]
Switching power supply	Power-Win Technology Corp.	PW-250B-1Y300PU	Rated input: 100–240V, 50/60 Hz, 4A Rated output: 30-V DC, 6.67A, 200W w/o convection; 30VDC, 8.34A, 250W w/ convection 17.1 CFM	IEC 60950-1:2005, EN 60950-1:2006+A11:2009 (CB) CSA C22.2 No. 60950-1-07, UL 60950-1:2007	NEMKO (Cert NO58990) CSA (LR94521)
IC U31 (Battery protection)	Maxim or equivalent	DS1339C-33 or equivalent	Provides protection against reverse charge	UL/CSA 60950-1	UR (E141114)
Plastic of Enclosure	Bayer	Bayblend FR3000	Rated: V-0 for thickness 1.5 mm, 5 VB for thickness 2.0 mm, RTI min 75 Thickness in the appliance min. 3mm at main parts of enclosure, 2.5mm at lid	UL746C, UL94	UR (E41613)
DC Fan	Delta Electronics or equivalent	AFB0524VHD	Rated: 24V, 0.15A, min. 17.02 CFM, max. 20.3 CFM	CSA C22.2 No. 113	CSA (LR91949)
Printed wiring board	Any	Any	Rated: min. 105°C V-0	UL 796	UL
Internal Wiring, (secondary)	Any	Any	Rated min. 300V, 60°C, VW-1 or FT-1 or better	UL758	UL
Protective device on USB output from management (PPC) card adapter (IC U2)	Texas Instruments	TPS2031D	Rated: 6-V DC, 0.6A, protection current 1.1-A max	UL2637	UL
Linear regulator U29 supplying 5-V DC to USB protective IC U2	Micrel	MIC29502WU	Rated Output: 5-V DC, 5A	-	Evaluated in the equipment during the type tests
Attachment plugs, fuseless	Qualtek Electronics	770W-X2/10	Rated: 250V, 2.5A Tmax: 85°C	UL 498	CSA, VDE, UL R/C: E139592
Fuse	Bel Fuse	RST 2.5	Rated: PCB Type T2.5/250V, Cover V-0, Toper 125°C	UL 248	VDE, S, UR E20624

Table 8.1 (continued)

Clause Number in Standard (e.g., 1.5.1 in IEC 60950-1; 8.10 in IEC 60601-1; and 24.1 in IEC 60335-1)			List of Critical Components		
Component/ Part Number	Manufacturer/ Trademark	Type/model	Technical Data	Standard (Edition or Year)	Mark(s) of Conformity[1]
NTC	CANTHERM	MF72-005D9	Rated: 5-ohm, current steady-state max: 3A	UL 1434	UR, E241319
Varistor RV1	Panasonic	ERZ-V10D391	Rated: 390V, 2,500-A peak, 70J, toper	-	UL, CSA
Capacitor - C8, C10, C12, C13	Johanson Dielectric	302R29W102KV3ESC	Rated: SMD 1808, 1nF, 250-V AC, X2	IEC60384-14, UL 60950-1, UL 60950-21	TUV, S, UR E212609
Thermistor R4	EPCOS/TDK	B57371V2103J060	Rated: 10-kΩ smd NTC 0603	UL 1434	UL, E69802
Power cord for United Kingdom	PHINO	P318-0328-1	U.K. power cord, 3A fused-C7, 1.2M, RAL7047 jacket		VDE
Optocoupler ISO1	Fairchild	FOD817SD or interchangeable	High input-output isolation voltage of 5,000 Vrms	UL 1577	UL R/C: E90700, VDE
Software	XXYY. Ltd.	Rev.3.02			Evaluated in unit

Supplementary information: [1] Provided evidence (e.g., certificate originator and number and NRTL file number) ensures the requested level of compliance.

ciated with electric shock; fires and arc flashes when working on systems operating between 50 and 600V are set to specific requirements from the EMC point of view. The main safety issue encountered with semiconductor components are static charges, and thus, when using such components, it is important to work closely with the EMC design team. In addition, depending of the category of the components, other characteristics should be considered, depending on the function that the component performs within the area of the equipment where it is used.

8.2.1   Integrated Circuits

Integrated circuits (ICs) are selected based on their operating temperature range and creepage distances between the pins, the electric strength between different internal circuits. There are ICs that should provide a certain insulation between input and output. The characteristics of the ICs are given generally at 25°C ambient. The derating for both the lowest and the maximum operating temperature of the equipment in which an IC is used should be used as a guide

Table 8.2
List of Components with Specific Ratings and Relevant Applicable Standards

Component	Characteristics, Technical Data, Ratings, etc.	Component Standards	UL CCN
Accessories for information technology: disk drives; barcode scanners; optical transceivers	Voltage; current;	No component standard; apply the requirements for end-use equipment standard: UL/IEC 60950	NWGQ NWGQ2
Appliance inlet /outlet	Voltage; current	UL 498 IEC 60309-1; -2 IEC 60320-1; -2-2	AXUT2 AXUT RTRT2 ZYVZ2
Appliance inlet with EMI filter; ON/OFF switch, fuse holder	Voltage; current; X2 capacitor; Y2 capacitors	UL 1283 UL 498 IEC 60940 IEC 60939-1	FOKY2 AXUT2 AYVZ2
Appliance wiring	Voltage; Cross-sectional area; max. temperature	UL 758 IEC 60317	AVLV2
Battery (lithium)	Voltage; max. charging current (for type B—rechargeable battery); protection means	UL 1642 IEC 62311	BBCV2
Battery pack (lithium)	Voltage, capacity (in mAh or Ah); PCM type; flammability (for cover)	UL 2054 IEC 62311	BBFS2
Battery (standard) (lead-acid)	Voltage, capacity (in mAh or Ah);	UL1989 UL2054 IEC 60086	BAZR2
Battery charger, nonautomotive type	Voltage; current	UL 1012 Apply the requirements for end-use equipment standard: UL/IEC 60335-1	BBML2
Bridge rectifier	Voltage; current	UL 1557	QQQX2
Bushing-insulating	Flammability; max. number of wires	UL 635 IEC 60137	NZMT2
Cable ties	Loop tensile strength; max. operating temp.; flammability	UL 1565	ZODZ2
Capacitor (X-Type, Y-Type) Y1 = double-insulated	Voltage; Capacitance; tolerance; insulation resistance	UL 1414 IEC 60384-14	FOWX2
Capacitor (general)	Voltage; capacitance; tolerance	UL 810 IEC 61071 IEC 61921 IEC 62391	CYWT2
Circuit breaker	Voltage; current	UL 1077 IEC 60934 IEC 60898	QVNU QVNU2 DIHS2 DKPU2 DKUY2

Table 8.2 (continued)

Component	Characteristics, Technical Data, Ratings, etc.	Component Standards	UL CCN
Coating-conductive (metalized)	Coating thickness; Substrate	UL 746	QMRX2
Coating for PWB (PCB)	Coating material (color, thickness; Flammability); Laminate (type; thickness); max. soldering temp;	UL 746 UL 94	QMJU2
Coating – Plastics - Component	Color; flammability; Minimum thickness; relative thermal index (RTI)	UL 746 UL 94 UL 1694	QMFZ2
Connector	Voltage; current	UL 310 IEC 61984	RFWV2
Contactors	Voltage; current	UL 508 UL 60947-1 UL 60947-4-1	NRNT2
Crimp connectors	Crimpedon closedloop or spade connectors for securing under screw terminals or quick-disconnect-type connectors with positive detent	UL 486	ZMVV2
Data processing cable	Voltage; cross-sectional area; max. temperature	UL 1690	EMRB
DC-DC converter	IN: voltage; current; OUT: voltage; current;	No component standard; Apply the requirements for end-use equipment standard: ANSI/AAMI ES 60601-1 IEC 60601-1 UL/IEC 60950	QQHM2 QQGQ2 NWGQ2
Diode	Voltage; current	UL 1557	QQQX2
Enclosure	Overall dimensions (a x b x c) in cm, thick in mm. color; flammability (for thermoplastic parts)	UL 94 UL 746	QMFZ2
Fan AC; DC	Voltage; current; air flow (m³/h; CFM)	UL 507	GPWV2
Filter (EMI/RFI)	Voltage; current; X2 Capacitor; Y2 capacitors	UL 1283 IEC 60940 IEC 60939-1	FOKY FOKY2
Fuse	Voltage ; current; type (FF, F, M, T, TT)	UL 248-1; -14 IEC 60127	JDYX, JDYX2
Fuse holder	Voltage; current; flammability	UL 512 IEC 60127-6	IZLT2 JAMZ2
Heating elements	Voltage; current	UL 1030 UL 499	UBJY2 KSOT2

Table 8.2 (continued)

Component	Characteristics, Technical Data, Ratings, etc.	Component Standards	UL CCN
Interconnection cables	Voltage; cross-sectional area; max. temperature	UL 758 UL 62 IEC 60227 IEC 60245	AVLV2 ZJCZ
Interlock switch	Voltage; current	UL 61058 IEC 61020 IEC 61058	WOYR WOYR2
Insulating tape	Voltage; flammability	UL 510	OANZ2
Inverter, converter	IN: Voltage; current; OUT: voltage; current	UL 1741 IEC 60146	NMMS2
Isolating devices (nonoptical)	RMS isolation; work voltage	UL 1557 Additional apply the requirements for end-use equipment standard: IEC 61010-1 UL/IEC 60950-1	FPPT2
Labels	Construction: (adhesive, base, ink, overlay material)	UL 969	PGDQ2
Laser module	Voltage; current; laser class	UL 60950-1 IEC 60825-1 IEC 60825-2 FDA 21 CFR, Sub-part J (I, II, IIa, IIIa, IIIb)	NWGQ2
LED non-laser	Colors; voltage	UL 1598 IEC 62504	IFAR
Motor (construction only)	Insulation class	UL 1004 IEC 60034	PRGY2
Motor (impedance-protected)	Voltage; current; power	UL 2111	XEIT2
Motor Start Capacitor	Capacitance; tolerance; voltage	UL 810	CYWT2
Optical fiber cable	Optical density; maximum flame spread distance	UL 1651	QAYK
Optical isolator	RMS isolation; spacings (air and along body) between input to output terminals	UL 1577 IEC 60747-5 VDE 884	FPQU2
Overcurrent protectors (solid state)	Voltage; protective current; temperature range	UL 2367 IEC TR 61912	QVRQ2
Plastic parts (e.g., insulator and foam)	Dimensions; flammability	UL 94 UL 746	QMFZ2

Table 8.2 (continued)

Component	Characteristics, Technical Data, Ratings, etc.	Component Standards	UL CCN
Plugs and socket	Voltage; current	UL 498 IEC 60884 IEC 60309-1 IEC 60309-2	RTRT
Power supply	Input: voltage; current; frequency; output: voltage; current; frequency	IEC/UL 60950 ANSI/AAMI ES 60601-1 UL 1310	QQGQ2 QQHM2 EPBU EPBU2
Power supply cords (United States, Canada, European Union, international)	Type; number of wires; voltage; cross-sectional area; max. temperature	UL 817 CENELEC HD-21 IEC 60799	ELBZ
Pulse transformer	Working voltage; insulation ratings; trigger current	UL 506	XTEX2
PWB (PCB)	Flammability	UL 796 IEC 60603-2	ZPMV2
Relay	Voltage coil; voltage and current (or power) contacts	UL 508 UL 1577 IEC 60255 IEC 60730-2-10 IEC 60947 IEC 61810 IEC 61811 IEC 61812 IEC 60747-5	NLDX2 NRNT2 NLRV2 NKCR2 NMFT2 FPQU2
Relay socket	Voltage; current; flammability	UL 508 IEC 60255	SWIV2
Resistor	Resistance; tolerance; power dissipation; dielectric withstanding voltage	UL 1676 IEC 60115-1	FPAV2
Resistor——fusing and temperature limited		UL 1412	FPEW2
Safety-related programmable components (e.g., microprocessors, ASICs, and EPROMS)—household		UL 60730-1	XAAZ2
Shrink tubing	Voltage; flammability	UL 224	YDPU2
Sleeving	Voltage; flammability	UL1441	UZFT2
Solenoid	Voltage; current	UL 906	VAIU2
Strain relief		UL 514B	NZMT2 QCRV
Surge suppressor	Breakdown voltage; clamping voltage; peak pulse current	UL 1449; IEC 61463-1 IEC 61644-1	VZCA2

Table 8.2 (continued)

Component	Characteristics, Technical Data, Ratings, etc.	Component Standards	UL CCN
Switch ON/OFF	Voltage; current; type (1-pole; 2-pole)	UL 61058 IEC 60669 IEC 61020 IEC 61058	WOYR WOYR2 NRNT2
Terminal block	Voltage; current; dielectric strength; working temperature; flammability	UL 1059 IEC 60947-7	XCFR2
Thermal cutoff	Voltage; current; trip temperature	UL 1020 IEC 60691	XCMQ2
Thermal protector (for motors)	Voltage; current; trip temperature	IEC 60730	XEWR2
Thermistor (NTC; PTC)	Voltage; hold current; trip current; nominal resistance	UL 1434 IEC 60539	XGPU2
Thermostat	Voltage; current; trip temperature	UL 873 UL 60730-1	XAPX2
Transformer (with overload protection)	IN: voltage; current; OUT: voltage; current	UL 506 ANSI/AAMI ES 60601 UL/IEC 60950 IEC 60044 IEC 60076 IEC 60742 IEC 60989 IEC 61050 IEC 61558	XPTQ2 NWGQ2 XODW2 FGQS2 XOKV2
Transformer (construction only; insulation system)	Class of insulation	UL 1446 IEC 60076-3	XORU2 OBJY2
Semiconductors devices (transistor, triac)	Type; voltage; current	UL 1557 IEC 60747	QQQX2
Triple insulated wire	Flammability;	UL 1446 IEC 60851	OCDT2
Tubing	Insulation; flammability;	UL 224	YDPU2
Valves	Type (e.g., air, gases, oils, refrigerants, steam, and water); voltage	UL 429 UL 60730-2-8 IEC 60534	YSYI2 YIOZ2
Varistor	Maximum clamping voltage; working current	UL 1449 IEC 61051-1	VZCA2
Voltage selector	Voltage; current	UL 61058 IEC 61020 IEC 61058	WOYR WOYR2

in the process of selection. It is very important to ensure that semiconductor devices at the safety interface, are made reliable enough to allow proper operation, even in the typical fail-short conditions. It is also important to keep software/

programmable devices out of the safety design as much as possible to avoid the significant engineering investment required in a safety evaluation.

Solid-state overcurrent protectors are a special category of ICs. These devices limit the output current to a safe level when the output load exceeds the current-limit threshold or when a load-side short circuit is present. Solid-state overcurrent protectors are intended to be used on the load side of an isolating transformer, power supply, or battery to provide a means of supplementary insulation. These devices, intended to be mounted on a printed wiring board (PWB) only (factory wiring), have no means for manual operation or reset, and the electrical spacings within the devices are not specified.

8.2.2   Diodes

Diodes can be used in a number of ways, such as to protect a current-sensitive circuit. A device that uses batteries will likely contain a diode that protects it when the battery is inserted improperly. The diode will stop the reversed current from traveling from the battery to the rest of the circuit; thus, the diode protects the sensitive electronics inside the circuit.

Diodes are selected based on the application and based on the working voltage to which they will be subjected. Other diode characteristics that need to be considered are rated working peak voltage and the peak pulse power dissipation (PPP), peak impulse current (IPP), and clamping voltage (VC), and the operating temperature range that must cover the equipment's operating temperature range.

A *light-emitting diode* (LED) is probably the most well known and most easily identified. LEDs emit visible light when electrons jump across the PN junction. The resulting light is referred to as *luminescence.* Some of these devices are considered to be laser devices. In order to be acceptable without any supplementary guards, these shall meet the criteria of laser Class 1, in normal functional conditions and in SFCs.

Photodiodes conduct only when they are exposed to light. These can be useful in making projects with a light-activated switch, so that a circuit is only active in the presence of the light.

Zener diodes are designed to conduct in the reverse direction, only when the breakdown voltage is reached will it conduct the circuit. That characteristic will be safety-sensitive along with the creepage and operating temperature range.

Rectifier diodes are designed to stop electricity from flowing in the wrong direction. Their power is a factor of finding the correct match for the circuit. It is valid, as well, for the bridge rectifiers.

Schottky diodes are designed to turn on and off very rapidly when the breakdown voltage is reached, responding quickly in digital circuits. When current flows through a diode there is a very small voltage drop across the terminals. Silicon diodes have a voltage drop, or loss; a Schottky diode voltage drop is significantly less. This lower voltage drop enables higher switching speeds and better system efficiency. When time represents a safety-sensitive issue, Schottky diodes should be considered.

8.2.3 Transistors

Selecting a transistor depends on the working voltage, current, and power dissipation: The positioning of such components of PCBs should be considered the overall product layout. Having a heat sink on a transistor may influence the correct function of the rest of the circuits and/or may generate a microclimate that should be taken in consideration when the operating temperature range is chosen for all the components.

Note: Power thyristors, transistors, diodes, bridge rectifiers, and any combination of these devices are considered electrically isolated semiconductor devices. These devices are provided with a heat sink or are intended to be connected to a heat sink in the end-use application. For these devices it is important that there is an isolation system between live parts (terminals) and the heat sink. For this reason, these devices are provided with an isolation voltage rating. These devices should be installed in end-use equipment considering the standard requirements for enclosure, mounting, electrical spacing, and segregation.

8.3 Passive

8.3.1 Resistors

Selecting these from the electrical safety point of view necessitates two considerations: the power dissipation and the electric strength test voltage at which they are rated. Using a resistor between two circuits that should be insulated could generate a huge problem in terms of the electric strength voltage test and the SFC. Having two resistors in series with the same value each may solve the problem; having more resistors in series will increase the electric strength voltage at which their sum will be able to pass the test.

A power resistor should be mounted some distance above the PCB; otherwise the CTI of the material will be severely diminished by the radiated heat that is absorbed by the board material.

8.3.2 Capacitors

Capacitors are used to store electrical energy. The capacitor consists of two plates with a separator electrically isolating the two plates. The plates are electrically charged, and the charge will remain in the capacitor until the capacitor internally discharges or the capacitor is discharged through a circuit.

The difference between electrochemical batteries and capacitors is that batteries store energy electrochemically whereas capacitors store energy electrostatically. The energy density of batteries may be higher than that of capacitors. In the case of supercapacitors, their power density may be higher than that of battery cells. The energy storage ability of a capacitor is measured in farads. The energy stored in small capacitors can be small or, in the case of supercapacitors, may be quite large and the peak current can be very high—this should be considered in an electrical circuit design.

8.3.2.1 Types of Capacitors and Their Failure Modes

There are many different types of capacitors, and each type has its own unique characteristics and application. Application overlap will exist between the different types of capacitors and cost, form factor, availability, and other factors may then become the differentiator in choosing a specific type of capacitor for a specific application.

Capacitors have different failure modes that vary from type to type. Depending on the capacitor type, capacitors can potentially fail, and the failure mode can range from open circuit to short circuit, or the capacitor capacitance can degrade outside its specification. The following is a list of popular capacitors, including discussion of some potential causes of capacitor failure [3].

- *Ceramic capacitors:* The ceramic capacitor dielectric is ceramic. Ceramic capacitors can fail due to mechanical cracking, surge currents, and dielectric breakdown. A noted failure mode is cracking of the part due to relatively low elasticity. There is no liquid electrolyte in the capacitors, and usually these capacitors fail in a benign manner. In rare and unique circumstances, these capacitors can fail thermally, with the appearance of a roman candle. Therefore, the part should be used in applications preventing mechanical stress that could result in cracking of the part. In the design and placement of these capacitors, the above should be considered.

- *Electrolytic capacitors:* An electrolytic capacitor is polarized and has a liquid electrolyte. The capacitors may fail when subjected to extreme heat conditions and excessive voltage, dielectric breakdown, and exposure of revere polarity. The capacitors usually fail benignly but can vent through a venting mechanism. There is a risk that the capacitor can leak electrolytes on energized areas on the circuit board; this should be considered in circuit board design and placement of these capacitors.

- *Film capacitors:* Film capacitors are also known as metalized film capacitors. They are constructed using alternating metalized film electrode and dielectric film layers, which are tightly wound. The films are typically made of polyester, polystyrene, polycarbonate, polypropylene, or paper. The capacitors may fail due to internal short circuits or excessive applied voltage, or due to an internal opening. Usually the capacitors fail benignly, but in unique cases they can potentially fail thermally.

• *Tantalum capacitors:* Tantalum capacitors are made of tantalum powder pressed into a pellet. The tantalum wire in the pellet forms the anode. The electrolyte is solid and formed from manganese dioxide. A conductive layer over the manganese dioxide forms the cathode. These capacitors can fail due to an internal short circuit, excessive ripple currents, or dielectric breakdown due to voids or excessive voltage exposure. These capacitor failures are usually benign, but in unique circumstances, these capacitors can fail thermally.

Derating capacitors and choosing capacitors suitable for the electrical, thermal, and mechanical stresses they may experience in their application should always be investigated, analyzed, and considered.

The fixed capacitors intended for use in mains parts of electronic equipment are class X and class Y capacitors.

Class X capacitors [4] are suitable for applications where failure of the capacitor would not lead to danger of electrical shock but could result in a risk of fire. Class X capacitors are divided into three subclasses: X1, X2, and X3 (see Table 8.3) according to the peak voltage of the impulses superimposed on the mains voltage to which they may be subjected in service. Such impulses may arise from lightning strikes on outside lines, from switching in neighboring equipment, or from switching in the equipment in which the capacitor is used.

Class Y capacitors [4] are suitable for applications where failure of the capacitor could lead to danger of electric shock. Class Y capacitors are further divided into four subclasses: Y1, Y2, Y3, and Y4 (see Table 8.4). These capacitors bridging basic insulation (connected between primary and ground) should comply with electric strength tests for basic insulation. (For a working voltage of 250 Vrms, the test voltage should be 1,500 Vac or 2,121 Vdc.)

The preferred values of rated AC or DC voltage are 125V, 250V, 275V, 400V, 440V, 500V, and 760V.

It is essential to consider the rate voltage of capacitors. It is important to be aware that capacitors will be subjected to an electric strength test voltage, and thus their rating should follow the peak impulse value of the required RMS voltage.

As well, the creepage distance between the terminals and from uninsulated parts and the metallic enclosure should fully meet the product standard requirements.

Capacitors should not be connected between live parts and nonearthed accessible parts. Any capacitors rated greater than 100 nF must be marked with

Table 8.3

Subclasses for X Capacitors

Subclass	Peak impulse voltage (kV)	Installation Category According to IEC 60664-1	Application
X1	> 2.5–4	III	High pulse
X2	≤ 2.5	II	General use
X3	≤ 1.2	-	General use

Table 8.4

Subclasses for Y Capacitors

Subclass	Type of Insulation Bridged	Rated Voltage [V]
Y1	Double or reinforced	≤ 500
Y2	Basic or supplementary	≤ 150–300
Y3	Basic or supplementary	≤ 150–250
Y4	Basic or supplementary	< 150

the voltage rating and capacitance. Capacitors should not be connected across thermal cutouts.

Another category of capacitor is represented by electrolytic capacitors. These capacitors consist of a wound capacitor element, impregnated with liquid electrolyte, connected to terminals and sealed in a can. The element is comprised of an anode foil, paper separators saturated with electrolyte, and a cathode foil. The rated capacitance is the nominal capacitance, and it is specified at 120 Hz and a temperature of 25°C. To reduce the risk of explosion due to excessive pressure from the hydrogen liberated during operation, the aluminum electrolytic capacitors are equipped with pressure-relief vent structures.

For electrolytic capacitors an additional and separate layer of insulation (i.e., extruded tubing) should be provided. The thickness of this layer needs to be in accordance with the product standard requirements for spacing.

Aluminum electrolytic capacitors contain materials that can catch fire and support ignition when contacted by flames. Flammable parts include plastic parts, insulating sleeves, paper, and the electrolytes. Hydrogen in the capacitor can ignite if sparking occurs during capacitor failure. In some applications one should consider the provision of fire-resistant shields.

8.3.3 Inductors

Inductors should have supplementary overload capacity as per the applicable standard along with the ability to fully meet the operating temperature range for which the equipment is rated. Their support should have an acceptable and determined flammability rating according to the product standard.

8.4 Temperature Control Devices

Sometimes within equipment it is necessary to control the maximum temperature. A relevant example is luminaires, where the hazard of fire may be raised if they develop a high temperature. There are several devices that may sense the level of temperature; when selecting this component, the application should be judged for possible damage in case of a failure and for all the consequences that may result. It is very important in such situations to consider within the design the function of the equipment, as well as the reliability of the sensing component for the operating temperature range of the device.

An overtemperature protection device should not operate in normal use (because of nuisance tripping). These devices operate in SFC and should be rated to interrupt the maximum voltage and current of the circuit in which they are employed. Overtemperature protection devices that operate in case of failure of a temperature-control system could be self-resetting only if the protected part cannot continue to function. Such devices are fusing resistors and temperature-limited resistors.

Thermal management is an increasingly critical function in today's high performances systems. Thermal management should start by measuring the temperature in a specific location (e.g., electronic circuits, motor windings, transformer windings, heating appliances, and user-accessible parts) and disconnecting the supply on the part that generates heating. This will establish protection against thermal hazards (e.g., burning and fires).

For measuring the temperature, select proper temperature sensors. Four main technologies are available: *thermocouples, RTDs, thermistors,* and *integrated circuit temperature devices*. The differences between these sensing devices are presented in Table 8.5.

To be more reliable, the output signal from sensors (which is a low voltage or current) can be converted in a more robust signal of 4–20 mA or digital output.

Thermocouples are based on the effect in which the junction between two different metals produces a small voltage that increases with temperature. Heating the sensing junction generates a thermoelectric potential proportional to the temperature difference between the two junctions. There are a few thermo-

Table 8.5

Differences Between Sensing Devices

	Thermocouple	RTD	Thermistor	IC Temperature Devices
Measuring range	Wide; up to 1800°C	Narrow; up to 850°C	Very Narrow; up to 150°C	Very Narrow; up to 150°C
Stability	Low	High	Moderate	High
Accuracy	Moderate	High	Low	High
Sensitivity	Low	High	High	High
Linearity	Moderate	High	Low	High
Response time	Fast	Slow	Slow	Fast
Output signal strength	Very low	Low	Robust	Robust
Supply	No	Requires an external power source	No	Requires an external power source
Application	measure high temperature	When accuracy is needed	When sensitivity is needed	Remote applications

couples groups, expressed as letters (B, E, J, K, N, R, S, and T) that have their own characteristics and ranges (see Table 8.6)

Resistance temperature detectors (RTDs) use the fact that some metals (usually platinum and nickel) increase their electrical resistance as they get hotter. The most widely used sensor is the 100-ohm or 1,000-ohm RTD or platinum resistance thermometer. To measure the change, the sensor output is fed into a Wheatstone bridge with a reference voltage. Platinum resistance thermometers can cover temperature ranges from −200 to 800°C.

Thermistors are resistive devices composed of metal oxides formed into a bead and encapsulated in epoxy or glass in which resistance decreases with increasing temperature. Because the resistance characteristic falls off with increasing temperature they are called negative temperature coefficient (NTC) sensors. Resistance drops dramatically and nonlinearly with temperature.

The standard catalog reference temperature for the NTC devices is 25°C, or sometimes, it is given the temperature of the thermistor body when supposed "zero-power resistance" is seen. This "zero-power resistance" is represented by the DC resistance value of the thermistor when measured at a specific temperature with a low enough power dissipation from the thermistor in certain conditions.

Using NTC devices provides high accuracy in temperature measurement, and close tolerances ensure a definitely improved control. Regarding these devices, we have observed that it is important to ensure that their stability in time is guaranteed by an appropriate aging process of the devices. Depending on the

Table 8.6

Thermocouples Groups

Type of Thermocouple	Junction	Characteristics
K	Nickel-chromium/ Nickel-alumel	Most common type of thermocouple, inexpensive, accurate, reliable, and wide temperature range.
J	Iron/constantan	Also very common. Smaller temperature range and a shorter life span at higher temperatures than the type K. It is equivalent to the type K in terms of expense and reliability.
T	Copper/constantan	A very stable thermocouple; used in extremely low temperature applications.
E	Nickel-chromium/ constantan	Stronger signal and higher accuracy than the type K or type J at moderate temperature ranges of 1,000 °F and lower.
N	Nicrosil/nisil	The same accuracy and temperature limits as the type K, but slightly more expensive.
S	Platinum rhodium—10%/ platinum	Used in very high temperature applications. Sometimes used in lower temperature applications because of its high accuracy and stability.
R	Platinum rhodium—13%/ platinum	Used in very high temperature applications. It has a higher percentage of Rhodium than the type S, which makes it more expensive. Very similar to the type S in terms of performance. Sometimes used in lower temperature applications because of its high accuracy and stability.
B	Platinum rhodium—30%/ platinum rhodium—6%	Used in extremely high temperature applications. Maintains a high level of accuracy and stability at very high temperatures.

application, the process of encapsulation of these sensors offers a wide range of applications with specific functions in maintaining the safety features of equipment, which makes NTC thermistors very versatile components.

Due to their advantages, NTC thermistors may be successfully used for protecting electrical power systems from overheating or cooling system failures.

The main disadvantage of these devices is their very slow response; NTC thermistors are not suited to detect rapid changes in temperature and therefore can only be used to protect a system from changes that have a slow patter in the temperature modification. NTC thermistors cannot be used for short-circuit or over-current protection.

An *integrated circuit temperature device* is a sensing temperature device with an output voltage linearly proportional to the temperature. For these devices, accuracy is defined as the error between the output voltage and 10 mV/°C times the case temperature of the device, at specified conditions of voltage, current, and temperature (expressed in degrees Celsius).

8.4.1   Thermostats

A thermostat is a device able to control heating or cooling of a system through targeted settings of the temperature. The thermostat makes or breaks an electrical contact when a certain temperature is reached. Thermostats can be constructed in many ways (commonly of two different metals) and may use a variety of sensors to measure the temperature; then, the output of the sensor controls the heating or the cooling device. Subsequently, the heating or cooling equipment runs at full capacity until the set temperature is reached; then it shuts off.

The following elements need to be considered when selecting a bimetal thermostat for temperature control: actuating temperature, electrical load, life expectancy, and ambient operating conditions (temperature and humidity).

The *actuating temperature* is the temperature when the thermostat opens or closes the circuit. The thermostat status can be normally open (N/O) or normally closed (N/C) with respect to ambient temperature. Referring to the electrical load it is important to know if the load is resistive or inductive as well as the values for the maximum and steady-state current and voltage.

8.4.2   Thermal Cutoff (TCO)

These devices are nonresettable thermal protectors that are included within the heat-generating area of electronic circuits and electrical equipment. The thermal element senses temperature changes and "breaks" the circuit when the "cutoff temperature" is reached. It is important to be aware of the fact that the time interval from the moment when the heat source starts to work abnormally and the "fusing-off" of the thermal element depends on several factors (e.g., mounting conditions, holding temperature of the device, and maximum temperature limit ranges of the thermal cutoffs).

The main advantage of thermal cutoff devices is their very simple construction. They feature a thermal element, a special resin that starts to liquefy when its ambient reaches the melting point. The thermal element is welded across a pair of leads of wires and coated with a compound that protects against oxidation, so it is hermetically sealed. The resin compound generates a surface tension that causes it to form a bulb-like shape that pulls the liquefied element apart. The size of these devices, which are miniaturized, offers them a wide range of applications, in areas such as power supplies, cellular phones, audio-video equipment, IT equipment, transformers, solenoids, electric fans, small electric motors, driers, gas home appliances, fluorescent lights, electric shavers, heating devices, ICs, batteries, and automobile industry. TCOs can also be used for overheating protection.

However, TCOs should not be used for life-support equipment or in applications for the aeronautical industry or nuclear power industry without a specific acceptance for those applications.

Depending on the application, manufacturers should select them from the point of view of the environment in which they are to be used. (When the TCO is continuously used at a temperature higher than the maximum operation temperature, the TCO may be degraded and may not operate normally at the specified temperature [5].) Specifically, manufacturers should consider the following:

1. Selecting the correct coating, (e.g., ceramic or phenolic type coating);
2. The rated functioning temperature;
3. The holding current;
4. The rated voltage.

Since TCOs perform an important safety function, it is vital to choose TCOs that are certified or recognized by testing agencies and to be aware of all of the thermal characteristics of the device in which the TCO will be used, including the differences between the rated functioning temperature, the holding temperature (the temperature at which it will work according to the standard conditions when the maximum rated current passes through it), and the maximum temperature limit (the temperature at which the device will not reclose when exposed for a certain duration of time). Equipment should be designed so that any thermal overshoot does not exceed the maximum temperature limit after the TCO operates.

In addition, measuring the resistance between lead wires (terminals) and checking the internal status with X-rays are effective means to confirm the status of the TCO on delivery and after mounting in the equipment.

Using TCOs is very convenient, and in order to obtain the best results, their use should involve attentive studies regarding the installation/positioning of the devices' body and the leads of the device for even heating. It is also important to ensure that the location is not subjected to continuous vibrations, avoiding any mechanical tension on the body and on the leads of the device. Manufacturers should test an adequate number of final products, repeating testing under normal and abnormal conditions.

8.5 Motors and Fans

Depending of the function of the motor or fan, they should be judged in terms of their intended load and the conditions of the environment in which the end equipment is to be used. It is strongly recommended that manufacturers ensure that evidence of safety tests is offered for motors and fans (e.g., overload protection, locked rotor, overvoltage, and prevention from starting). Designers should choose those parts that can be protected effectively against the moving parts of these devices.

It is necessary to ensure that motors do not cause a fire hazard. Therefore, manufacturers should avoid motors approved for construction only, since these motors have not been investigated for locked rotor and running overload protection. Manufacturers should use only motors that are recognized as having impedance or thermal protection. For fans, an important parameter is the necessary airflow rate (volume flow).

The steps for evaluating flow rate are listed as follows [6]:

1. Determine the amount of heat generated inside the equipment P;

2. Decide the permissible temperature rise inside the equipment ΔT;

3. Calculate the air flow rate necessary for transfer of the heat: Q (CFM) = $(1.76 \times P)/\Delta T$, where P is the internal heat dissipation in W, ΔT is the allowable temperature in °C and air flow rate in CFM (cubic feet per minute).

The airflow rate can be also expressed in: m^3/hour = 1.6 CFM; m^3/min. = 0.028 CFM; m^3/sec. = 0.00045 CFM or liter/sec. = 0.47 CFM.

Critical systems that incorporate fan cooling should be provided with thermal warning or shutdown mechanisms when loss of airflow is detected.

8.6 Thermoplastic Materials

The proprieties that describe a thermoplastic material are: physical (specific gravity, area factor, pencil hardness, water absorption, flammability); optical (light transmission, haze, yellowness and refractive indexes); mechanical (tensile strength and stress) yield and break; elongation (strain); tensile modulus of elasticity; tear, impact and burst strengths, fold endurance); thermal (tensile heat distortion, deflection temperature under load, specific heat, coefficient of thermal expansion, Vicat softening temperature); and electrical (dielectric constant, dissipation factor, volume and surface resistivity, arc resistance Tungsten-comparative tracking index) [6].

It is important to choose thermoplastic materials according to the applicable requirements of the used standard(s). Enclosure, supports, and insulating walls should be judged first based on the operating temperature at which the plastic material will work, the proximity to any heating source, the position which material will have in normal use, and the required flammability rating.

The required flammability is for the minimum used thickness within the equipment. The mechanical designer should provide proof that after manufacturing, the plastic will not be subject to a shrinkage due to molding.

When a thermoplastic material is molded into the desired shape of the finished product, internal molding stresses may be present in the final part. With time and elevated temperature, the internal stresses may cause gradual distortion and possible exposure of the internal parts. After placement in an oven for seven hours at a specified temperature, the sample of the complete products are removed and examined for possible mold stress relief distortion. Any distortion, war page, or opening of the enclosure is considered unacceptable if it results in exposure to electrical hazards or moving parts of tested equipment [6].

It is also necessary to ensure that any colorants that are used along with the base material will not reduce the flammability rating of the final material.

The level of burning performance of polymeric materials is characterized by relative thermal index and classified by the flame rating (flammability). The relative thermal index is assigned in various thicknesses for both electrical and mechanical properties. All polymeric parts and printed wiring (circuit) board must have an acceptable flame rating. Common flame ratings are 5V, 5V-A, 5V-B, V-0, V-1, V-2, and HB. The least flammable is 5-V material. For foaming materials, the common flame ratings are HF-1, HF-2, and HBF. For thin materials, the common flame ratings are VTM-0, VTM-1, and VTM-2.

To evaluate the suitable polymeric material of an application according to flammability requires the following steps [6]:

- Identifying the polymeric materials that will be used in the product;
- Determining the function that each material played in the product;
- Obtaining information concerning material properties;
- Evaluating the suitability of the material in the end product application by checking the end product standard.

The Vicat softening point of the plastic material should be taken in consideration when it is used for enclosures hosting components that are producing heat. (e.g., heating elements).

8.7 Terminal Blocks

The terminal blocks are often used for connection (by screw, push-in, spring-cage, bold, etc.) to the mains of permanent installed products or for interconnections inside the equipment. When they reside in the primary circuit, terminal blocks must be the approved type.

Terminal blocks' ratings should meet manufacturer ratings of the equipment to ensure that that they are able to operate at the required maximum temperature under the maximum normal load, to withstand the electric strength test voltage between adjacent terminals, and to permit connection of specific wires with an adequate cross-sectional area.

It is very important to verify which standard was used for approval of the terminal block designed to be used for a permanent connection to the mains. Having an approval may not be sufficient; manufacturers are often faced with the rejection of a terminal block due to the size of the screws that are used for connection, or due to the inability to pass specific tests for which the product standard is asking (e.g., a field wiring test). Another failure experienced in the use of terminal blocks is the connection of more than one wire in one clamping part, exceeding the allowed cross-sectional area.

8.8 Connectors

Connectors should be judged according to the type of circuits that will be connected to them. Having TNV circuits connected along with SELV circuits at the same connector will imply a certain breakdown voltage between adjacent terminals and a certain creepage and clearance between them. Connectors that are keyed and are used with this feature for safety purposes (e.g., to prevent a reversed battery connection) should meet mechanical requirements for the number of connections that the design team assumes may happen during the life of the equipment.

8.9 Internal Wiring

Internal wiring [6] is vital for assuring the safety of any electrical equipment. Wires should be certified/listed. Such a qualification ensures the uniformity of the insulation quality thickness, as well as its flammability. It also ensures that wire will meet environmental conditions; depending on the application, wires may need to be oil- or water-resistant or to perform well at ow temperatures, for example. In addition, wires' rated voltage, their gauge that dictates their current capability, and the temperatures to which the wires are subjected should be considered. A factor of 1.25 is recommended for the gauge of the wires. The insulation required based on the application should be checked; the capability of being used as twisted wires is sometimes an issue, and if it is necessary, it should be taken in consideration. If the insulation of wiring from different circuits contacts to one another (e.g., mains supply and low voltage), the insulation for each wire must be rated for the highest voltage in either of the wires. The wire must be insulated with PVC, PFE, PTFE, FEP, or neoprene. Most wire characteristics are marked on the wires themselves or on the packaging (spool). The wiring that provides the connection to the mains must be certified/listed.

References

[1] MECA, "*Critical Component Table*," Franklin, USA (http://60601-1.com)

[2] UL Standards Info Net, "Catalog of UL Standards for Safety" (http://ulstandards-infonet.ul.com/).

[3] Swart J., et al., "Case Studies of Electrical Component Failures," Failures 2006, South Africa, 2006.

[4] IEC 60384-14, "Fixed Capacitors for Use in Electronic Equipment—Part 14: Sectional Specification: Fixed Capacitors for Electromagnetic Interference Suppression And Connection to the Supply Mains," Geneva, 2013

[5] Uchihashi Estec Co., Ltd., "Application Instructions for Elcut Thermal Cutoffs," 1998.

[6] Bolintineanu, C., and S. Loznen, "Product Safety and Third Party Certification," *The Electronic Packaging Handbook,* edited by G. R. Blackwell, Boca Raton, FL: CRC Press, 2000.

Selected Bibliography

Dowlatshahi, S., "Material Selection and Product Safety: Theory Versus Practice," *Omega 28,* 2000, pp.467–480.

ECMA-287, European Association For Standardizing Information and Communication Systems, "Safety of Electronic Equipment," Geneva, 2002.

Harris, K., and C. Bolintineanu, "Electrical Safety Design Practices Guide," Tyco Safety Products Canada Ltd, Rev 12, March 14, 2016.

IEC 60950-1+AMD1+AMD2, "Information Technology Equipment—Safety —Part 1: General Requirements," Geneva, 2005–2013.

Interpower Products, "Designer's Reference Catalog," No.16, http://www.interpower.com/ic/designers/designing-for-export/guides-and-charts.html.

Karana, E., P. Hekkert, and P. Kandachar, "Material Considerations in Product Design: A Survey of Material Aspects Used by Product Designers," *Materials and Design 29,* 2008, pp.1081–1089.

Littelfuse, "Electronic Designer's Guide," EC101-E, February 1998.

Martin, P. L., *Electronic Failure Analysis Handbook,* New York: McGraw-Hill, 1999.

Wickmann, Circuit Protection Design Guide, W1/0008, 2012.

9

Batteries

9.1 Introduction

The adoption of mobile electronic products today is tremendous. Mobile products have become an integral part of life; the need for more portability in products is driven by the consumer's need for mobility. In mobile products, a power source needs to power the product in the form of a battery. Battery technology has improved since the first zinc-copper battery was developed by Alessandro Volta in the 1800s.

There are two categories of batteries, primary and secondary batteries. Primary batteries are not rechargeable batteries, and the one-time use of the battery allows for the disposal of the battery once the battery is discharged. Secondary batteries are rechargeable batteries and allow the user to recharge and reuse the battery. Therefore, a primary battery has a one-time discharge life cycle, and a secondary battery has multicharge discharge life cycle.

Safety plays an important role in both primary and secondary batteries. Therefore, the safety design and verification of the battery and its product safety performance is necessary.

9.2 Secondary Batteries

Rechargeable batteries are used in products where the option of primary batteries may not be suitable for the market. Initially mobile products relied on rechargeable lead acid, nickel cadmium (NiCAD), and nickel metal hydride (NiMH) to power the portable products. These cell chemistries used a water-based electrolyte. However, the introduction of lithium-ion technology and the light weight and high-energy density of the cells in the battery allowed for smaller portable products. Its light weight, energy density, and increasingly low cost is propelling lithium-ion technology into new products, and there is a migration from the older battery chemistries toward lithium-ion energy storage in portable products.

Today the predominant rechargeable battery in mobile product applications is lithium-ion chemistry, and the focus of this chapter will be on this chemistry. A typical battery system is shown in Figure 9.1.

The typical lithium-ion battery system consists of essentially four components. The first is the power adapter, which can be a 12-V car adapter, USB adapter, or 120-V/230-V AC adapter. The power adapter conditions the power that is routed to the product charger circuit to charge the battery. The AC adapter needs to be subjected to safety evaluation and certification.

The charger circuit is the circuit within the product that ensures that the battery is charged within the normal operating range of the battery cell with respect to the charge current, upper voltage, and charge temperature. The charger circuit can be part of the product or separate from the product device. The charger may need to be subjected to safety evaluation and safety certification.

The battery typically has a secondary redundant set of current, voltage, and temperature controls. These controls are independent of the charger and the product device. Depending on the design, the primary function of this circuit is to act as an independent safety circuit that is only called upon to operate

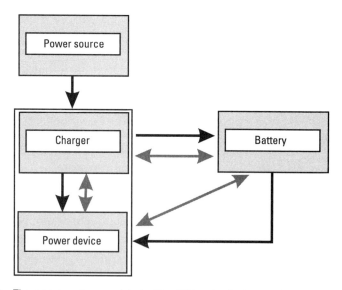

Figure 9.1   The components associated with a lithium-ion battery system.

when the control circuits in the charger and the product fail. The battery needs to be subjected to safety evaluation and safety certification.

The product device is powered by the battery, and the battery is designed to provide the power needed to power the product. Selecting the right cell for the application is important to ensure battery system reliability and safety. Where the charger system manages the charging of the battery with respect to charge temperature, voltage, and current, the product often manages the discharging of the battery with respect to discharge current, lower cutoff voltage, and discharge temperature. The product device and all its subsystems and components need to be subjected to safety evaluation and safety certification at both a subsystem and systems level. This evaluation can take a systems approach, ensuring that the combination of the control system in the product device and in the battery system and does not allow for gaps or stresses outside the cell, battery, or power adapter specification.

9.2.1 Rechargeable Batteries

Lithium-ion chemistry did not evolve from lead acid or nickel-based chemistry but was developed as a completely new cell chemistry in the 1990s by Sony (Figure 9.2).

A lithium-ion cell consists of a set of electrodes that are housed in a casing, often referred to as a cell can or cell pouch. There are typically two cell geometries associated with lithium-ion cells, namely the cylindrical-shaped cell and prismatic-shaped cell. (The prismatic cell may have a can construction or a pouch construction.) The dimensions can vary considerably depending on the capacity of the cell and the application. The cell casing can either be a pouch construction, which is a polymer with an aluminum lining, or a metal can construction, typically aluminum. The electrodes will be housed inside the sealed cell casing or pouch. The electrodes consist of an anode and a cathode and

Figure 9.2   A cylindrical lithium-ion cell.

sandwiched between the anode and the cathode, is a polymer separator. An organic electrolyte used in the cell can be absorbed in the separator or can be free-flowing in the cell between the anode and the cathode (Figure 9.3).

From a safety perspective, lithium-ion cells act differently than lead acid and nickel-based cell chemistries. The cell may go into thermal runaway and overheat, but the severity of the thermal event is dependent on the cell state of charge (SOC). In a worst-case failure mode, the lithium-ion battery thermal runaway event may result in venting of the cell or rapid disassembly of the cell and/or ignition and flaming, and venting of potentially combustible gasses.

In multicell batteries, individual cell failures may propagate from one cell to the adjacent cells and may continue until all of the affected cells in the battery system have failed. Cell thermal failure propagation may not always be observed and is affected by many factors including the battery design.

The reasons for the increased risk for flaming combustion are described as follows:

- *Flammable electrolyte:* Most lithium-ion cell eletrolytes contain components that are flammable.

- *Sustained exothermic chemical reaction:* Once the cell has entered thermal runaway, various degradation and/or oxidization processes maintain

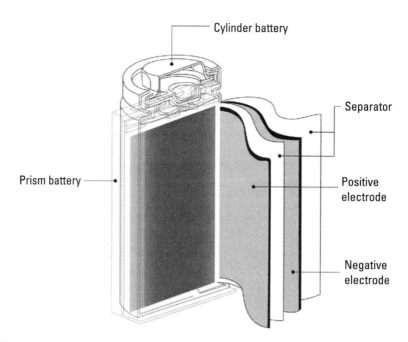

Figure 9.3   The construction of a lithium-ion cylindrical cell and a lithium-ion prismatic cell.

temperatures in the battery cell above 500°C. The risk to ignite secondary combustibles is always there.

Cell failures can occur early in the life of the cell as well as later in the life of the cell. It just depends on the failure mechanism that caused the cell to fail. Failure of the cell can be caused by a poorly designed cell, a cell manufacturing defect, battery management design defect, battery management failure, electrical abuse, mechanical abuse, or thermal abuse. In addition to these potential failure mechanisms, late-life and end-of-life failure can also occur but these failure mechanisms may be unique and very cell-model-specific.

Because of the above limitations, lithium-ion batteries need a control system for charging and discharging cells in a very precise manner. If the battery management system does not fulfill this task there is a risk that the cells may be electrically stressed and that battery reliability and safety will be compromised. This behavior of the cell electrochemistry requires that the cell be managed by a battery management unit (BMU) and a charger designed to charge lithium-ion cells.

9.2.2 Lithium-Ion Batteries

The lithium-ion battery is also different in construction when compared to lead acid and nickel-based battery systems. Typically, in lead acid and nickel-based chemistries, the battery will consist of a single cell or multiple cells making up the battery voltage and current specification. The cells may be housed in a wrapper or in a case, combined with a set of extensions to form the battery contacts. The chargers for lead acid batteries and nickel-based batteries can range from fairly simple to quite complex (Figure 9.4.)

In contrast, from a systems perspective, lithium-ion batteries are more complex due to the addition of precise control of voltage, current, and temperature as well as safety circuitry redundancy. The cells may be housed in a wrapper or a case, but typically a circuit board, often referred to as the battery protection circuit or BMU, is also housed in the case to form the battery. This protection circuit is there to protect cell(s) against such variables as over-voltage charge, over-current charge, and over-temperature charge. The charger system for these batteries is a precise device, and the amount of charge going into a lithium-ion battery should be very well controlled to prevent overcharge.

The reason for this is that there is currently no mechanism in lithium-ion cell chemistries to manage overcharge of the battery cell. In lead acid- and nickel based batteries the water in the electrolyte during overcharge is split into oxygen and hydrogen, and if this process evolves at a slow rate, it is possible for the gasses to recombine and form water again, effectively preventing overcharge of the cells' active materials. This slow overcharge is used to balance the cells

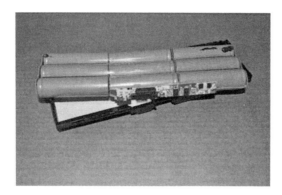

Figure 9.4 The lithium-ion battery pack showing the cells, battery management circuit board, and the plastic enclosure.

in the battery cell stack. If overcharge occurs at a higher rate, the excess gas buildup is often released through venting valves.

Electrochemical instability in a Li-ion battery cell during overcharge may cause several reliability and safety issues within the cell, including degradation of the electrolyte, lithium plating, and gas generation, as well as thermal runaway.

9.2.3 Lithium-Ion Battery Failure Causes

There are many reasons for a lithium-ion battery to fail in an unsafe manner. The lithium-ion cell can fail for the reasons shown in Figure 9.5. This information can be used in the safety failure modes and effects analysis (SFMEA).Figure 9.5 lists the stresses and defects on its left and the potential failure modes of the cell on its right.

The safety evaluation should consider the battery system design, which includes the product device. When this evaluation is performed, a systems approach, for example, similar to IEEE1625 and IEEE1725 may be performed.

In these two standards, the approach is to evaluate the battery system from the perspectives of the environment, users, power supply, host device, battery pack, and ultimately the cell. The cell is the component in the battery system that essentially dictates the battery pack, user, and environment limitations.

For example, if the cell is rated to be safely discharged up to a maximum temperature of 70°C and a product is rated to be operated at 80°C, the cell safety specification will not be compatible with the cell, and hence, irrespective of the product specification, the cell safety specification in this case limits the product specification. This is relevant to all operating parameters of the cell and components in the battery system. Hence the systems approach ensures

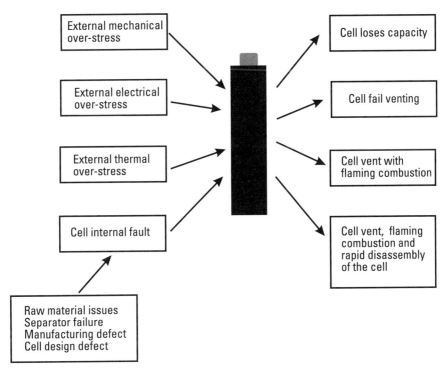

Figure 9.5 Potential causes and failure modes of lithium-ion cells.

that the battery system is engineered to the finest detail of compatibility at the component, subsystem, and systems level.

9.2.3.1 Mechanical Over-Stress

Lithium-ion cells can potentially experience a safety-related failure when the cell is mechanically stressed or damaged. In addition, external mechanical stress relates to mechanical damage that can occur to the cell or to the circuit board powered by the cell. Damage to these components can lead to immediate failure of the battery or can induce a defect that has some latency before the failure actually occurs. The failure mode of the cell will depend on factors such as extent of the mechanical damage, ambient temperature, age of the cell, and the state of charge. For example, the lower the state of charge of the cell, the less severe the cell failure may be. The higher the state of charge, the more severe the cell failure may be, for example. The mechanical stress on the cell may cause the separator to fail within the cell and result in an anode-to-cathode short circuit—this will cause internal cell heating and the cell may go into thermal runaway. Damage to the circuit board and component may cause a malfunction or even result in propagating circuit board safety-related failure. The lithium-ion cell and control circuits should be sufficiently protected against reasonable mechanical stresses to prevent damage to the cells and circuit boards.

9.2.3.2 Electrical Over Stress

In a lithium-ion battery, various components are sensitive to electrical overstress and may fail compromising the safety of the battery pack. These include discrete electronic components [1] and the lithium-ion cell [2]. Various electronic components (e.g., transient suppressors) can be overstressed and will then fail thermally. A component can heat or ignite adjacent surfaces, which can result in a burn hazard or fire hazard to the user. The lithium-ion cell, when electrically stressed during charge or discharge, may overheat, or during low temperature charge, lithium plating can potentially occur, compromising cell performance and cell safety. Therefore, lithium-ion cells require a control circuit that ensures that the cell is only operated within the cell-design operating window for charge and discharge voltage, and current.

9.2.3.3 Thermal Over-Stress

A lithium-ion battery is sensitive to temperature. The cells in the battery have a specific temperature range in which the cell will operate. When operated below its designated operating temperature, lithium plating could potentially occur, which is undesirable. At high temperatures, the cell may overheat.

Venting of the lithium-ion cell can cause electrolyte to migrate to the BMU circuit board or to the product device circuit board. The electrolyte can cause propagating circuit board failures [3], which represent a safety-related failure mode as they can result in external heating of the cells and force the cell into thermal runaway. Externally excessive heating of lithium-ion cells in a lithium-ion battery is a burn or fire risk.

However, internal heating of the cell can also be caused by internal faults inside the cell. In these cases, the safety of the lithium-ion cells depends on various factors.

9.2.3.4 Cell Internal Fault

An internal lithium-ion cell fault is a fault inside the cell and can be induced by an internal or external event in the cell. A lithium-ion cell with an internal cell fail can also experience a safety-related failure.

There are many potential reasons for an internal cell fault to occur (e.g., contaminated or out-of-specification raw materials used to manufacture the cell, manufacturing defects with in the cell, separators that fail, or cells that were designed incorrectly).

To minimize lithium-ion cell internal faults, the design and manufacturing of lithium-ion cells needs to be evaluated and tested. The design of the cells can be evaluated through internal testing and utilizing safety standards and obtaining safety certification. The manufacturing of the cells can be managed by safety audits and certification and also by implementing quality processes at the factory to ensure that the manufacturing process is consistent and follows the manufacturing requirements of the cell designers.

9.3 Secondary Battery Safety Standards

In battery-powered products the amount of energy in the battery can be significant, and any unintended release of uncontrolled energy always carries the risk of injuring a person or causing damage to property. The design of the lithium-ion cell, battery charger, and product device are evaluated through safety testing and certification. Following this evaluation process, the various components are stressed and tested to ensure that they operate at fail-safe, minimizing the risk of injuring the operator. There are currently two distinct types of batteries on the market: primary batteries, which are not rechargeable, and secondary batteries, which are rechargeable. This section discusses secondary batteries.

In various countries, governments regulate products where a significant hazard can be presented by the product. FCC and FDA regulations are mandatory for consumer products sold in the United States, but when it comes to consumer product safety, the regulation of manufacturers and product distributors is voluntary. This means that a manufacturer can decide to have the product certified or will have it certified as a result of a customer requirement. In some cases the certification is transferable across countries, and having the product certified in the United States may facilitate the product being certified in other countries where certification is required or vice versa. In the United States, certification companies may carry their own certification mark. For example, Intertek may certify products using their ETL label; Underwriters Laboratories may certify the same products using their UL mark; and there are others. These organizations may approve independent laboratories to test to their respective standards, but the markings will be under the various safety certification organizations. In addition to the product safety certification, a government controlled body called the Consumer Product Safety Commission (CPSC) monitors product safety. This agency monitors safety-related product failures and has the authority to fine companies that do not report safety-related issues with their products. In addition, the CPSC has the authority to investigate unsafe products and initiate product recalls with the product manufacturer.

Cell and battery safety standards are developed to evaluate a cell, battery, or product device as a single entity or as a combination for compliance and certification against a specific battery safety standard. The safety standard is designed to test the design and manufacturing of the cell, battery, and product device to ensure that the safety requirements for the specific standard are met.

Each country has its own safety standards for products, and the same trends are observed from rechargeable battery standards. Various countries have developed their own standards or adopted standards from other countries. In many cases, batteries cannot be sold in a country if the batteries are not certified to the standards applicable in the specific country.

Although there is some degree of harmonization within the battery certification world, various countries have their own standards or harmonized standards with IEC standards. Table 9.1 lists several countries and their associated standards.

Table 9.1
Secondary Batteries Standards List

Country	Applicable Standard	Standard Description
IEC	IEC 62133 In final phases of approvals: IEC 62133-1 IEC 62133-2	Secondary cells and batteries containing alkaline or other nonacid electrolytes; safety requirements for portable sealed secondary cells, and for batteries made from them, for use in portable applications Secondary cells and batteries containing alkaline or other nonacid electrolytes; safety requirements for portable sealed secondary cells, and for batteries made from them, for use in portable applications—Part 1: Nickel systems Secondary cells and batteries containing alkaline or other nonacid electrolytes—Part 2: Safety requirements for portable sealed secondary lithium cells, and for batteries made from them, for use in portable applications
USA	ANSI C18 ANSI 18.2	For all battery types ranging from primary alkaline batteries to rechargeable batteries For portable rechargeable cells and battery safety; covers both lithium-ion battery systems and nickel-based battery systems
European Union	EN 62133	Based on the IEC 62133
Taiwan	CNS 15364:2010 and CNS 14857-2	For a secondary Li-ion battery cell/pack (excl. button battery, batteries installed in the product as the accessory); harmonized with IEC 62133
Japan	JIS C8714	Lithium-ion batteries used for portable electronic applications
India	IS16046	Based on the IEC 62133
Russia	GOST 62133:2004	Based on the IEC62133
South Korea	KC 62133	Based on the IEC 62133
China	GB31241:2014	Test of rechargeable battery

9.3.1 Other Standards Developers

9.3.1.1 United Nations (UN) and the United States Department of Transportation (U.S. DOT)

The UN provides recommendations for the transport of dangerous goods. These recommendations can be formalized and adopted as requirements by a country for shipping batteries. In the United States, the DOT adopted these recommendations for the safe packaging and transportation of lithium-ion and lithium metal batteries. The test criteria are captured in "The Recommendation on the Transportation of Dangerous Goods, Manual of Tests and Criteria, Part 3, Section 38.3.

UN/DOT 38.3

UN DOT tests are often referred to as the UN/DOT T- tests and consist of eight tests. Batteries in the consumer product and automotive space have to conform to this standard in order to be eligible for shipping. There are other international organizations related to the transportation industry, and the relevant standards pertaining to these industries also need to be adhered to. This standard is a self-certification by the manufacturer of the battery and a NRTL; a third party is not required to certify the battery.

9.3.1.2 UL

UL is both a standards organization and a certification laboratory. UL standards are not just popular in the consumer product area, but UL also develops standards for electrically powered vehicle batteries. Specifically, to lithium-ion batteries, UL has two dominant battery standards for consumer products.

UL1642

This standard is specifically for lithium-ion electrochemical systems and is used for testing lithium-ion *cells*. When the lithium-ion cells are integrated into batteries, UL2054 is used to test the batteries.

UL2054

This standard pertains specifically to *batteries*. This means that one or more cells were integrated into an enclosure to form a battery. All battery chemistries can be tested using this standard with the exception of lithium-ion cells, and UL1642 will replace the cell testing section of this standard.

In the light vehicle and automotive space, the following standards may be relevant.

- *UL 2271:* This standard pertains to batteries in light electric vehicles.
- *UL 2272:* This standard pertains to batteries used in hover boards.
- *UL2580:* This standard pertains to electric vehicle batteries.

9.3.1.3   IEEE

The IEEE operates in the electrical space and hence all its governed areas relate to electricity, which includes battery standards. Following are two battery standards developed specifically for the consumer product market, and they relate specifically to lithium-ion battery systems. What makes these standards so unique is the fact that the standards below do not just focus on individual components but also evaluate the battery as a system integrated into a product. This is a key element in lithium-ion battery system design, as a battery system needs to be engineered and cannot, as in the past with some other battery chemistry systems, just be integrated without becoming very cell-specific.

IEEE1625

This standard was developed specifically for notebook computer batteries consisting of multiseries cell battery packs. However, the standard is applicable to all mobile multiseries cell consumer products, specifically computing devices. The standard addresses the electrochemical cell, the battery, the device charger system, and the wall power adapter. The standard is based on a systems approach, evaluating the integration of the various components to operate in an environment to promote product safety. CTIA used this standard to develop its testing, evaluation, and auditing lithium-ion battery certification protocol for multiseries cell mobile devices.

IEEE1725

The standard was developed specifically for single-series cell cellular devices. It was based on IEEE1625 but can be used for several single-series cell consumer products using lithium-ion batteries. The standard addresses the electrochemical cell, the battery, the device charger system, and the wall power adapter. The standard is based on a systems approach, evaluating the integration of the various components to operate in an environment to promote product safety. CTIA used this standard to develop its testing, evaluation, and auditing lithium-ion battery certification protocol for single-series cell mobile devices.

9.3.1.4   CTIA—The Wireless Organization

The CTIA Wireless Organization is an international trade group providing standards specifically for the cellular telephone industry. CTIA developed two battery standards for cellular products using lithium-ion batteries. The first focuses on a single-series cell battery, and the second focuses on a multiseries battery system.

CTIA IEEE1625

The standard was developed specifically for multiseries cell batteries used in mobile computing devices' single-series cell cellular devices. The CTIA requires this standard for the certification of cellular devices and their batteries. The CTIA standard requires testing, evaluation, and auditing of the cellular device battery system, which includes evaluation and testing at cell level, battery level, and systems integration level and the evaluation of the adapters powering and charging the device battery system.

CTIA IEEE1725

This standard was developed specifically for single-series cell cellular devices. The CTIA requires this standard for the certification of these cellular devices and their batteries. The CTIA standard requires testing, evaluation, and auditing of the device battery system, which includes evaluation and testing at the cell level, battery level, and systems integration level and the evaluation of adapters powering and charging the device battery system.

9.4 Primary Batteries

Primary batteries can be purchased in many different forms, ranging from button cells to AAA, AA, B, C, and D forms; 9-V batteries; and other form factors (see Figure 9.6). Currently, in the market the predominant primary battery chemistries are zinc-carbon, alkaline, and lithium iron disulfide and lithium batteries. These batteries chemistries dominate the market and are sold in high volumes.

Zinc carbon batteries are the oldest of the three chemistries in the market. These batteries have a 1.5-V chemistry and are likely less costly than alkaline and lithium-ion disulfide. However, their battery capacity is less than alkaline and lithium iron disulfide batteries, and the batteries will not last as long. Also, these batteries may leak corrosive electrolyte when they are fully discharged.

Figure 9.6 Various sizes of alkaline primary batteries.

Alkaline batteries, also known as alkaline manganese batteries, are the second oldest of the trio and much improved in their energy capacity and current delivery. The batteries have a very low internal discharge rate and can be stored for extended periods of time. The batteries may leak corrosive electrolyte and are not leak-proof. The output voltage of these batteries is also 1.5V.

Lithium-iron disulfide is the youngest of the three chemistries discussed in this section. There are many different types of lithium metal batteries, and the other versions may have output voltages between 3V and 4V—most common may be button cells offering a 3-V output voltage. This cell chemistry has a capacity improvement over alkaline batteries and also offers a 1.5-V output voltage. This is due to the lower internal resistance of the cells and its ability to power energy-intensive products (e.g., digital cameras).

The safety concerns with these batteries are higher when compared to zinc carbon and alkaline batteries. In 2004, the DOT and the U.S. Federal Aviation Administration banned the bulk shipment of lithium metal batteries on passenger aircraft although passengers can carry them onboard if the maximum lithium content is not exceeded. These batteries are heat-sensitive and may fail exothermically when rapidly discharged or heated by an external heat source. The batteries may be equipped with a current-limiting device to prevent excessive discharge current and to promote cell safety.

There are safety risks associated with primary cells. Primary cells can overheat and become a burn risk for the user. The cells may vent hot gases, or they may fail, causing the cell to rapidly disassemble. The electrolytes may be corrosive or, when coming in contact with a person's eyes or skin, may result in injury.

Button cells (Figure 9.7) may be zinc carbon or lithium metal-based and pose an additional risk. This risk is associated with children swallowing the

Figure 9.7   Various sizes of button cells.

button cells. Every year children are hospitalized for swallowing button cells batteries, which can cause severe internal injury.

9.5 Primary Battery Safety Standards

There are safety standards pertaining to primary batteries. Table 9.2 shows a subset of standards associated with primary batteries in general; Table 9.3 is more specific, focusing on lithium metal primary batteries.

Primary batteries are intended to be discharged only once and disposed of when discharged. The batteries are not rechargeable and should not be recharged. Recharging a primary battery may pose a safety risk.

Table 9.2
A Subset of General Standards Associated with Primary Batteries

Standard Number	Standard Title
IEC 60086-1, BS 387	Primary Batteries—General
IEC 60086-2, BS	Batteries—General
ANSI C18.1M	Portable Primary Cells and Batteries with Aqueous Electrolyte—General and Specifications
ANSI C18.3M	Portable Lithium Primary Cells and Batteries—General and Specifications

Table 9.3
A Subset of General Standards for Lithium-Based Primary Batteries

Standard Number	Standard Title
Standard Number	Standard Title
BS 2G 239:1992	Specification for Primary Active Lithium Batteries for Use in Aircraft
BS EN 60086-4:2000, IEC 60086-4:2000	Primary Batteries. Safety Standard for Lithium Batteries
IEC 61960. Ed.1. 02/ 208497 DC	Secondary Cells and Batteries Containing Alkaline or Other Nonacid Electrolytes. Secondary Lithium Cells and Batteries for Portable Applications
BS G 239:1987	Specification for Primary Active Lithium Batteries for Use in Aircraft
BS EN 60086-4:1996, IEC 60086-4:1996	Primary Batteries. Safety Standard for Lithium Batteries
ST/SG/AC.10/27/ Add.2	United Nations Recommendations on the Transport of Dangerous Goods

9.6　Battery Safety Design

A lithium-ion battery system should be designed and engineered to ensure that the cells in the battery fulfill the battery requirement and that the battery in the product device fulfills the product requirements throughout its useful life in the field. During the design process, the safety design of the battery system should be evaluated and tested. The safety standards will evaluate the effectiveness of the in-house design for safety processes. Although the brand of the product will define the safety levels of the product, compliance to the safety standards can be viewed as a standard with which the product should comply.

Battery system safety does not just entail a safe design but also entails the manufacturing process and quality control of the cell and battery. The cell quality control is critical. The battery system design may be safe and the cell may be safe, but a manufacturing defect in the cell can override the battery system safety and cause the battery system to become unsafe. Therefore, single ownership and continuity from the system level down to the component level is an effective way to manage both design safety as well as manufacturing quality. A SFMEA is a good tool to incorporate all the risks identified in battery system design, battery components, and the environment in which batteries will operate. This approach will facilitate minimizing product safety risk.

References

[1] Swart J, et al. "Case Studies of Electrical Component Failures," *Failures 2006*, South Africa, 2006.

[2] Swart J, et al. "Going Beyond Industry Standards in Critically Evaluating Lithium-Ion Batteries," *Advancements in Battery Charging, Monitoring and Testing,* Vancouver, Canada, 2005.

[3] Slee, D., et al., *"Introduction to Printed Circuit Board Failures,"* IEEE Symposium on Product Compliance Engineering, Toronto, CA, 2009.

Selected Bibliography

Batteries and Energy Storage Technology Magazine (BEST Magazine), http://www.bestmag.co.uk.

Battery Council International. "Failure Modes Study: A Report of the BCI Technical Subcommittee on Battery Failure Modes," 2010, Chicago, IL.

BatteryUniversity, Internet site, http://www.BatteryUniversity.com.

Gates Energy Products, *Rechargeable Battery Applications Handbook,* Boston, MA: Butterworth-Heinemann, 1992.

IEEE 1725, "IEEE Standard for Rechargeable Batteries for Cellular Telephones," 2011.

Linden, D. (ed.), *Handbook of Batteries*, (4th ed.)., New York: McGraw-Hill, 2010.

Perez, R. A., *The Complete Battery Book*, Philadelphia: Tab Books, 1985.

Swart, J., et al., *"Lithium-ion batteries for hybrid electric vehicles: A safety perspective,"* 5th International Advanced Automotive Battery (and Ultracapacitor) Conference, Hawaii, 2005.

Van Schalkwijk, W. A., and B. Scrosati, *Advances in Lithium-Ion Batteries,* New York: Kluwer Academic/Plenum Publishers, 2002.

Vincent, C., and B. Scrosati, *Modern Batteries,* Second Edition, New York: John Wiley & Sons, Inc., 1997.

10

Power Source

10.1   Introduction

From a safety perspective, the power source components can be considered the most significant part of products because they feed power to all the rest of the components. Additionally, this part of the product provides the principal separation between hazardous voltages (the mains) and the nonhazardous parts (the low-voltage secondary).

10.2   Power Supplies: Plugs, Connectors, and Cord Sets

Connecting power to an electrical product can be done in several ways. Power supplies intended for connection to a *mains supply* may be provided with one of the following means of connection:

1. Power supply cord, which may be detachable or nondetachable, fixed to, or assembled with the power supply;
2. Simple plug;
3. Permanent connection, using terminal blocks.

The detachable power supply cord is a flexible cord intended to be connected to the power supply by means of a suitable appliance coupler (e.g., IEC60320, NEMA type).

The nondetachable power supply cord may be either ordinary, a flexible power cord that can be easily replaced without special preparation or any special tool, or special, meaning that it has to be specially prepared, that it requires the use of a special tool for replacement, or that it cannot be replaced without damaging the power cord and/or the power supply. Power supply cords may be equipped with nonindustrial type plugs (type A) or industrial type B, depending on the end application in which they are used.

The simple plug with a power supply or direct plug-in power supply is a type of equipment with no mains on/off switch. The plug of the direct plug-in power supply is intended to serve as the disconnecting device if the equipment must be quickly disconnected. It is imperative that access to the mains plug and the associated mains socket/outlet, is never obstructed. The installation instructions of such power supply should include adequate safety instructions.

Permanently connected power supplies require a special means of connection to the mains supply, equipment that is intended for connection to the building installation wiring using screw terminals or other reliable means (e.g., terminal blocks or screws). This type of equipment should be installed in the field by service persons or by licensed electricians according to the local electrical codes and/or regulations.

10.2.1 Attachment Plugs

The characteristics of an attachment plug are the *pattern (according to national requirements—see Table 10.1)* and the rated *current* and *voltage.* Plugs for use with aluminum wire rated 20 amperes or less should be properly marked with the copper aluminum revised (CO/ALR) marking.

One of the features of receptacles and attachment plugs is that the grounding connection must make first and break last, meaning that when the plug is inserted the ground contact connects first and when pulling out the plug, the ground is the last to disconnect. This feature allows for the safety of having a complete grounding path during the connection and disconnection process. The mains plug must be rated at least 125% of the product current rating.

Tests done for attachment Plugs include the following: security of blades and pins, temperature, plug grip test, blade pull test at elevated temperature, abrupt pull test, push back force test, conditioning cycles for blade retention test, depth of cavity test, retention of blades test, overload test, resistance to arcing, and improper insertion test.

Depending on the country in which the product is used, the attachment plug (appliance coupler) has to have the configuration required in that country. There are countries with specific supplementary requirements for the appliance coupler; in those countries a specific approval for the plugs may be required (e.g., in Australia and New Zealand, compliance with the AS/NZS 3112 is mandatory). Due to this fact, it is recommended that manufacturers and suppliers not supply detachable power cords with the product, leaving this task to the discretion of the local distributors. Table 10.1 presents the worldwide plug and socket patterns and the voltages and frequencies at which they may be used.

Note: Plug and socket pattern codification presented within Table 10.1 is made according to the IEC TR 60083:2015 [1].

Table 10.1
Worldwide Plug and Socket Patterns, Voltages, and Frequency

Country/Area	Volts	Frequency (Hz)	Plug and Socket Pattern	Comments
Abu Dhabi, Bahrain, Dubai, England, Gambia, Grenada, Guernsey, Ireland, Rep. of, Jersey, Macau, Malaysia, Malawi, Malta, Mauritius, North Ireland, Saint Helena, Ascension and Tristan da Cunha, Scotland, Singapore, United Kingdom, Wales	230	50	G	G (BS 1363)
Afghanistan, Azerbaijan, Belarus, Cape Verde, Egypt, Georgia, Iran, Kazakhstan, Kyrgyzstan, New Caledonia, North Korea, Sao Tome and Principe, Tajikistan, Turkmenistan, Uzbekistan	220	50	F Used also C socket Socket C accept also E, F plugs, but without ground Socket F accept also C and E plugs	F (Schuko; CEE 7/4 plug & CEE 7/3 socket) C (Europlug; CEE 7/16)

Table 10.1 (continued)

Country/Area	Volts	Frequency (Hz)	Plug and Socket Pattern	Comments
Albania, Algeria, Andorra, Armenia, Austria, Azores, Balearic Islands, Bosnia-Herzegovina, Bulgaria, Croatia, Estonia, Finland, Germany, Greece, Hungary, Iceland, Kosovo, Latvia, Lithuania, Luxembourg, Macedonia, Moldova, Montenegro, Netherlands, Norway, Portugal, Romania, Russian Federation, Serbia, Slovenia, Spain, Sweden, Turkey, Ukraine	230	50	F Used also C socket Socket C accept also E, F plugs, but without ground Socket F accept also C and E plugs	
Angola, Eritrea, Gabon, Guinea-Bissau, Mauritanie, Paraguay, Somalia, Togo	220	50	C	Eritrea: 230V
Anguilla, Antigua, Belize, British Virgin Island, Colombia, Cuba, Dominican Rep., El Salvador, Guam, Haiti, Honduras, Jamaica, Mexico, Montserrat, Panama, Peru, Philippines, Taiwan, Trinidad & Tobago, Virgin Islands	110	60	A, B	Anguilla: Only socket A Jamaica: 50 Hz Mexico : 127V Antigua : 230V Montserrat : 230V El Salvado: 115V Trinidad & Tobago: 115V Belize: additional 220V Peru: 220V Philippines: 220V
Argentina	220	50	I Used also C socket Socket C accept also E, F plugs, but without ground	I (IRAM 2073)

Table 10.1 (continued)

Country/Area	Volts	Frequency (Hz)	Plug and Socket Pattern	Comments
Australia, Christmas Is., Cocos Is., Cook Is., Fiji, Kiribati, Nauru, New Zealand, Papua New Guinea, Pitcairn Islands, Samoa, Tonga, Tuvalu, Vanuatu, Western Samoa	230	50	I	AS/NZS 3112 Papua New Guinea: 240V Tonga: 240V Cook Islands: 240V Fiji: 240V Kiribati: 240V Nauru – 240 V
American Samoa, Aruba, Bahamas, Bermuda, Canada, Costa Rica, Cayman Islands, Ecuador, Guatemala, Liberia, Marshall Islands, Micronesia, Nicaragua, Palau, Puerto Rico, United States of America, Venezuela	120	60	A, B	A (US NEMA 1-15) B (US NEMA 5-15; IEC 60906-2)
Bangladesh	220	50	C, D, G	D (BS 546 5 A)
Barbados	115	50	A, B	
Belgium, Congo, Czech Rep., France, Ivory Coast, Poland, Saint Pierre and Miquelon, Slovakia, Tunisia	230	50	E Used also C socket Socket E accept also C plug	E (CEE 7/6 plug & CEE 7/5 socket)
Benin, Burkina Faso, Burundi, Cameroon, Central African Rep., Comoros, Djibouti, Equatorial Guinea, Madagascar, Mali, Mongolia, Morocco, Syria, Tahiti	220	50	C, E	Tahiti: 60 Hz
Bhutan	230	50	D, F, G	

Table 10.1 (continued)

Country/Area	Volts	Frequency (Hz)	Plug and Socket Pattern	Comments
Bolivia	115, 230	50	A, C	
Bonaire, Curacao Is.	127, 220	60, 50	A, B, F	
Botswana, Dominica, Ghana, Hong Kong, Iraq, Nigeria, Qatar, Saint Kitts and Nevis, Sierra Leone, Sri Lanka, Tanzania, Yemen, Zambia, Zimbabwe	230	50	D, G	Zimbabwe: 220V Hong Kong: 220V Qatar: 240V Saint Kitts and Nevis: 60 Hz
Brazil	127, 220	60	N Socket N accept also C plug	NBR 14136
Brunei, Cyprus, Falkland Islands, Gibraltar, Isle of Man, Kenya, Kuwait, Oman, Santa Lucia, Seychelles, Uganda, United Arab Emirates	240	50	G	United Arab Emirates: 220V
Cambodia	230	50	A, C, G	
Canary Islands, Svalbard	220	50	F	Svalbard: 230V
Chad	220	50	D, E, F	
Chile	220	50	L Socket L accept also C plug	
China, People's Rep. of	220	50	A, G, I	
Congo, Democratic Rep. of, French Guiana, Guadeloupe, Martinique, Senegal	220	50	C, D, E	Guadeloupe: 230V Senegal: 230V
Denmark	230	50	K Socket K accepts also C, E and F plugs	K (DS 60884-2)
Ethiopia	220	50	D, J, L	

Table 10.1 (continued)

Country/Area	Volts	Frequency (Hz)	Plug and Socket Support	Comments
Faeroe Islands, Greenland	230	50	C, K	Greenland: 220V
Guinea	220	50	C, F, K	
Guyana	240	60	A, B, D, G	
India, Nepal, Pakistan	230	50	C, D, M	
Indonesia	230	50	C, F, G	
Israel	230	50	H Socket H accept also C plug.	H (SI 32)
Italy, San Marino	230	50	F, L Socket F accept also C, E plugs. Socket L accept also C plugs	
Japan	100	50 (East Japan), 60 (West Japan)	A, B	
Jordan	230	50	B, C, D, F, G, J	
Laos	230	50	A, B, C, E, F	
Lebanon	220	50	A, B, D, G	
Lesotho	220	50	M	M (15 A BS 546)
Libya	230	50	C, D, F, L	
Liechtenstein, Switzerland	230	50	J Socket J accept also C plug	J (SEV-1011)
Maldives	230	50	D, G, J, K, L	
Monaco	230	50	C, D, E, F	
Mozambique	220	50	C, F, M	

Table 10.1 (continued)

Country/Area	Volts	Frequency (Hz)	Plug and Socket Support	Comments
Myanmar	230	50	C, D, F, G	
Namibia	220	50	D, M	
Netherlands Antilles	115, 220	60/50	A, B, F	
Niger	220	50	C, D, E, F	
	230	50	D, G	
Reunion, Saint Martin	220	50	E	Saint Martin: 60 Hz
Rwanda	230	50	C, J	
Saint Vincent	110, 230	50	A, B, G	
Saudi Arabia	220	60	G	
Solomon Islands	220	50	G, I	
South Africa	230	50	D, M, N	
South Korea	220	60	C, F	
Sudan	230	50	C, D	
Suriname	127, 230	60, 50	A, B, C, F	
Swaziland	230	50	M	
Thailand	220	50	A, B, C, F, O Socket O accept also C, E and F plug, but for E and F no ground	O
Timor East	220	50	C, E, F, I	
Uruguay	230	50	C, F, I, L	
Vietnam	110, 220	50	A, C, D	

10.2.2 Power Supply Cords

There are several factors that need to be considered when selecting a power supply cord for a specific application. The most common factors are described as follows:

- *Ampacity* (current-carrying capacity): The amount of current (electrical flow) a conductor can carry. The larger the wire size, the greater the amount of current (Table 10.2).

- *Voltage:* The voltage rating depends primarily on the insulation thickness. The thicker the insulation, the higher the voltage rating (e.g., 0.4-

mm nominal insulation wall for 300V; 0.8-mm nominal insulation wall for 600V).

- *Temperature:* This would involve both the upper and low-end temperatures required for the product or environment (e.g., usually 80°C, 105°C, and 200°C).

An electrical product should be supplied in the EU with a European harmonized cord set suitable for the rating of the unit, according to EN 60245 designation 53 (rubber sheathed) or EN 60227 designation 53 (PVC sheathed). Alternatively, the equipment can be provided with an appliance inlet, while each country will supply a European harmonized detachable cord set.

The product using a nondetachable cord must be provided with bushing and a strain relief. It must enter the product through an inlet bushing and have a smooth, well-rounded surface, and it should withstand the cord anchorage test.

For a unit rated up to and including 6A, the cross-sectional area of the conductors in the power supply cord must be a minimum 0.75 mm². For products rated between 6A and 10A the minimum cross-sectional area required is 1.0 mm² (Table 10.2).

Table 10.2
Maximum Ampacity of Cords and Cable

Conductor Size (Copper)		Current (A)	
AWG	Cross-Sectional Area (mm²)	Maximum Product Rated	Protective Rating External to Product
18	0.75	I ≤ 6	10
16	1.0	6 < I ≤ 10	16
14	1.5	10 < I ≤ 16	25
12	2.5	16 < I ≤ 25	32
10	4.0	25 < I ≤ 32	40
8	6.0	32 < I ≤ 40	63
6	10.0	40 < I ≤ 63	80
4	16.0	63 < I ≤ 80	100
2	25.0	80 < I ≤ 100	125

The conductor size represents approximately the dimensional equivalence.
AWG = American wiring gauge.

If the cord set is supplied without a plug, appropriate installation instructions must be included.

Any clamping screws used as part of anchorage should not bear directly on the cord, and at least one part of the cord anchorage should be securely fixed to the product. The terminals used to make the AC connection between the product and its cord can be of stud, pillar, or screw types. All these have to meet the dimensional requirements.

When preparing power supply cords for permanent attachment to a product, the protective-grounding conductor should be made slightly longer than the circuit conductors, so that the protective-grounding connection will be the last to break in the event of failure of the strain relief mechanism.

For power supply cords, the following tests are applicable:

- Conductor secureness test;
- Security of insulation test; Dielectric voltage-withstand test;
- Insulation resistance test;
- Accelerated aging test;
- Crushing test;
- Impact resistance test;
- Flexing test;
- Jacket retention test;
- Adhesion test;
- Cycling heat test;
- Abrasion resistance;
- Cut-through resistance;
- Elongation;
- Tensile strength.

When the power supply cord is not supplied with the product, it is necessary to include applicable ratings; in this manner, a properly rated power cord, will be acceptable to the local authorities. Any additional requirements applicable for the power supply cord (e.g., retention, location, and special openings) should be fully described within the installation/user's instructions/manuals.

Within the EU market the power supply cords use HAR marking coding (Figure 10.1). According to the HAR agreement, the CBs that are signatories to the agreement consider cables and cords bearing any one of the HARmonisation markings of the other signatories unconditionally, as bearing their own approval mark and, should accept them accordingly. HAR mark coding was

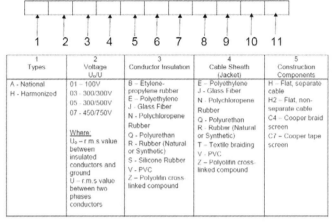

Figure 10.1 EU HAR coding [2].

established and is operating with the full support of the cable manufacturers located in the EU countries, represented by the Europacable, the European cable manufacturers association.

If in North America the color coding of the conductors is typically black (line), white (neutral), and green (ground), the European harmonized conductors are brown (line), blue (neutral), and green/yellow (ground) (Figure 10.2) Due to the differences between the European and North American color coding of conductors on power supply cords and their standards and thus the construction of these, it is necessary to have different cordage for the same equipment when it is intended to be put in service in *both* markets. Table 10.3 presents the codification of North American cable types.

The following are specific requirements for plugs and cords used in medical application in some countries.

Conductor Color Coding		
Conductor	**International Color Coding**	**North American Color Coding**
3 Conductors		
Line	Brown	Black
Neutral	Blue	White
Ground	Green / Yellow	Green
5 Conductors		
Line	Brown	Black
Line	Black	Orange
Line	Gray	Red
Neutral	Blue	White
Ground	Green / Yellow	Green

Figure 10.2   Color coding for mains conductors.

- Australia: In Australian medical applications, hospitals prefer to have a clear, transparent plug and orange, flexible cable. These plugs and connectors must carry one of the many Australian approvals.

- North America: Hospital-grade plugs are subject to special requirements contained in the plug standards: UL 498 and CAN/CSA C22.2 no 42. The hospital-grade plugs, connectors, and receptacles carry the "green dot," signifying that they have been designed and tested for grounding reliability, assembly integrity, strength, and durability. Specifically, they meet the requirements of UL Standard 498 (attachment plugs and receptacles) for abrupt plug removal; ground pin retention; fault current; terminal strength; ground contact temperature and resistance; assembly security; cord grip strain relief and cord pull; and various durability and impact tests of the material. Locking terminals ensure reliable power connections, which is very important on patient-connected medical equipment.

- Denmark: The Danish hospital-grade plug and socket are recommended for use in medical applications and specifications are being added to the standard SB 107-2-D1. The socket is designed to prevent "normal equipment" from being connected and disrupting the mains circuit in specific medical settings.

10.2.3   Strain Relief: Cable Glands

In order to be acceptable to the local authorities, the nondetachable power supply cords must pass several tests; one of the most important tests is the strain re-

Table 10.3
North American Cable Types [4]

North American Cable Types
SVT: Thermoplastic insulated vacuum cleaner cord, with or without third conductor for grounding purposes, 300V (PVC);
SJT: Junior hard service, thermoplastic insulated conductors and jacket, 300V (PVC);
SJTW: Same as SJT except outdoor-rated (PVC);
SJTO: Same as SJT but oil-resistant outer jacket (PVC);
SJTOW: Same as SJTO except outdoor-rated (PVC);
ST: Hard service cord with all thermoplastic construction, 600V (PVC);
STW: Same as ST except outdoor-rated (PVC);
STO: Same as ST but with oil-resistant outer jacket (PVC);
STOW: Same as STO except outdoor-rated (PVC);
SPT-1: Parallel jacketed thermoplastic cable, 300V. With or without third conductor for grounding. (PVC)
SPT-2: Same as SPT-1 but heavier construction (PVC);
SPT-3: Same as SPT-2 but heavier construction (PVC);
SJE: Hard service cord, thermoplastic elastomer insulated, and jacketed, 300V (TPE);
SJEW: Same as SJE except outdoor-rated. (TPE)
SJEO: Same as SJE but with oil-resistant jacket (TPE);
SJEOW: Same as SJE except outdoor-rated (TPE);
SJEOO: Same as SJE but conductor insulation and jacket BOTH oil resistant. (TPE);
SJEOOW: Same as SJEOO except outdoor rated. (TPE);
SE: Extra hard service cord, thermoplastic elastomer conductor insulation and jacket, 600V. (TPE);
SEW: Same as SE except outdoor-rated. (TPE);
SEO: Same as SE but with oil resistant jacket (TPE);
SEOW: Same as SEO except outdoor-rated (TPE);
SEOO: Same as SE but with oil-resistant conductor insulation and jacket (TPE);
SEOOW: Same as SEOO except outdoor-rated (TPE);
S: Extra hard service cord, thermoset-insulated conductors and thermoset jacket, 600V;
SO: Same as S but with oil-resistant jacket (thermoset);
SOW: Same as S except outdoor-rated. (thermoset);
SOO: Same as S but both conductor insulation and jacket are oil-resistant (thermoset);
SOOW: Same as SOO except outdoor-rated (thermoset);
SJ: Hard service cord, thermoset insulated conductors and thermoset jacket, 300V (thermoset);
SJO: Same as SJ but with oil-resistant jacket (thermoset);
SJOW: Same as SJO except outdoor-rated (thermoset);
SJOO: Same as SJ but both conductor insulation and jacket are oil-resistant (thermoset);
SJOOW: Same as SJOO except outdoor rated (thermoset).

Nomenclature Key
S = Service grade (also means extra hard service when not followed by J, V, or P);
J = Hard service;
V = Vacuum cleaner cord (also light-duty cable);
P = Parallel cord (also known as zip cord)—always light-duty;
E = Thermoplastic elastomer (UL/NEC designation ONLY);
O = Oil-resistant*;
T = Thermoplastic;
W = Outdoor-includes sunlight-resistant jacket and wet location rated conduc tors (formerly "W-A");
H = Heater cable;
VW-1 = Flame-retardant;
FT2 = Flame-retardant.
*When only one "O" appears in a classification (i.e., SJEOW), only the outer jacket material is oil-resistant. If two "O's" are in the classification (i.e., SEOOW), the insulation covering the conductors and the outer jacket insulation are all oil-resistant.

lief test (cord anchorage test). It is performed with some variations, to conform to the applicable standard for the intended market. This type of test is a pull type test, which will ensure that during the test and after, the power cord will not expose the user to any risk: The pull force should not damage the internal terminations, and, there should be no loss of electrical continuity. Strain reliefs extend cord life and reinforce the cord connection to product.

Many styles of strain reliefs are threaded and can be assembled in two different ways. The mounting threads of the strain relief can be threaded directly into the panel of the product, or the strain relief can be eased through a clearance hole in the panel and fitted with a locking nut. Obviously, each of these options requires a different sized clearance hole in the product panel.

The strain reliefs can be provided in different types of mounting threads: national pipe thread (NPT) is the American standard, and Panzer Gewinde (PG) is a European standard. PG threading is sometimes referred to as metric threading; however, these threads are not truly metric. There is a metric system of threading that is replacing PG threads. The choice of the thread system depends on the location of equipment. Equipment intended for use in North America should make use of NPT strain reliefs, and equipment intended for use in Europe should make use of metric threaded strain reliefs.

At the opposite end of the strain relief body are threads that are used to attach the dome nut and flex nut. This style of threading is designed to handle pressure under high-torque conditions.

10.2.4 Terminal Blocks

Terminal blocks (see also Section 8.7) are intended specifically for use in making the internal connection between the power supply cord and the primary circuitry of the permanent connected and nondetachable power supply cords connected products. Three-contact terminal blocks provide connection points in single-phase applications with terminals for line, neutral, and ground. Five-contact terminal blocks are used in three-phase applications with terminals for three lines, neutral or common, and ground.

International standards require that equipment using permanently attached power cords be constructed such that cords can be disconnected and removed from the product without the use of any specialized tools, such as soldering irons. Screwdrivers and wrenches are allowed. The theory behind these requirements is that product repair is likely to take place at the user location and be performed by personnel who have a limited understanding of the product itself. The assumption is that tools and skills may be limited and that therefore, the power cord connection process should be simple.

Figure 10.3 illustrates an installation that complies with international requirements. The cord enters the product through a strain relief, which can be

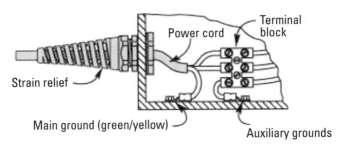

Figure 10.3   Strain relief and terminal block use [5].

released by using a wrench. It does not have to be removed from the panel in order to release the cable.

The cord is attached to a terminal block, which is constructed so that a screwdriver is the only tool required to connect or disconnect it. Solder-type terminal strips are not permissible.

The terminal block is constructed so that creepage and clearance distances between lines, as well as line and ground, are maintained. The insulation construction must prevent contact with current-carrying surfaces in an attempt to eliminate the possibility of accidental electrical shock. This is accomplished on the terminal blocks by recessing screws and terminals so that they are screwdriver-accessible only. In this case, screwdriver accessibility means that the standard test finger, which is described in international standards, cannot touch current-carrying surfaces when the terminal block is assembled with wires in place.

10.3   Fuses/Fuse Holders

The circuits within electrical equipment are subject to destructive overcurrents; overloads due to a harsh environment; unexpected conditions or component failures; deterioration over time due to the aging and functioning of some of the components and very often due to the user's misuse. These are just a few of the factors that contribute to the generation of the aforementioned overcurrents/overloads.

Fuses are circuit-protection devices that provide protection in the event of circuit overload by restricting the fault currents to low values.

A fuse is considered to be a non-resettable type of protective device; it is designed to safe-interrupt a circuit when the current that goes through it generates an excess of energy that could melt the fusing element.

Under normal operation, the fuse behaves as a conductor. The essential component in a fuse is a metal wire or strip that will melt when the current exceeds the amount that the fuse is designed to withstand, opening the circuit path, and disconnecting the equipment from the power source.

International fuses come in the 5 × 20 mm and 6.3 × 32 mm size. The standards covering international fuses are IEC 60127-1 and IEC 60127-2, and for fuse holders it is IEC 60127-6. North American fuses come in two sizes: ¼ × 1¼ inch or 5 × 20 mm. Standards to refer to include UL 248-1 and CSA 22.2 no. 248.1.

One important parameter in the relation product and the mains is the protective current rating, which represents the rating of an overcurrent protective device (e.g., fuse or circuit breaker) provided external to the equipment (i.e., in the building wiring, in the mains plug, or in an equipment rack).

In most countries, 16A is considered to be suitable as the protective current rating of the circuit supplied from the mains. In Canada and the United States, this rating is 20A, and in the United Kingdom and Ireland it is 13A—this being the largest rating of fuse used in the mains plug.

The fuse could be one of the following types:

- *Fast-acting:* A fast-acting fuse will open on overload and short circuits very quickly. These fuses are used in equipment where there are no transient in-rush currents. They offer protection for equipment that cannot withstand current overloads, even briefly.

- *Time-delay:* Time-delay fuses are designed to withstand a heavy amount of current overload for a limited amount of time (in rush current). They are used in equipment that can sustain a brief overload situation, typically, where the loads are inductive (e.g., in equipment utilizing fans and transformers).

The time-current characteristics of fuses are known by the following abbreviations and color codes: FF = very quick-acting (black); F = quick-acting (fast blow) (red); M = medium time, lag (yellow); T = time , lag (slow blow) (blue); TT = long time, lag (gray).

Fuses may have single or multiple elements. Single-element fuses are normally the fast-acting fuses. Within circuits subjected to surge currents, the fuses should not cause nuisance openings, and thus, the slow blow fuses are recommended. Fast-acting fuses (type F) are recommended in equipment with surge (in rush) currents that are 10 times the full load current during the first 10 msec. of operation [6].

An important characteristic of the fuses is represented by the breaking capacity (minimal ability of the fuse to remain physically intact when overloaded). It is usual to refer to low (L) breaking capacity on the order of magnitude of 30–200A, and high (H) breaking capacity from 1,500 to 15,000 A. The fuse with high-breaking capacity is usually constructed with a ceramic body, rather than glass, and filled with silica sand to absorb a large overload and protect the fuse itself. The sand and ceramic ensure that the fuse remains in one piece and does not allow arcing, when clearing a fault current.

It is important to verify that the fuse that is selected has a greater breaking capacity than the maximum available current that can be supplied to the product. If the breaking capacity is too low, the fuse could literally explode or create an electric arc of unacceptable duration, causing damage to the product or injury to an operator, when clearing a short.

The maximum AC short-circuit current that can be delivered by the mains depends upon such things as the rating of the distribution transformer, the size of the conductors, and the distance from the transformer to the product. Some miniature glass fuses may have a rating 10x their rated current and may be sufficient for many applications. However, if extra protection is needed, then a high-breaking capacity fuse may be desired.

In choosing the correct type of fuse (protective device), consider the ability of the fuse to withstand the fault current; otherwise, the fuse may rupture and will cause supplementary damage. The rating that defines the ability of a fuse to maintain its integrity while reacting to overcurrents is the interrupting rating (also known as the breaking capacity or short-circuit rating). This is defined as the maximum approved current that the fuse can safely interrupt at rated voltage. This requirement is stated within most of the national electrical codes. The latest edition of the NEC 2017 edition at section 110.10 "Circuit Impedance, Short-Circuit Current Ratings, and Other Characteristics" specifies: "The overcurrent protective devices, the total impedance, the equipment short-circuit current ratings, and other characteristics of the circuit to be protected shall be selected and coordinated to permit the circuit protective devices used to clear a fault to do so without extensive damage to the electrical equipment of the circuit."

Each fuse standard also dictates nonfusing and fusing time current limits. Nonfusing time defines the minimum time that a fuse can carry for a specified current without clearing/opening a circuit. Fusing time is defined as the allowable time range (min-max) that a fuse can carry for a specified current before clearing/opening a circuit.

A few design hints for using fuses are provided as follows:

• Fuses should be located on the supply side of the mains circuits in the product, including any mains switch, and should preferably be fitted in all supply conductors. In equipment generating high frequencies, it is essential for the interference-suppression components to be located between the mains supply and the fuses.

- Fuses should not be fitted in the protective earth conductor and in the neutral conductor of permanently installed products and multiphase equipment.

- A fuse should be provided in each supply lead for class I products (grounded) and for class II products having a functional earth connection, and in at least one supply lead (phase) for other single-phase class II products.

- If in a product two MOP(s) are present between all parts connected to earth and primary circuit (including opposite polarity part), or the subject product has no connection to earth (no protective, no functional), fuses can be omitted for protection against earth faults.

- In some products, the operation of the fuses may need to be detected and indicated.

- IEC 60127 requires fuses to withstand currents of 120% of product-rated current, but North America standards specify that the fuse must open with load conditions less than 110% of product-rated current.

- The fuse current rating must be selected on the basis of fault-mode current and should be higher with 1.25 to 1.5 than the full load current (rated input current for the product). The fuse voltage rating should be at least equal to the line voltage;

- If fuses complying with IEC 60127 are used in primary circuits, they should have high breaking capacity (1,500A) if the prospective short-circuit current exceeds 35A or 10 times the current rating of the fuse, whichever is greater.

- The type and rating of any operator-replaceable fuses should be marked adjacent to each fuse holder.

- Fuses in accordance with IEC 60127 should be marked with the rated current, voltage, and type of fuse as in the following example: "IEC symbol for fuse" (⊏▭⊐) T1AL250V (slow blow–rated 1A/250V with low breaking capacity) or F1AH250V(fast blow–rated 1A/250V with high breaking capacity).

- If a fuse is not intended to be replaceable, fuse ratings need not be marked.

- To select the correct fuse, one should consider the following characteristics:

- Rated current and voltage of the equipment/circuit;

- Rated current/voltage of the fuse;

- Ambient temperature for use the product;
- Ambient temperature of the location of the fuse;
- Maximum available fault current;
- Expected surges, inrush current, start currents, transients;
- Size, mounting style, ease of removal/replacement, visual indication of the location;
- Fuse holder style, mounting style, clip, soldered, PCB mount, RFI.

Moreover, agency approval status should be assured for the intended fuse. For correct use of fuses, one should do sufficient testing and study applications instructions to determine the optimal fuse. During the preliminary evaluation, the fuses should be mounted properly exactly as they will be mounted in the equipment, using the intended sized wiring, ensuring good connections of the fuse and of the fuse holder; the evaluation should be performed in normal conditions, under overload and under any foreseeable fault conditions.

When using resettable fuses (e.g., PTC type), in which resetting after an overload has occurred removes power and allows the device to cool down), other aspects should be considered during the design as well, including the position of the fuse within the equipment during its normal use. The temperature has a huge influence on this type of fuse, and we have observed more than once that nuisance tripping may occur just due to the fact that a PTC was mounted above a heat-generating component within an equipment.

10.3.1 Fuse Holders

A fuse holder is mounted in the product and is designed to hold the fuse. Fuse holders can hold both North American and international sized fuses.

A fuse carrier is the "cap" to the fuse holder. It carries the fuse into the holder and secures the fuse in place. One of the benefits of using a fuse carrier in conjunction with a fuse holder is that they are touch-proof.

Regarding fuse holders, the recommendation is to operate them at a temperature lower than the rated value specified by the testing house. The designer should consider from this point of view the value of the ambient in which the evaluation is taking place, versus the intended full operating temperature range of the product in which the fuse with the fuse holder will be used, and these shall be judged. Generally speaking, at an ambient of 25o C the fuse holders should not reach more than 60% of the maximum rated temperature. From this point of view the stated derating of 40% represents in the literature an acceptable value. Be sure that the maximum admissible power acceptances and temperatures defined by the manufacturer of the fuse holder are followed.

Factors to consider when evaluating the thermal influences in fuse holders are listed as follows:

1. The influence of the power dissipation in the fuse holder contacts;
2. Rated power dissipation of the chosen fuse;
3. Admissible power acceptance, temperature ratings, and operating current of the fuse holder;
4. Ambient air temperatures both inside and outside of the equipment;
5. Electrical load alternation (cycle loading);
6. Long-term operation with a load > 0.7 In;
7. Heat influences of surrounding components;
8. Heat dissipation/cooling and ventilation designed into the equipment;
9. Length and cross-section of connecting wires;
10. Mounting orientation of the fuse holder.

Fuse holders with fuses intended to be operator-replaceable should not permit access to live parts during a fuse replacement. The regulations specify details for fuse holders—how they should be designed and installed so that they are de-energized while a fuse is being replaced. A legible sign should be installed immediately adjacent to the fuse holders and should be worded as follows: Danger—disconnect circuit before replacing fuses.

Design considerations must take into account both the fuse and fuse holder together to ensure that a suitable pairing is selected. Such considerations include the following:

• What size fuses would be most appropriate?
• What are the load ratings for where the product is being used?
• Does the equipment have a large in-rush at start-up?
• How long can the equipment handle an overload?
• Is the overload large enough to physically destroy the fuse?

Thermal considerations:

• Power dissipation of the fuse link;
• Ratings of the fuse holder;
• Ambient temperatures inside and outside equipment;
• Electrical load changes;

- Long operation times;
- Ventilation, cooling, and heat dissipation;
- Wire lengths and sizes.

For internal fuses on PC boards fuse clips can be used as fuse holders. It takes two of the clips for one fuse.

In which types of applications should we consider fuses? This is a question with no straight answers within the applicable safety standards for electrical products.

10.3.2 Effects of Overcurrents

As previously specified, the main abnormal issues that occur during the operation of an electrical product are overcurrents. An overcurrent that can generate an unacceptable risk is either an overload current or a short-circuit current. When a protective device cuts off a short circuit very fast (in less than one-quarter cycle before it reaches its highly destructive value, the device is called current-limiting). Most modern fuses are current-limiting.

According to our experience (please refer Figures 10.4–10.6 as relevant examples), the most difficult scenario for protecting a piece of electrical is the presence of an overload current. Short-circuit currents, on the other hand, can be solved using simple solutions as fuses.

Accordingly, overload currents should be regarded as a very important factor when first designing electrical equipment, and as well later on, when the equipment is tested and evaluated. Otherwise, situations like that shown in

Figure 10.4 Effect of overload current in a transformer that is only short-circuit protected.

Figure 10.5   Effect of the overload current in a transformer with a thermal cutoff that is incorrectly rated.

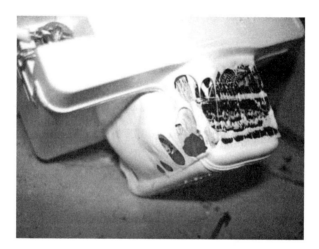

Figure 10.6   Effect of an overload current in a nonprotected transformer.

Figure 10.6 may occur, where the whole transformer has come out through the plastic walls of an enclosure in front of a horrified and scared end user.

The direct plug-in power supply in Figure 10.4 was protected against a short-circuit overcurrent only. When the power supply was overloaded, it overheated to a temperature that melted the plastic of the enclosure, and in the position in which it was installed, due to its weight, the transformer from inside started to exit the enclosure through the plastic wall of the external enclosure (Figures 10.5 and 10.6).

This example shows a power supply that was protected properly against short circuits, but that protection was not able to cover the overload protection when the current was slightly lower than the short circuit on the load side.

10.4 Power Entry Modules

Using a power entry module for connection of an electrical product to the mains reduces the risk of accidents. The design of most modules makes it necessary to remove the power cord assembly from the unit prior to making any changes like fuse replacement and/or voltage selection. Interlocking the power entry connector with access to other module functions reduces the probability of accidental shock by the user. When selecting a module, functions and mounting orientation need to be addressed. Power entry modules are available with a variety of component (e.g., AC power inlet, on/off switch, fuses and fuse holder, voltage selector, and EMI/RFI filter) combinations (Figures 10.7 and 10.8). These combinations are described as follows.

AC power inlet: The modules direct power into the equipment using a power inlet for a Class I grounded connection or for a Class II (without ground) connection.

- *Power switch:* The power switch keeps the power control near the source of power on the product. Many switches used in the modules are double-pole (control both the line and neutral conductors), single-throw switches. Module power switches are normally rated at 4–10A at 250 VAC. The availability of vertically or horizontally marked switches makes it possible to meet standards for correct marking alignment on switches. Some power switches have a light to indicate the ON position. Since the power inlet terminals are live after switching ON the unit, they must be protected by means of shrink tubing or by insulated

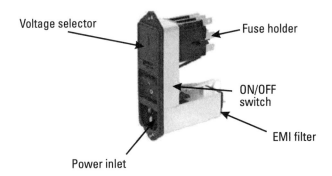

Figure 10.7 Typical power entry module [7].

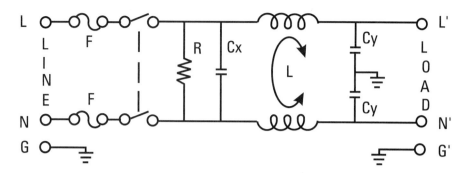

Figure 10.8   Electrical schematic of a power entry module [8].

quick-disconnect type connectors. If shrink tubing and insulated quick-disconnect type connectors are used, they must be rated a minimum 300V and 105°C.

- *Fuse holder:* The power entry modules can be used with either 1/4 in x 1-1/4 in or 5 × 20 mm fuses. They are available in single- or double-fused versions. The design of the power entry modules allows users in some cases to quickly change a single-fused module to double-fused by simply removing the fuse substitution clip. In a single-fused module, the clip must be positioned on the neutral side of the circuit for the module to work.

- *Voltage selector:* The voltage selection allows equipment to be designed and manufactured to operate on 120 or 230 VAC. Changing the selection device allows the user to define the correct input voltage. In some power entry modules, the voltage selection changes are made by removing the fuse holder and rotating it.

- *EMI (RFI) filtering:* EMI is also called radio-frequency interference (RFI). The terms EMI and RFI are often used interchangeably, but EMI is actually any frequency of electrical noise, whereas RFI is a specific subset of electrical noise on the EMI spectrum, the radio frequency band.

An EMI filter is an electronic passive circuit used for two actions:

1. To prevent the product from radiating conducted noise, generated by the product, that might interfere with other products. The typical frequency filtered is 10 kHz–30 MHz for noise picked up and conducted through external wires or power cords (Figure 10.9).

2. To suppress conducted interference that appears on a signal or power line and can enter the product (increase the immunity of the product).

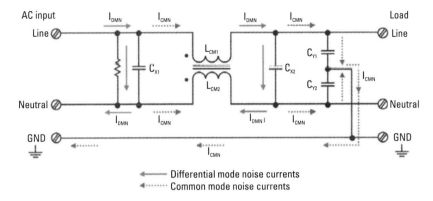

Figure 10.9 Typical EMI filter used to suppress conducted EMI noise [9].

The disturbances may interrupt, obstruct, degrade, or limit the effective performance of the circuit(s) of the product. The source of disturbances may be any object, artificial or natural, that carries rapidly electrical currents.

An important parameter of such filters is the insertion loss, which represents the value (in decibels) determined from a ratio of the voltage passed through the product without filtering, versus the voltage passed through the product with filtering. Common mode insertion loss is used to express the amount of signal lost on both the line and neutral conductors (when referenced to ground), due to removal of interference or noise by the filter circuit. Differential mode insertion loss is used to express the amount of signal lost on either the line or neutral conductors [when referenced to the other (i.e., between line and neutral)] due to removal of interference or noise by the filter circuit. Insertion loss values are typically based on the results of a 50-ohm test circuit.

When looking for a correct EMI filter(s), the parameters that should be taken into account are the following:

- Type of filter—if known what it shall suppress (e.g., capacitor type and LC combined type);
- Case size/dimension;
- Operating temperature range (check if it is in line with the range imposed for the end product);
- Rated current, rated voltage;
- Dielectric strength test voltage;
- Maximum value of the leakage current that is acceptable for the end product.

When choosing an EMI (RFI) filter, it is very important from the point of view of electrical safety to consider the ratings that the supplier of the filter offers versus the requirements specified within the applicable safety standard for the end product considering the leakage (touch) current, dielectric strength test voltage, and any applicable requirements for the components that are part of the filter as specified within the end equipment standard.

Be aware that some suppliers are giving the ratings for a wide range of input voltage (e.g., a 100–240 Vac), but the leakage current maximum value is given for the lower limit voltage. The value should be multiplied with the ratio that gives the expected maximum voltage in the field for the equipment (e.g., if the equipment is rated 100–240 Vac and the leakage value is given as max 1.8 mA at 120 Vac, when the equipment is connected to 240 Vac, the leakage current value may reach the value of 240/120 x1.8 = 3.6 mA, which for any equipment assumed to be Class 1, under the IEC 60950 series of standards, the value would not comply.

To reduce the disturbance that affects an electrical circuit due to electromagnetic conduction from an external source the EMI (RFI) filters use capacitors between the conductors and ground; thus, a small amount of current is conducted via the filter to the ground. This current can generate a hazard of an electric shock if the leakage current has a value higher than the maximum acceptable limit imposed by the applicable standard.

The general criteria should be the approval status of the filter: Being connected in the primary circuit, it will be considered a safety-critical component, and thus, it should be acceptable to the local authorities for the intended market(s).

10.5 Switches

Electrical products should have a means of disconnecting all current-carrying conductors. This could include a switch or circuit breaker, an appliance coupler that can be disconnected without the use of a tool, or a main plug (without a locking device) that can be removed from a wall socket outlet, without the use of a tool. For permanently connected products and multiphase products, only the switch or circuit breaker is allowed. If the plug is considered to be the disconnection device, it must be easily accessible, and safety instructions should specify it accordingly. For single-phase portable products, a plug on a cord of a length not greater than 3m is considered to be easily accessible.

Any designer should observe first—along with the ergonomic aspects and the field of application of the equipment—that any power supply switch meets the following criteria:

- It is properly rated (current and voltage) for the intended application.

- It is easy accessible and able to operate immediately.

- It has a clear position ON and OFF for secure locking.

- It is an easy-mounting type for the application and from the point of view of manufacturability.

- It is approved for the intended market and for the intended application.

Switches in the mains circuit are considered critical safety components, and thus these must be an approved type.

Note that different colors of the contact blocks (e.g., normal open (N/O): blue; normal close (N/C): red) will help the manufacturability (by preventing errors in wiring, and serviceability (in the identification of circuits) of the equipment.

When there are multiple power supplies turned ON by the same switch, the designer should consider the sum of the currents of the involved power supplies.

A switch that is placed in a cord set or power-supply cord that is not polarized should simultaneously open all of the supply conductors, in contrast to the switch that is placed in a polarized cord set or power-supply cord, which should only open the current-carrying conductors.

A switch should never open the grounding conductor of a power-supply cord or cord set.

The ergonomic aspects of switches should be considered by the mechanical designer of the enclosure of the equipment, considering as a "must" the easy access to the mains supply switch and a very clear path to it.

Switches must be rated as equal to or must exceed the load they control and must disconnect all ungrounded conductors [double-pole, single-throw (DPST) switch types]. Switches need to be mounted securely so they do not rotate in normal use. "O" and "I" symbols for the ON and OFF position should be marked adjacent to the mains switch, circuit-breakers, and push-button switch.

Spacing for switches DPST comply with IEC 60328 requirements (with a minimum 3-mm contact gap per pole). If a product includes a one-third or greater horsepower motor, a separate switch is required. The indicator lights (if provided) should comply with IEC 60073 in regard to coloring. The disconnect switch should not have a red actuator (as red is reserved for emergency stops).

10.5.1 Emergency Stop

An emergency stop is defined as a fail-safe control switch or circuit that, when de-energized, will stop the operation of the product and will shut off all potential hazards outside the main power enclosure.

Emergency stops, also known as E-stops, are special types of pilot devices that perform the emergency shutdown operation on an electrical system. E-stops are different from typical "OFF" buttons in that they must pass a rigorous line of testing and meet a long list of specifications.

The types of emergency stop device include a push-button operated switch, a pull-cord operated switch, or a pedal-operated switch without a mechanical guard.

The devices should be of the self-latching type and should be positioned so as to be readily accessible and nonhazardous for the regular operator and others who may need to operate them. They should be available and operational at all times, regardless of the operating mode and should override all other functions and operations.

Types of actuators that may be used include mushroom-type push button, wires, ropes, bars, handles, and foot-pedals without protective cover. Actuators of E-stop devices should be colored red with a yellow background (if used); in certain circumstances, it may be useful to provide labels in addition.

The E-stop function should not impair the effectiveness of safety devices or of devices with safety-related functions. The reset should not initiate a restart.

The operation of an E-stop should never depend on electronic logic or on the transmission of commands over a communications network or link.

10.5.2 Solid State Relays (SSRs)

There are ON-OFF control devices in which the load current is conducted by one or more semiconductors. The SSR may be designed to switch either AC or DC to the load. It serves the same function as an electromechanical relay but has no moving parts. The classification of SSR is related to the means by which input-output isolation is achieved. On reed-relay-coupled SSRs and on photo-coupled SSRs, the input-output isolation is achieved by reed relay or by light; on transformer-coupled SSRs the degree of input-output isolation depends on the design of transformer. On direct-control AC or DC types of SSRs, there is at present a great disadvantage as no isolation exists between the control and load circuits.

The minimum breakdown voltage from control circuit to both the SSR case and the load circuit should correspond with basic insulation.

10.6   Varistors

Varistors [or voltage-dependent resistors (VDRs)] together with spark gaps, gas-filled surge voltage arresters (gas discharge tubes), carbon blocks, and suppressor diodes are known as surge voltage protection devices, which are used against hazards generated by transient surge voltages. These voltages, which may be released either in a predictable manner via controlled switching actions, or randomly induced into a circuit from external sources (e.g., due to lightning, ESD, inductive-load switching, or electrical noise), occur for a very short time on signal inputs and low-voltage AC or DC power lines.

Due to varistors' high-energy dissipation, these components can absorb much higher transient energies than transient suppressor diodes and can suppress positive and negative transients. When a transient occurs, the varistor resistance changes from a very high standby value to a very low conducting value. Accordingly, the transient is absorbed and clamped to a safe level.

The most usual varistor is the metal-oxide varistor (MOV), which primarily consist of arrays of zinc-oxide (ZnO) balls, in which the ZnO was altered with small amounts of other metal oxides such as bismuth, cobalt, or manganese. In the MOV manufacturing process, these balls are sintered (fused) into a ceramic semiconductor. This produces a crystalline microstructure that allows these devices to dissipate very high levels of transient energy across their entire bulk. After sintering, the surface is metallized, and leads are attached via soldering.

Varistors may be used in any circuit of electrical equipment—in the primary or secondary circuits. In fact, according to several safety standards, if in the primary circuit a surge suppressor is used, it should be a VDR.

During the lifetime of a VDR, after a number of switching cycles, the leakage current that flows through this type of component increases. This leakage current causes a permanent and continuously increasing temperature stress, which may cause at some point the VDR to burn or burst; in such situations, the VDR generates a hazard. Thereby, a component that supported the safety of the equipment for a while may create a fire hazard and/or lead to electric shock hazards.

The varistor's absorption of the transient energy during a surge event produces localized heating within the component, which may lead to its degradation over time. If left unprotected, the degradation of a varistor can increase heating and thermal runaway. As such, a growing number of varistor-based surge-protection devices offer a built-in thermal disconnect function. This function provides added protection from catastrophic failures and fire hazards, even under extreme circumstances of varistor end of life or sustained overvoltage.

MOVs are rated for specific AC-line operating voltages. Exceeding these limits by applying a sustained abnormal overvoltage condition could result in overheating and damage to the MOV. Safety standards have taken this possibility into consideration, specifying that VDRs should be protected, in turn, against the following:

- Temporary overvoltages above the maximum continuous voltage;
- Thermal overload due to leakage currents within the VDR;
- Burning and bursting of the VDR in the event of a short-circuit fault.

An important condition of acceptability for using VDRs in primary circuits is the introduction as mandatory of an interrupting means (fuse) having an adequate breaking capacity that should be connected in series with the VDR.

The VDRs shall pass a specific impulse test after which the clamping voltage should not suffer a variation more than 10% from the initial value.

Depending on the source of surges, the transients can be as large as hundreds of volts and hundreds of amperes, with durations of 400 ms. Due to varying load sizes, there will be variance in wave shape, duration, peak current, and peak voltage of the transients. Once these variables are approximated, circuit designers will be able to select a suitable suppressor type. When using varistors, designers should consider all of the applicable safety standards with which the circuit/product must comply to ensure that the circuits/products are as safe as possible. When choosing an appropriate varistor (MOV) for a specific overvoltage-protection application, they should consider the following characteristics:

- Circuit conditions such as the peak voltage and current during the surge event;
- The operating temperature of the equipment in which the varistors are used;
- The MOV continuous operating voltage (which should be at 20% above product maximum rated voltage under normal conditions);
- The number of surges the MOV must survive;
- The leakage current at maximum-DC working voltage;
- The acceptable let-through voltage for the protected circuit.

10.7 Transformers

A mains transformer is an electrical device that, by the principles of electromagnetic induction, transfers electrical energy from one electric circuit to another, without changing the frequency. The energy transfer usually takes place with a change of voltage and current. Transformers either increase or decrease AC voltage. The core of the transformer is used to provide a controlled path for the magnetic flux generated in the transformer by the current flowing through the windings (coils).

There are five parts to the basic transformer. The parts include the input connection (from mains), the output connection (to load), the windings (primary and secondary), the bobbin, and the core.

Different types of transformers are used for electrical products as part of their power sources: (1) power transformers and (2) isolation transformers. A power transformer is used primarily to couple electrical energy from a power supply line to a circuit system, or to one or more components of the system.

An isolation transformer is a 1:1 turn's ratio and does not step voltage up or down. Instead, it serves as a safety device. It is used to isolate the grounded conductor of a power line from the chassis or any portion of a circuit load. Using an isolation transformer will not reduce the danger or shock if contact is made across the transformer's secondary winding.

Technically, any true transformer, whether used to transfer signals or power, is isolating, as the primary and secondary are not connected by conductors but only by induction. However, only transformers whose primary purpose is to isolate circuits (opposed to the more common transformer function of voltage conversion), are described as isolation transformers. If an isolation transformer is connected between the AC power source and the power supply input terminals, it should be rated for at least 200% of the maximum RMS current required by the power supply.

From the core construction point of view the most common mains transformers are of laminate steel (E–I–shaped) or toroidal (ring-shaped) format.

Mains supply transformers should comply with the following requirements:

- Overheating of insulation in the event of short circuits or overload on any output winding should not cause an unacceptable risk;

- They should have dielectric strength (after the humidity conditioning treatment);

- Their creepage distances and clearance should have at a the values required by the type of insulation.

To evaluate the compliance of a mains transformer, it needs to be analyzed together with the overheating of insulation. See the cross-sectional diagram in Figures 10.10 and 10.11 for the construction and the materials used in such an analysis.

The most common method of achieving compliance is by properly gauging the transformer primary and secondary fuse values with respect to the ampacity of the transformer. If the fuse alone is not sufficient to protect against overheating of insulation in the event of short circuit or overload on any output winding, a suitably rated thermal cutoff may be included in the primary.

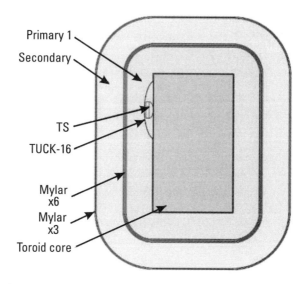

Figure 10.10   Cross section for a toroidal core transformer.

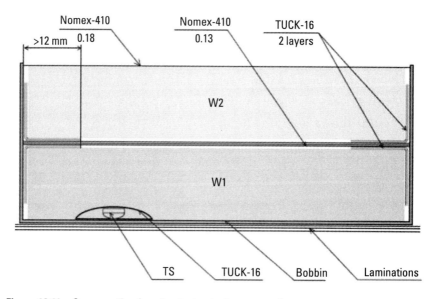

Figure 10.11   Cross section for a laminate steel core transformer.

If the short circuit is terminated by the opening of a fuse, and if the fuse does not operate within approximately 1s, the current through the fuse should be measured. Evaluation of the prearcing time/current characteristics should be performed to find out whether the minimum operating current of the fuse is reached or exceeded and to determine the maximum time before the fuse operates. The current through the fuse may vary as a function of time.

If the output voltage is designed to collapse when a specified overload current is reached, the overload is slowly increased to the point that causes the output voltage to collapse.

The following constructional recommendation should be considered:

- The tape used as interleaved insulation should not be hygroscopic and should be made of a material such as polyester film, PVC, PTFE, aramid paper, polyamide, or glass cloth. The product standard requirements for electric strength, spacing (clearance and creepage), distance through insulation, and heating should be fulfilled.

- The bobbin material is considered acceptable if it has a minimum thickness of 0.71 mm and a minimum flammability of 94V-2.

- Insulation between a primary and secondary must be at least two layers and have a total thickness of at least 0.3 mm, or one layer and total thickness of at least 1 mm.

- Sleeving of wires exiting the windings must be at least 0.3-mm-thick and extend at least 20 mm from winding.

- Leads connecting the primary to AC power source should be sized to carry at least the maximum input current and a min. 300V, min. 105oC.

- The load wire size should be heavy enough to carry the output current that would flow if the load terminals were short-circuited.

A description of the construction details for a mains transformer should be provided in the following format:

Ratings:
- Input: V; A;
- Output: V; A.

Construction:
- Core: EI Laminations Overall mm by mm by mm, by mm stack

Insulation system: Temperature/class rating
Wire Insulation:
- Material max temperature;
- Primary winding, W1;
- Secondary winding, W2.

UL Recognized, File No: E _____

Bobbin: Material—Designation—Thickness—Flammability rating
UL Recognized, File No: E _____

Insulation between windings:
Material no. of layers per layer (mm)
Primary—Secondary
Primary—Secondary
Secondary interwinding
Primary Crossover
Secondary Crossover
Outerwrap
UL Recognized, File No: E _____

Thermal Protector TS:

• Manufacturer:

• Designation:

• Type

• Ratings:V; A

• Connections:

• Terminations:

UL Recognized, File No: E _____

Fuse (if applicable):

• Manufacturer:

• Type/Size: Glass/Ceramic cartridge, mm/in by mm/in, link type

• Ratings: V,A.

Fuse holder (if applicable):

• Manufacturer:

• Cat No.:

• Ratings:

• Terminations:

• Mounting:

Enclosure (if applicable):

• Overall mm by mm by mm, by mm thick

Openings: No Dimensions Location

Potting Compound:

• End bells: (material)

• Dimensions: Overall mm/in by mm/in by mm/in

• Lead Entry:

Transformer Mounting:
Terminations:
Type of terminals Primary Secondary
• No. of terminals;

• Current bar Material and thickness;

• Spring Material and thickness;

• Method of securing to mounting surface.

UL Recognized, File No: E _____

Dielectric Voltage Withstand:
• Primary to Core V;

• Primary to Secondary V;

• Secondary to Core V;

10.8 Power Supplies

The power supply unit (PSU) is the heart of any electrical product. If the PSU fails, it affects everything, and, in some cases, if the PSU has inefficient protection features, a malfunction of the PSU may damage other components within the product or those that work in conjunction with the product being powered.

Two major types of power supplies are distinguished: regulated power supplies and unregulated power supplies. Regulated power supplies are further divided into linearly regulated power supplies and switch-mode power supplies (Figure 10.12).

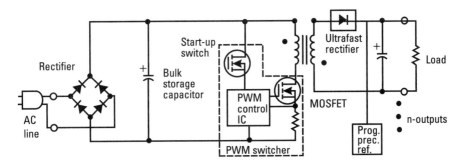

Figure 10.12 Simplified diagram of a switch-mode power supply [10].

All modern power supplies are of the switch-mode type, as these are smaller and more efficient than the old linear types. It's necessary to understand a little about how switch-mode power supplies work.

First, these power supplies convert AC power from the mains into DC. This DC is then rectified and smoothed and then switched (chopped = the DC voltage is switched periodically at a frequency of 40–200 kHz using a power transistor) to provide pulsed DC, but at a much higher frequency than the mains supply, so that it can be applied to a high-frequency compact transformer to produce the secondary voltages. The quantity of energy transformed to the secondary circuit is controlled, depending on the load, by varying the chopping rate. The longer the transistor is conductive, the higher is the quantity of energy transformed to the secondary circuit (pulse width modulation). The outputs from the transformer are rectified and smoothed to produce the required DC output voltage. Since the output voltage does not directly depend on the input voltage, these units can be used for a wide input voltage range and can even be supplied with DC voltage.

The switching circuit in the power supply, coupled with the stray capacitance of switching components to earth and between primary circuits and the output, is main source of EMI from a switch-mode power supply.

Digital control (microcontroller-based) combined with a 4-kVac reinforced input to output isolation and other specifications such as an output-to-ground isolation of 1,500 Vac enables these power supplies to meet the safety standards.

Various output characteristics are available for power supplies to provide electronic protection of the devices against damages due to overload or short circuit.

Power supplies are usually able to deliver a current of 1.1 times the rated current. They automatically switch off if the current consumption of the connected load exceeds this value or if a short circuit occurs. After a defined period of time, the power supplies try to restart the load and automatically switch off again if the overload or the short circuit still exists. In this case, the power supply either immediately cuts the output voltage to zero (rectangular current-limiting) or performs slow lowering of the output voltage; that, however, can possibly lead to a further increase of the output current (triangular current-limiting). Since the current does not sag in case of an overload, this method enables reliable starting of high loads.

Power supplies with a U/I characteristic (fold-forward behavior at overload—no switch-off) and power reserves are able to deliver output currents of up to 1.5 times the specified rated current at the rated output voltage. In addition to this reserve, the power supply is able to manage a further output current increase of up to 50%—at decreasing output voltage, however. The amount of current reserves the power supply can deliver and how long it is able to deliver the reserves primarily depends on the ambient temperature. The temperature inside of control cabinets can rise to more than 60°C due to the waste heat of the internal devices, solar irradiation, or its place of installation. Starting from a certain temperature value, the maximum available output power will decrease depending on the temperature. The limit value starting from which this derating process takes place, ranges from 40°C to 60°C, depending on the technical design and the manufacturer of the power supply. The difference between the ambient temperature and the internal temperature of the power supply is approximately 25°C. As a result, no reserves will be available, and the internal components will be operated at their temperature maximum (60°C + 25°C = 85°C), if a manufacturer specifies a maximum ambient temperature of 60°C for a power supply the internal components of which are specified with a rated operating temperature of maximum 85°C. Depending on the device it is also possible that power supplies are not able to deliver their full output power at very low ambient temperatures. This behavior is caused by an NTC thermistor attached to the input circuits to limit the inrush current. In case of very low temperatures, the resistance of this thermistor rises so high that the power supply is not able to deliver its full output power. When operating a power supply under extreme conditions for a long duration (e.g., in case of permanent operation within the power limits or in case of very high ambient temperatures), the power supply can heat up to a degree where safe operation is no longer guaranteed.

There are several methods to protect the power supply against damaging due to overtemperature:

- Reducing the maximum output power to allow the power supply to cool down.

- Switching off the device completely and necessitating that operation cannot resume until a manual reset is performed. Depending on the manufacturer, the reset is done either using a corresponding switch or by disconnecting the supply voltage.

- Switching off only the output and not switching it on until the temperature falls below a certain limit value (action performed by the device).

- Additional recommendations for design of a safe power supply are listed as follows:

- Components and materials used should have prior safety certification.

- From mechanical point of view a rigid construction with all components securely attached should be provided.

- All areas containing hazardous voltages, hot components, fan blades, or any other item that might cause harm should be protected from access by the user, including through any openings in the enclosure.

- Grounding connections and bonding straps must be provided where necessary.

- Creepage and clearance spacings must separate all hazardous voltages from user accessible points.

- There should be a very clear channel separating primary and secondary circuits (Figure 10.13).

- An effective current limiter in low-voltage outputs may be required.

The switching-mode power supplies ensure a wide range input. This means that the PSU can be operated with any voltage within the specified limits. Therefore, many modern power supplies can be operated with AC voltages between 85 and 264V (allowing them to be included in a product rated 100–240V) and DC voltages between 100 and 350V without any loss of power. (The PSU is able to deliver the specified rated power over the entire input voltage range.)

Power supplies with wide range inputs can be connected to almost any power supply system all over the world and thus reduce costs and logistics, since one power supply is able to cover almost all needs.

Modern electrical products require power supplies that are compact, lightweight, efficient, cost-effective, Restriction of Hazardous Substances (RoHS)-compliant, reliable, and super-safe. Switch-mode power supplies (SMPSs) can

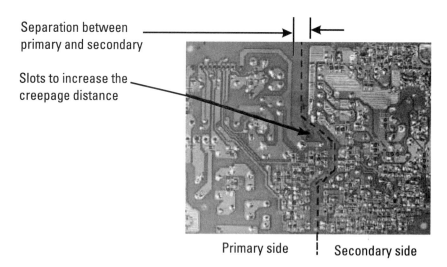

Figure 10.13 Channel separating primary and secondary circuits [11].

meet all of these needs, but not all SMPSs are created equal. Take care to choose power supplies from a reputable supplier, preferably with proven experience in the field, and with a good understanding of the demands of the involved standards.

In selecting a PSU, think first about the standard(s) that the end-use equipment is required to meet; the PSU chosen should be one that was tested and evaluated based on that standard, or, on an equivalent or more severe standard. It is important to ensure that the approval on the PSU is current. The difficulty is that each of the new editions and amendments of standards for products introduces changes to the requirements. Power supplies meeting the requirements of IEC 60601 (medical products) can generally be used in information technology and laboratory products, but the reverse is not necessarily true.

It is essential to choose the PSU based on the following specifications:

- Input voltage;
- Input current;
- IEC1000-3-2 for all load conditions);
- Hold-up time;
- Inrush current (must be less than the ratings of input components);
- Touch current (leakage current);
- Dielectric strength voltage;
- Output voltage(s);
- Output current;
- Temperature (operating and storage);
- Temperature derating;
- Efficiency at full load.

The PSU should come as a listed/certified component. It does not mean that it will accomplish all of the requirements that are applicable to the end equipment in which it will be used. Factors like conditions of acceptability that limit use may apply to the PSU. These may include the end equipment enclosure, the ventilation and separation requirements, the EMC requirements for the end equipment, and the specific requirements for the end equipment depending on its application (e.g., military, medical, or laboratory). This may generate more questions than answers.

When acquiring a PSU was considered, users should obtain several documents from the supplier:

1. Approval status;

2. Declaration of conformity including the full test and evaluation report that may be used to offer the proof of compliance of the PSU with the standard against which it was tested;

3. Declaration regarding the routine (production line) tests;

4. Technical documentation and all of the applicable conditions of acceptability, including the mounting conditions, ventilation requirements, conditions regarding accessibility, clearances and creepage distances that should be met and maintained when it will be used within the end equipment.

References

[1]   IEC TR 60083 "Plugs and Socket-Outlets for Domestic and Similar General Use Standardized in Member Countries of IEC," Geneva, 2009.

[2]   HD 361 S3, "System for Cable Designation," CENELEC, Brussels, Belgium, 1999.

[3]   Interpower, "Conductor Color Coding," Oskaloosa, IA, 2016.

[4]   Interpower, "North American Cable Types," Oskaloosa, IA, 2016.

[5]   Interpower, "More Information on Terminal Blocks," Oskaloosa, IA, 2016.

[6]   Bolintineanu, C., and S. Loznen, "Product Safety and Third Party Certification," The Electronic Packaging Handbook, edited by G. R. Blackwell, Boca Raton, FL: CRC Press LLC 2000.

[7]   Schurter, "Product Catalog," Lucerne, Switzerland, 2015.

[8]   Delta Electronics, "Product Catalog," Karnataka, India, 2016.

[9]   Berman, M., "All About EMI Filters," Electronic Products, October 2008, pp. 51–53, http://electronicproducts.com.

[10] ON Semiconductor, "SWITCHMODE™ Power Supply Reference Manual," 2002.

[11] Mullet, C., "Inside the Power Supply," PPT Presentation, ON Semiconductor.

Selected Bibliography

ABB STOTZ-KONTAKT GmbH, "Power Supply Units Application Manual," Heidelberg, Germany, 2006.

Benatti, J., "MTBF and Power Supply Reliability," Electronic Products, August 1, 2009.

Brown, M., Power Supply Cookbook, Boston: Butterworth–Heinemann, 2001.

ECMA-287, European Association for Standardizing Information and Communication Systems, "Safety of Electronic Equipment," Geneva, 2002.

Flynn, D., "Challenges for Power Supplies in Medical Equipment," IEEE Power Electronics Magazine, June 2015, pp. 32–37.

Hammond Manufacturing, "Power Transformer Guide, Design Guide for Rectifier Use," 2016.

Harris, K., and C. Bolintineanu, "Electrical Safety Design Practices Guide," Tyco Safety Products Canada Ltd, Rev 12, March 14, 2016.

IEC 60320-1, "Appliance Couplers for Household and Similar General Purposes—Part 1: General Requirements," Geneva, 2015.

IEC 60884-1, "Plugs and socket-outlets for household and similar purposes—Part 1: General requirements," Geneva, 2006.

IEC 60950-1+AMD1+AMD2, "Information Technology Equipment—Safety—Part 1: General Requirements," Geneva, 2005–2013.

Littelfuse, "Transient Suppression Devices and Principles," Application Note AN9768.

STI, Scientific Technologies GmbH, "Selection of Positively Driven/Force Guided Contacts."

11

Product Construction Requirements

11.1   Introduction

Together with the selection of components, construction requirements represent the second of three criteria of compliance with any product safety standards, in addition to testing. Once a product is defined and the design started, the hardware team needs to implement construction requirements that fully meet the requirements stated within the PDD.

11.2   Enclosures

This section discusses electrical equipment designated to be used in *nonhazardous locations only.*

Requirements for enclosures depend on the equipment type, the environment in which the equipment will be installed, and the duration of the equipment's life, as well as the method of installation and the relative position of the equipment within the environment.

Enclosure types can be categorized as *internal* or *external.* Each type has different functions, and thus when designed and evaluated, they are judged and tested accordingly. Internal enclosures may be used to segregate circuits that are at a hazardous voltage, to provide supplementary protection against radiation, or just to protect service persons or provide compliance with certain requirements.(e.g., regarding the IP degree of protection for the enclosure when the external enclosure is not able to fully protect the equipment). (For example, internal enclosures can provide protection against the presence of water for some circuits that do not display the presence of water after the test.) Internal enclosures are also often used to protect against moving parts and against radiation hazards.

Enclosures can be categorized *based on the hazards mitigate* and include electrical, fire, and mechanical enclosures. (See Section 7.7.) Enclosures can also be categorized based on *the environmental conditions in which they are used,* as described in the following:

- *Enclosures for indoor use:* Provide a degree of protection for the *user* against access to hazardous parts and for the equipment hosted inside the enclosure against the ingress of solid foreign objects. They also provide a degree of protection from harmful effects on the equipment due to the ingress of water that might be expected within an indoor environment. (See Section 7.7.)

- *Enclosures for outdoor use:* Provide a degree of protection for the equipment inside the enclosure against the ingress of solid foreign objects (including dust); in addition, these enclosures offer a degree of protection from the harmful effects on the hosted equipment caused by the ingress of water (e.g., rain, sleet, snow, ice, and UV radiation). Enclosures for outdoor use also protect against corrosion, which can occur due to the conditions that electrical equipment is subjected to during its use. (See Section 7.7.)

Enclosures can also be categorized based on *the materials from which they are made,* described as follows:

- *Metallic enclosures:* Enclosures whose external walls are made of metal or are primarily composed of metal;

- *Nonmetallic enclosures:* Enclosures that are not made from metal. Instead, they are constructed of plastic materials or fiberglass.

To further their ability to meet specific characteristics, different organizations, such as the IEC and NEMA, have built their own systems of standards and classifications for enclosures. (See Section 7.7.)

Not surprisingly (and we will not speculate on the reasons), these two systems of standards and classifications for enclosures define enclosures differently, and thus, a perfectly equivalent conversion from the enclosure types covered by the IEC's 60529-classification and NEMA's standard classifications is not possible.

Due to these differences in requirements between the IEC and NEMA classifications for enclosures, when choosing the correct enclosure, it is important to be aware of the standards against which the equipment hosted by the enclosure will be judged during its evaluation. The PDD should specify clearly from the beginning the intended market and the type of the required enclosure, including its electrical safety and *performance* requirements.

The mechanical designer of an enclosure should take in consideration all relevant requirements, listed as follows:

- Mechanical strength and rigidity;
- Flammability ratings of the materials;
- Durability and stability of the materials;
- Ventilation requirements;
- Means and method of installation of the hosted equipment;
- Location of the components within the enclosure in the normal position in which it will be installed;
- Performance requirements for the designed enclosure, including packaging and transportation;
- Degree of protection against internal and external influences;
- Multifunctionality of the enclosure;
- Stability and durability of the materials during the life of the hosted equipment;
- Ergonomic design;
- Cost.

Based on IEC 60950 series of standards, construction of an enclosure as listed below satisfies the requirements without the need for testing.

- No opening in the bottom of a *fire enclosure;*
- Openings in the bottom of any size under PVC-, TFE-, PTFE-, FEP-, and neoprene-insulated conductors and their connectors;
- Baffle plate type constructions in the walls of the enclosure;
- Metal bottoms of *fire enclosures* conforming with the dimensional limits imposed by the applicable standards;
- When *openings* are necessary for ventilation, baffle plate construction, slanted openings, screens or the like, are provided.

Openings in the tops and sides of fire enclosures and electrical enclosures, excluding openings in the operator access areas within an enclosure, should comply with the appropriate standard requirements. It is necessary to emphasize here that the operator access may have to be judged when the operator is not using any tool to gain access, or, in some situations, the access of the operator must be judged from a safety point of view when the tool supplied with the equipment is used. (Sometimes suppliers offer tools for adjustments, and by having those tools available, safety must not be impaired by gaining access to hazards.).

Openings in the sides of fire enclosures and of electrical enclosures should be located so that an object, upon entering the enclosure, is unlikely to fall on bare parts at hazardous voltages. Similarly, where louvers are provided for ventilation purposes, they should be shaped to deflect outward external vertically falling objects.

During the evaluation of an enclosure, the following aspects are observed in order to determine the compliance:

- *Protection in the operator area:* There should be no energy in the operator area;

- *Provisions for earthing:* Class 1 equipment should be provided with a protective earth terminal;

- *Mechanical strength of the enclosure:* This preserves the required creepage and clearances between the conductive parts and the end user and protects against the risk of personal injury by hazardous moving parts that are located within the enclosure or by the construction itself (e.g., sharp corners, burrs, and sharp edges).

- *Protection against contact with hazardous voltages circuits, including the tele-communication voltages circuits.*

- *Protection against other hazards that may be involved (e.g., radiation and chemicals):* During the tests that are performed on the enclosures, no test should show signs of interference with the operation of safety features; damages to the finish and cracks, dents, and chips that do not adversely affect the safety are ignored.

- *A certain degree of protection is evaluated according to the manufacturer's specifications, following the performance-related aspects.*

Specific requirements may be imposed by insurance companies, national and local codes, and organizations with a specific profile (e.g., police and military); these performance aspects, may regard specific accessibility degree (IP code), specific impact degree (IK code), minimum thickness of the metal sheet or of the plastic walls, presence of tampers, and specific interlocks requirements, and attack resistance.

All of these requirements should be evaluated in conjunction with all the safety-related aspects, and the most stringent requirement should be applied to the enclosure.

Any enclosure that hosts hazardous voltages and/or is required to be a fire enclosure should be designed and evaluated to meet the following minimal requirements:

- *Accessibility:* No access within the enclosure without the use of a tool or with the tool supplied with the equipment; for tools, it is acceptable to have a screwdriver or a key to remove screws or locks to gain access to the enclosure. It is not be acceptable to recommend a coin as a tool to open an enclosure; it may jeopardize the safety of the equipment and of the people who are in its proximity.

- *Mechanical strength:* An external enclosure should be able to resist appropriately during such test as steady force test, impact tests (steel ball tests), and drop tests, as applicable

- *Flammability rating and minimum thickness of the used material:* This applies to nonmetallic enclosures, and the flammability class of the used material should meet the applicable requirements for the minimum thickness of the enclosure. When the enclosure is a metallic one, then no flammability aspects are involved. The minimum thickness should be judged based on the mechanical strength evaluation.

- *Degree of protection, accessibility and impact, and IP and IK codes:* Specific determination of required IP or IK degrees of protection is performed using access probes and tests.

Another important consideration relates to the *intended openings* that are provided on the enclosures. The permanently connected equipment, with metallic or nonmetallic enclosures, may be provided with intended openings for connection of it to the mains and/or for interconnection with other equipment using conduits. Such intended openings are provided with knockouts (KOs), and they should be designed with the following considerations in mind:

- KOs that will not be used in the field have to resist all the mechanical strength tests specified within the product standard;

- KOs used in the field should be safely removable, using the recommended tools, to present a safe area for the installer after removal (i.e., smooth with no sharp edges, no burrs);

• After the intended wiring and connections are made, the KOs need to be protected by using bushings, fitings, and gaskets to be able to provide the same degree of protection as the enclosure had with the KO in place.

11.3   Circuit Separation

The circuit separation should be assured based on the type of circuits (e.g., unearthed SELV, earthed SELV, ELV circuits, earthed hazardous voltage circuits, primary circuits, secondary circuits, and TNV circuits), and according to the required insulation between the circuits (functional, basic, supplementary, or reinforced) (Figure 11.1).

For each type of the separation, the product standard gives the acceptable construction along with the required spacings (creepage and air clearance distances), and the adequate withstand voltage between circuits (when solid insulation is used).

The methods of separation include permanent separation, barriers, clamping, routing or fixing, using a protective screening that is permanently connected to the main protective earth terminal, and other constructions that assure equivalent separation (including internal enclosures).

It is known that the components are mechanically assembled, mounted, on PCBs, or wired. During the normal operation of equipment, all of the conductive parts of any part should be separated from the rest of the conductive

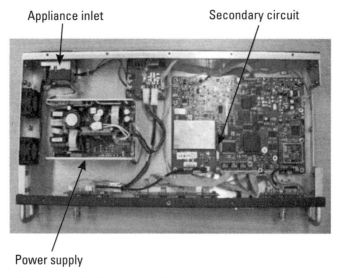

Figure 11.1   Equipment with adequate circuit separation.

parts at a degree imposed by the working voltages that appear in normal and single-fault conditions.

In terms of spacing as it regards the assemblies or components within equipment, the following should be considered:

- Where shortage of space on a PCB is an issue, especially between primary and SELV circuits, techniques such as slots or grooves can be used to attain the desired creepage distance. Slots must be wider than 1 mm; otherwise, they are not considered acceptable. For a groove (>1 mm wide) the only depth requirement is that the existing creepage plus the width of the groove and twice the depth of the groove must equal or exceed the required creepage distance. The slot or groove should not weaken the substrate to a point that it fails to meet mechanical test requirements.

- Components should be located so that their body is a minimum 2.5 mm from the board edge of the PCB.

- The PCB should be designed so that the components are mounted flat on the board rather than positioned vertically.

- Areas around metal brackets, or components with metal bodies that are free of circuit paths to prevent shorting should be taken in consideration;

- All secondary circuit wiring should be positively routed away from all uninsulated live parts of different circuits, either secondary or primary, and from insulated conductors of other circuits unless the secondary circuit wiring is rated for the highest voltage involved.

- All wiring should be routed away from sharp edges, screw treads, burrs, fins, moving parts, drawers, and other hazards that could abrade the wire insulation.

- A hole through which insulated wires pass in a sheet metallic wall should be provided with a well-rounded bushing.

- All wired electrical connections should be made by quick-connect terminals with positive engaging, closed-loop eyelets, open type eyelets with upturned ends, leads made mechanically secure and then soldered, or leads inserted into PCB holes and soldered.

- Resistors that actually dissipate more than a half-watt should be mounted away from the board surface and adjacent components. Consider adequate spacing and orientation when locating several components in a local area. The position in normal use should be taken into account (e.g., orientation of the heat-sink profile for natural convection cooling).

- Power resistors over 5W should have a series of cooling holes, approximately the size of the resistor diameter, in the board below the resistor to allow natural air circulation (natural convection cooling).

- As a general design practice, components dissipating power that would cause the adjacent PC board surface temperature to rise above 110°C should not be mounted on PCBs.

- Physically large components should have suitable mechanical support to ensure that the spacing is not affected during the mechanical strength tests.

- Electrolytic capacitors installed on PCBs require a clearance hole in the PCB directly under the pressure sensitive vent plug to allow the release of dangerous internal pressures in the event of circuit failure.

- The hazardous live circuits should be spaced away from other circuits by at least the values given in the applicable standard. Different standards require different values, and designers should use the most stringent value among them.

- A continuity test is to be carried out between all exposed parts of the separated circuit to ensure they are all equipotential bonded together.

- The protective conductor contact in any socket should be connected to the protective bonding conductor;

- A verification of the fault loop impedances between live conductors should be conducted to ensure that safe disconnection times are met during fault conditions.

- A test of resistance of insulation is required if the cables of an SELV circuit are grouped with circuits of different voltages. This test is between the live conductors of the SELV circuit and the protective conductor of the highest voltage circuit present. The test voltage should be 500 Vdc, and the resistance of insulation should be at minimum 1 MΩ.

- The live parts of the separated circuit should be electrically separate from other conductors in the same enclosure, including earth.

- In electrical equipment used with oxygen, the electrical connectors should be located as far as possible from an oxygen inlet/outlet source.

- Where the fire enclosure constitutes only a part of the equipment, careful analysis should be performed to assure that a reliable barrier to the propagation of fire exists.

11.4   Grounding and Bonding

The terminology that addresses grounding and bonding is given in each product safety standard and in NEC, CEC, and, generally speaking, in the electrical codes of countries where such documents exist.

Within the definitions chapter of the standards, grounding and bonding are clearly described. Their simple definitions follow:

- *Grounding (or grounded):* Connected to ground or to a conductive body that extends the ground connection;

- *Bonding (or bonded):* Connected to establish electrical continuity and conductivity.

It is very clear that the grounding conductor also performs bonding.

To understand the importance of grounding and bonding fully, it is useful to be aware that a ground fault represents an unintentional electrical conductive connection between an ungrounded conductor of an electrical circuit and the normally non-current-carrying conductors, metallic enclosures, metallic raceways, metallic equipment, or earth.

Earth as a whole is conventionally considered to be a conductor; thus, the electric potential of earth is considered to be zero. To eliminate electric shocks, all of the conductive accessible parts of electric equipment should have zero potential.

There is due variation (from one area to another one) in the composition of earth (with so many different materials present and varying levels of humidity and temperature and variations in chemical composition), leading to corresponding variations in the resistance of earth, but looking at our planet as a whole, the Earth may be regarded as a reference potential with a value considered and accepted to be zero.

Grounding and bonding should be done in such a manner as to serve all the following purposes:

- To protect life from the danger of electric shock and properties from damage;

- To facilitate the operation of electrical equipment and systems;

- To limit the voltage to ground during the normal operation of equipment;

- To prevent excessive voltages due to overvoltages (e.g., lightning, line surges, and accidental contact with hazardous voltages).

Once we take care to connect all of the accessible conductive parts of a piece of equipment to earth, the users in direct contact with this solidly grounded equipment will not be subjected to electric shock.

"Solidly grounded" is defined by the NEC as "connected to ground without inserting any resistor or impedance device."

In abnormal situations, hazardous potential (which is above the earth potential may be present. This is the case when any of the following are true:

- When the grounding conductor is broken;
- When the grounding conductor is inadequate in size ;
- When the grounding conductor is is not solidly grounded (or has poor contact, and the resulting presence of resistance/impedance).

All the product safety standards provide detailed information regarding proper grounding and bonding, starting with the parts that are expected to be properly grounded, and continuing with all of the details. In addition, each product standard provides a very clear and simple method of verification.

The *ground bond test* performs a measurement of resistance to determine if the equipment would remain safe in the event that internal live conductors touch the case. This test stresses the ground connection with a high current and causes a failure on a weak connection. All accessible conductive parts of the product that could become hazardous live in case of a fault must be grounded or separated from hazardous live circuitry by double or reinforced insulation. Alternatively, a conductive protective screen or barriers bonded to protective ground terminal can be used. The grounding lead from the appliance inlet or terminal block (for nondetachable power supply cords or permanent installed equipment) should be terminated by means of a closed-loop connector secured to a threaded stud or screw (of a suitable size for the bond wire, but not smaller than M4 = No.6) on the chassis (with at least three turns of the screw engaged) by means of a nut and washer (Figure 11.2). The grounding terminal should not be used for other purposes such as fixing mechanical parts. Where accessible plugs and sockets are used, the plug/socket combination must be such that the ground connection is made first and broken last.

The ground conductor for each component must be at least as large as the largest current-carrying conductor for that component. The ground conductor may be uninsulated, but if insulated it must have green/yellow- or green-colored insulation. Soldered ground connections must be mechanically secured prior to soldering. Crimping connections should crimp both the conductor and the insulator with the tools recommended by the connector manufacturer. It is important not to confuse the ground-bonding test with the ground continuity test. This last test only verifies that the protective ground connection exists.

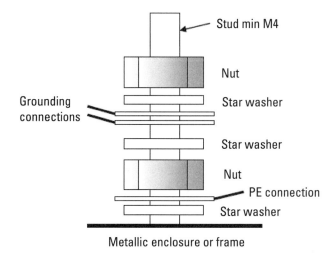

Figure 11.2 Grounding stud.

Since it is a low-current test, it does not verify the capability of this connection to withstand fault current.

In recognition of the importance of grounding and bonding, the majority of certification bodies ask that the protective earth conductivity (continuity) test be performed routinely in production (see Section 15.5).

11.5   Resistance to Fire and Flame Rating

Besides all the conditions that enclosures for electrical equipment should be ready to face during normal service conditions—including temperature; relative humidity; condensation; altitude (air pressure); heavy pollution of the air by dust, corrosive or radioactive particles, vapors, smoke, and salt; exposure to strong electric and magnetic fields; exposure to extreme temperatures (thermal shocks); radiation from the Sun; attack by fungus or even animals; heavy vibrations and shocks—a very important consideration is the ability of an enclosure to protect the spread of any fire outside of it and to be able to resist as well any external fire that may damage the equipment.

Metallic enclosures are able to fulfill this requirement with few concerns. Nonmetallic enclosures, on the other hand, prompt many concerns about the flammability of the material used for enclosure, as well as concerns about the colorant of that material, the minimum used thickness, and the molding process. All of these factors may drastically reduce the flammability rating, and consequently the resistance to fire, of the final enclosure.

To determine the correct flammability of a material, the standards specify methods of testing for the finished product (or the whole enclosure). When it is not possible to perform such tests, smaller-scale flame tests on standardized specimens may be used in order to issue a sound engineering judgement.

It is an imperative for a manufacturer to be aware of these options and to choose the one that better fits their product and budget. As well, when small components have to be evaluated and cannot be fabricated into standardized test specimens, the "small component flammability testing" described by UL1694 may be performed.

The flammability testing performed is based mainly on several fire hazard testing standards: UL 94, IEC 60695, and the VDE 0471 series. (See Section 8.6.) The tests that are chosen to be performed are requested by customers according to the standard requirements. For the purpose of testing, it is necessary to consider the different types of materials. For each of them, different types and methods may be used, including raw materials, with or without colorants, different thicknesses, different types of burning tests, vertical or horizontal burning tests, needle flame tests, hot-wire ignition tests, high-current arc ignition, and glow wire ignitability tests.

Along with the flammability evaluation of the nonmetallic materials used for enclosures for electrical equipment, there are several tests on these materials to determine the mechanical strength of the material in relation to the high temperatures to which these materials may be exposed within the electrical equipment; tests like ball pressure tests, thermal softening tests, and mold stress-relief and heat deflection tests provide useful information to mechanical designers for each application where the temperature may become a decisive factor in having a compliant enclosure that will behave safely and be compliant for the duration of the equipment's life, protecting the end users and the involved properties.

It is essential to establish for any piece of equipment the appropriate type of enclosure and the minimum thickness of that enclosure. Special attention should be paid to choosing the flammability of the material according to the minimum used thickness as it emerges from the design and, finally, from the molding processes.

Each product standard provides detailed information regarding the minimum flame rating that the materials should have when used within each application. As an example (from IEC 60950-1:2005), the flame-resistance requirements for wire insulation, when used inside a fire enclosure, are the following:

- Minimum flame rate of V-2 when tested in accordance with IEC 60695-11-10;
- Insulation with PVC, TFE, PTFE, FEP, polychloroprene, or polyimide.

It is useful to be aware that due to aging, a nonmetallic material may suffer over time due to the internal temperature, and thus its flammability rating may decrease in time. This consideration should lead the design team to choose an even better flame rating than the one specified within the product standard for those enclosures/or for parts of it. In doing so, the team will prevent future issues that may appear in the field, and overall, the price paid will be a wise investment in the safety of the equipment.

Last but not least, designers should consider, along with the flammability of the material, all of the rest of the properties of it: resistance to ignition; mechanical, physical, electrical and tracking resistance; RTI; softening temperature; and aging information. These considerations will depend on the material's function (e.g., enclosure or insulating barrier), whether it has direct or indirect contact with hazardous voltages, or whether nonmetallic materials are used as internal supports.

All of these considerations will give designers a better idea of how the material will behave depending on the style in which the equipment will be used (e.g., attended equipment, portable, intermittent, heavy-duty, household, or commercial).

In order to raise the degree of confidence in the plastic materials that are used during molding of the enclosures, it is important to seek molders who are in a *recognized molders program*. This will bring a supplementary level of knowledge and awareness by working with people who have in place production control measures from materials procurement to finished products. Participation in such programs means as well that the manufacturer is under continuous surveillance by the responsible party.

11.5.1 Circuit Boards

Circuit boards are a fundamental part of various products. They are used in equipment produced by makers of advanced microelectronics, telecommunications, aerospace and military, automotive, industrial, and medical equipment and in computers and watches, among other applications.

The term circuit board is often used interchangeably to either imply the part itself or the part populated with electronic components, which should be referred to as a circuit board assembly or electronic assembly and can include connectors and other circuit-related components (Figure 11.3). The reliability of the electronic circuit board assembly can therefore be evaluated at various levels (for example, the circuit board as a part, or the manufacturing of the circuit board and materials to make the circuit board). Then there is also the electronic circuit board assembly, which includes the components populating the circuit board, solder joints or parts, wiring and connectors, and other mechanical and thermal parts.

Figure 11.3   Circuit board populated with electronic components and connectors.

Circuit boards consist of a glass fiber mat, impregnated by a binder and then laminated with a copper layer. The circuit board provides the platform for the copper layer, and the copper layer is etched to form the circuit and the PCB. Electronic components, relays, and connectors are then soldered to the circuit board, and the copper traces from the electrical connections between these parts to form a working circuit board.

The circuit board design can change and may consist of a single-layer circuit board or a multilayer circuit board. In multilayer circuit boards, layers can be found on both sides of the circuit board as well as inside the circuit board, often referred to as inner layers. Components are mounted via SMD (surface-mount) or through-hole methods.

The circuit board is therefore a fundamental part in the product design. Accordingly, the circuit board and electronic circuit board assembly need to be considered from a reliability and safety perspective.

Circuit boards and circuit board assemblies can fail and cause products to become unreliable or to malfunction or fail. Electronic circuit board assembly reliability may be compromised by poor soldering, copper trace cracks, connectivity, and component reliability. In addition, circuit board failure has the potential to fail thermally and, in unique circumstances, result in charring of the circuit board. This rare phenomenon is known as a propagating circuit board failure [1, 2].

11.5.1.1 Propagating Circuit Board Failures

A propagating circuit board failure typically manifests itself as a charred circuit board or a charred area in a circuit board. The cause of the charring is often difficult to understand as most circuit boards are UL-94 V-0 rated and will not support burning combustion. However, this failure mode is very unique and complex, with temperatures high enough to melt the copper traces.

The failure mechanism is as follows. The binder in the circuit board is made of an organic material, which when exposed to extreme temperatures, will form carbon. Carbon is conductive and has a negative resistance temperature coefficient. Therefore, the higher the carbon temperature, the lower the resistance, which means that more power can be dissipated in the carbonized faulted area. As a result, when the isolation, between two adjacent copper traces or copper planes with carbonized organic material, a differential voltage potential, below-critical clearance or separation, and sufficient power are compromised and carbonized, then the carbon resistor temperature will thermally run away and result in thermal stressing and charring of the circuit board in the faulted region. The thermal event is "fueled" by the electrical power in the circuit. When the faulted region in a circuit board that is UL 94V-0 rated, is deprived of power, then the propagating circuit board fault will stop. Power fusing may not prevent this type of failure mechanism.

The initial localized heating event resulting in the circuit board binder to carbonize can stem from circuit board contamination, resistive contact heating, the failure of a discrete component, or any other heat source.

To minimize the risks of circuit board and electronic circuit board assembly failures, standards and experience can be used to guide the design of the circuit board and the electronic circuit board assembly.

11.5.1.2 Circuit Board and PCB Standards

The IPC standards are popular standards for circuit boards and electronic assemblies. The IPC was originally formed in 1957 and known as the Institute of Printed Circuits. Today the organization is known as the Association Connecting Electronics Industries. The IPC is accredited by ANSI as a standard developing organization.

The following are relevant IPC standards [3]:

- IPC-2221 Generic Standard on Printed Board Design;
- IPC-2223 Sectional Design Standard for Flexible Printed Boards;
- IPC-2612 Sectional Requirements for Electronic Diagramming Documentation (Schematic and Logic Descriptions);
- IPC-2615 Printed Board Dimensions and Tolerances;
- IPC-3406 Guidelines for Electrically Conductive Surface Mount Adhesives;

- IPC-3408 General Requirements for Anisotropically Conductive Adhesives Films;
- IPC-4101 Laminate Materials Standard for Printed Boards;
- IPC-4202 Flexible Base Dielectrics for Use in Flexible Printed Circuitry;
- IPC-4203 Adhesive Coated Dielectric Films for Use as Cover Sheets for Flexible Printed Circuitry and Flexible Adhesive Bonding Films;
- IPC-4204 Flexible Metal-Clad Dielectrics for Use in Fabrication of Flexible Printed Circuitry;
- IPC-4562 Metal Foil for Printed Wiring Applications;
- IPC-6011 Generic Performance Specification for Printed Boards;
- IPC-6012 Qualification and Performance Specification for Rigid Printed Boards;
- IPC-6013 Specification for Printed Wiring, Flexible and Rigid-Flex;
- IPC- 6202 IPC/JPCA Performance Guide Manual for Single- and Double-Sided Flexible Printed Wiring Boards;
- IPC-7351B Generic Requirements for Surface Mount Design and Land Pattern Standards;
- IPC-A-31 Flexible Raw Material Test Pattern;
- IPC-A-600 Acceptability of Printed Boards;
- IPC-A-610 Acceptability of Electronic Assemblies;
- IPC-D-325 Documentation Requirements for Printed Boards;
- IPC-ET-652 Guidelines and Requirements for Electrical Testing of Unpopulated Printed Boards;
- IPC-FA-251 Assembly Guidelines for Single and Double Sided Flexible Printed Circuits;
- IPC-FC-234 Pressure Sensitive Adhesives Assembly Guidelines for Single-Sided and Double-Sided Flexible Printed Circuits;
- IPC-T-50 Terms and Definitions;
- IPC-TF-870 Qualification and Performance of Polymer Thick Film Printed Boards;
- PAS-62123 Performance Guide Manual for Single and Double Sided Flexible Printed Wiring Boards.

These standards are available to provide guidance on the best practices in circuit board materials and manufacturing, circuit board layout and design, and circuit board assembly.

11.6 Interlocks

Interlocks are generally devices that fit as a part of equipment to synchronize some or all actions, to operate together with some other functions in a prearranged order, and to coordinate the imposed action as per the intended design.

As an example of interlock, we can refer to a device for preventing a mechanism from being set in motion when another mechanism is in such a position that the two operating simultaneously might produce undesirable results (e.g., a hazard situation). Such interlocks are very often used within the robotics industry.

We focus on the safety interlock (guard locking switches) and on interlocks as machine safety devices. In product safety standards, an interlock is described as a device or system, electrical, mechanical, or electromechanical, that serves to prevent exposure to an electric shock, or physical injury (or excessive radiation emission), when a door, cover, or access panel is opened or removed.

Some product standards lack the term of "safety interlocks." On the other hand, there are standards that pay attention to this real safety feature, such as the UL 923 standard. This standard even highlights the difference between primary interlocks (e.g., the door interlock that de-energizes the microwave generator upon opening the door, before microwave radiation emission exceeds the levels specified in the the standard) and secondary interlocks, (e.g., one of the door interlocks whose operation intends to prevent microwave radiation emission from exceeding the level specified in the applicable standard when the door is open).

We also found a short and clear definition of the safety interlock within the IEC 60950 standard for IT equipment: "a means either of preventing access to a hazardous area until the hazard has been removed or of automatically removing a risk when access is gained."

According to the above definitions, we can conclude that a safety interlock performs a safety function: It enables the equipment (or the system) to achieve a safe state when an inappropriate maneuver is performed by the operator, or it adjusts the equipment (or system) to a safe state in such situations.

In the context of electrical equipment safety, interlocks are mandated to prevent a user from making unsafe actions or to minimize the hazard of unsafe actions by setting the machine in a safe state when an unsafe maneuver occurs. Safety interlocks may have additional or combined features to reduce hazards at which the operator and even the equipment may be exposed.

An interlock should do one of the following:

• De-energize power supplies by disconnecting their power source;

• Stop moving parts;

- Advise users via a message or signal that higher risk than acceptable temperatures/radiation levels are becoming accessible and instruct about the measures that should be considered. (Such messages might read, for example, "do not look into the beam," "wait until parts cool down," or "do not go near certain parts of the equipment.")

As is specified in Chapter 12, warning labels placed on equipment are part of the safety design and in such situations; those labels will play the role of safety interlocks. Such markings should be placed on covers, doors, and other parts that, when removed, will give access to hazards. Product ssafety standards mandate interlocks in both industrial equipment and consumer products.

Examples of consumer products incorporating interlocks are described as follows:

- Removal of a guard on a food processor prevents the operation of the motor and blade, thereby eliminating the opportunity for blade spinning injury.

- Removal of the filter access door on a forced-air furnace prevents operation of the blower motor and possible contact with the blower blade.

- When the door on a clothes dryer is opened during the rotation of the drum, it stops.

When a cover of a laser is removed, the source turns off automatically.

- Modern interlocking mechanisms may take the form of simple switches or complicated sensors and actuators. Several safety standards address both interlocked guarding and interlocked controls on industrial equipment. Machinery represents a big chunk of the equipment that is designed and manufactured with interlocks in mind.

The "British Standard Code of Practice for Safety of Machinery," PD 5304, addresses both interlocking and the failure mode needs for interlocks.

Moreover, some standards authors are even discussing and imposing interlock monitors (electrical, mechanical, and electromechanical systems that serve to render appliances incapable of generating energy in the event the designated interlock do not perform their intended function).

The National Safety Council Publication *Safeguarding Illustrated Concepts* uses the term "interlocked" as one of the three categories that it recommends. This publication offers examples of interlocked features on industrial machines or devices, several of which are not even required by codes or by product standards. This NSC publication also provides a list of interlock guard advantages and disadvantages.

When designing and including interlocks within their equipment, designers and manufacturers should judge and apply engineering principles, keeping in mind the following factors: the best possible protection; the ergonomics of the equipment, including accessibility; reliability; and the ability to do not be defeated.

The OSHA publication *Concepts and Techniques of Machine Safeguarding*, OSHA 3067, lists interlocks second in a grouping of four options for guards, after the fixed guards. The OSHA standard specifically requires that at the point of operation, "the guarding device shall be in conformity with any appropriate standards therefore, or in the absence of applicable specific standards, the interlocks shall be so designed and constructed as to prevent the operator from having any part of his body in the danger zone during the operating cycle."

Many machines are not required to have interlocks per OSHA criteria, but interlocks may be required by other voluntary standards or by practice; the decision to have a voluntary interlock system, or a mandatory interlock device, relies heavily on a well-designed, high-reliability configuration and on a well-documented technical construction file for machinery and/or electrical equipment that is intended to be placed on the market.

It is interesting to note that some publications include the interlock in a category of devices that also may "...increase the danger of the protected system." Despite any negatives, the safety interlocks remain very important safety features of electrical equipment.

11.7　Moving Parts

One of the main mechanical hazards within electrical equipment consists of the hazardous moving parts. These are the moving parts that have the potential to cause injury.

It is necessary to arrange, enclose, or guard these parts in such way to reduce and eliminate the risk of injury to persons who come into contact, intentional or unintentional, with the equipment.

In an operator access area, protection should be provided by a suitable construction reducing the likelihood of access to hazardous moving parts or by locating the moving parts in a separate enclosure dedicated to those parts or an enclosure provided with mechanical or electrical safety interlocks that remove the hazard when access is gained in that area.

Special considerations should be given to moving fan blades. According to product standards, those should be evaluated first based on the likelihood of injury from moving fan blades.

It is necessary to determine the probability that pain or injury will be caused by the moving fan blades. The standard for IT equipment in IEC 60950 series offers a clear and simple calculation of the likelihood of the moving blades of a fan generating pain or injuries.

Where the guarding of hazardous moving parts is not possible due to the functionality of the equipment (i.e., moving parts are directly involved in normal operation), and the hazard is obvious to the operator, a warning statements such as the following should be affixed "in a prominent position, readily visible and accessible from the point where the risk of injury is greatest."

WARNING!
HAZARDOUS MOVING PARTS
KEEP FINGERS AND OTHER BODY PARTS AWAY!

In addition, the user's guide or operator manual and installation instructions should provide a detailed description of the hazard and how it could be averted.

11.8   Constructive Aspects Related to EMC

To fulfill the EMC standards requirements, the construction aspects that need to be considered refer to metallic enclosure, wiring, PCB layout, grounding and shielding, and usage of RFI suppression components. Related to these the following aspects take an important place on the design stage:

• Gasket and metal parts tolerance in the enclosure;
• Ventilation openings size and shape;
• Critical components location;
• Metal materials;
• The bonding of metallic part of the chassis;
• I/O connectors;
• Cables and power harnesses;
• Cover, doors, faceplates;
• Power distribution;
• PCB design.

A few constructional "rules of thumb" regarding the above issues follow:

• Cables should be shortened to the necessary length and routed in defined ways to minimize inductance and loop area.

- Where cable crossings cannot be avoided, a 90° crossing should be used for maximum decoupling.

- Never cross input and output connections of a filter.

- Where cable loops of different cables are laid out too close to each other, inductive coupling can occur.

- Harmonic currents can cause overheating in the local supply distribution transformer if it is inadequately rated, or if it is rated on the assumption of low harmonic levels.

- Power factor correction capacitors can overheat as well, due to the much higher harmonic currents they experience because of their lower impedance at higher frequencies, leading to failure.

- Equipment with timers and thermostats (e.g., laser printers, heaters, and air conditioners), which cause frequent changes of the load, will also cause voltage changes and fluctuations.

- Shielded enclosures should be grounded plainly and made of metal or other conductive materials.

- To achieve a high reflection loss at a sealing interface in an enclosure, and thus effective sealing and shielding of the joint, a low-impedance material is required.

- A shielded enclosure should use conductive painting and conductive gaskets (rubber used for IP reasons).

- When ventilation apertures (note that any opening acts as an antenna) are present in a shielded enclosure, the relation between size of apertures and wavelength of the disturbance to be attenuated should be considered.

- Conduits, metal films, braided wires, double-braided wires, or two separate shields can be used for cable shielding.

- The best effect of cable shield is obtained with a 360°ground connection on both ends of the shield.

- Coupling between susceptible paths and paths with high emission and coupling from external radiated fields should be reduced.

- Each electrical circuit should have an independent ground connection in order to avoid different potentials; if more than one system grounding point is used, a low-resistance connection between those points is recommended. Plain connections are therefore more effective than point connections. Flat, braided cables should also be preferred over round solid wires.

- For low frequencies, grounding on one side is sufficient and should be done on the transmitter side, with the receiver side floating.

- For high-frequencies, cables with well-known characteristic impedances should be used and grounded on both ends; additionally, grounding at several points along the signal path can be useful.

- For circuits with low- and high-frequency signals use of triaxial cables would be the best solution.

- When a PCB filter is used, it must provide a low-impedance connection to protective earthing terminal to minimize the noise radiation voltage from the mains inlet connection.

- An EMI filter should be installed as close as possible to the area that needs to be protected against the entrance of unwanted signals; the connection between the filter and source circuit should be kept as short as possible.

- The filter should be installed on the product enclosure in a surface part without painting.

- The chokes used to attenuate differential-mode or symmetrical interference generated by phase angle control devices must be connected as closely as possible to the semiconductor-switching device (thyristor or triac).

- In a SMPS to diminish fluctuations in the output voltage, a capacitor can be added in parallel with the load.

- The PCB should be a four-layer board with signal traces on the top and bottom layers; the middle two layers should be a ground plane and a power plane.

- All components on the PCB should be placed into functional groups (analog, digital, interface circuitry, and power supply groups).

- All ground connections must be made directly to the ground plane to prevent ground loops.

- The ground lines on the PCB should be arranged in the form of a star, with the common point of origin at the power-feed entry point.

- All conducting traces should be separated so that there is at least 1 mm of ground space between them.

- Slots and bottlenecks should be avoided as well; slots can be avoided by simply arranging the conducting traces in a zigzag pattern.

- The length/width ratio of the PCB must be less than 5 to minimize the inductance of the ground plane.

- Angles less than 45 degrees must be used to prevent signal reflection. When 90-degree angles or greater are used, high-frequency signals are reflected back through the trace;

- To reduce parasitic inductance, the optimal trace width is 0.495 mm, or 20 mils (1 mil=1 thou=0.001 inch; not to be confused with millimeters!).

- Traces with high switching current should also be placed at least 3 mm away from other parallel signal traces.

- Device decoupling capacitors must be placed very close (less than 1 mm preferred) to the VCC and GND pins.

- Bulk capacitors must be decoupled with a smaller capacitor with a lower effective series inductance.

- High-frequency, low-inductance ceramic decoupling capacitors should be used on each power pin.

- Decoupling capacitors of $0.1\mu F$ should be used for lower frequencies (below 15 MHz) and $0.01\mu F$ capacitors should be used for higher frequency applications (above 15 MHz).

- The emission (conducted and radiated) standard requirements need to be fulfilled by at least 3–4 dB (a margin for manufacturing uncertainty).

- The clock should be kept well away from input or output (I/O) circuitry to minimize coupling.

- The bandwidth of the clock signal should be limited, where possible, by filtering components.

- A resistor in series with a clock output may be used to reduce peak switching currents and limit the tendency to overshoot.

- An inductor in series with a clock output may be used to provide a high level of attenuation at high frequencies; a self-resonant inductor will maximize the attenuation at the particular frequency.

- Keep the fast logic away (i.e., in the center of PCB) from connectors to reduce cross-coupling and minimize the effects of ground noise.

11.9 Parts Subjected to Pressure

Parts subject to pressure in normal use are frequently found in electrical equipment (e.g., machinery, medical, and household equipment). Types of systems considered include: pneumatic pressure systems, hydraulic pressure systems, steam pressure systems, and combinations thereof. These systems might or might not include pressure vessels. The *Oxford Dictionary* defines a pressure vessel as "a container designed to hold material at high pressures."

The pneumatic and hydraulic parts included in such equipment should remain safe when the following failures occur:

- Loss of pressure or loss of vacuum;
- Fluid jet caused by leakage or a component failure.

For remaining on the safe side the following requirements specified in product standards for such parts need to be considered [4]:

- When pressure is greater than 50 kPa (1 Pa = $1N/m^2$) and energy limit (pressure × volume) exceed 200 kPa x l, the part should withstand the hydraulic test pressure.

- No leakage is allowed for pressure vessels intended for toxic, flammable, or otherwise hazardous substances.

- The maximum pressure to which a part can be subjected in all conditions should not exceed the maximum permissible working pressure for the part, which is specified by the manufacturer.

- Pipes and hoses should be protected against harmful external effects.

- Elements that can remain under pressure after disconnection of the equipment from its power supply should be provided with clearly identified exhaust means and a warning label drawing attention to the necessity of depressurizing these elements before any setting or maintenance.

- Adjacent to each pressure input connector should be present a marking specifying the maximum supply pressure from an external source, and the flow rate.

- There should be a suitable safety factor between the maximum permissible working pressure and the bursting pressure (the pressure at which a part suffers from permanent (plastic) deformation or leakage). Industry standards for pressure parts recommend safety factors of 3 ×, 4 ×, and sometimes 5 × (ISO, ASME, SAE).

- Equipment should incorporate an overpressure protection device where excessive pressure could occur.

Note: An overpressure safety device should not operate in normal use. Also, such a component should comply with ISO 4126 and with following requirements:

- To be connected as close as possible to the part intended to protect;
- To have an adequate discharge capacity;
- To permit an easy access for inspection, maintenance, and repair;
- To be incapable of being adjusted without the use of a tool;
- To have its discharge opening not directed toward any person;
- To avoid a shutoff valve between an overpressure safety device and the parts intended to protect;
- The minimum number of cycles of operation should be 100,000, except for one-time-use devices.

11.10 Serviceability

During design, manufacturing, and use of electrical equipment, one needs to consider the product serviceability. This is an expression of the ease with which the product can be maintained (preventive maintenance) and repaired (corrective maintenance) for providing a specific service (intended use).

Preventive maintenance (PM) includes all the actions taken to replace, service, upgrade, or patch a system to retain its operational or available state and prevent system failures. *Mean preventive maintenance time* (MPMT) is a measure commonly used to quantify the time required to perform PM.

Corrective maintenance (CM) includes all the actions taken to repair a failed system and get it back into an operating or available state. The failure can be unexpected or expected, but it is usually an unplanned outage. MTTR is the measure used to quantify the time required to perform CM.

Electrical equipment deteriorates with age and use; this necessitates that end users inspect and test equipment at regular intervals if it is still within the initial designed range.

It is imperative to preserve not only the correct functionality of the equipment but to ensure that no safety-related hazards may appear in the field during the use of the equipment; it is easier to prevent than to fix a major failure.

A proper serviceability program will speed up the service and reduce the out-of-service time for the product. To establish such a program, the manufacturer needs feedback from clients; that information will dictate the list of the operations that should be done in order to keep the equipment functions within the original parameters. A lack of feedback from customers about product behavior in the field may have a significantly negative impact on the service of the equipment. A few key elements of serviceability are described as follows:

• Equipment should feature backup power sources, including batteries, UPSs, and generators to keep systems operational during extended interruptions in commercial power.

• Parts requiring frequent changing or regular maintenance should be easily accessible.

• For safety-critical components manufacturers should have alternate components included in the initial approval of the product; safety-critical components that fail in the field may be replaced by an already accepted component, and it is not sufficient to be only an equivalent component

• Remote electronic diagnostics features should be implemented to verify and to update the functionality of product.

• From the point of view of serviceability of electrical equipment, the following aspects should be considered on the design and manufacturing stages.

• When the size of the PCB requires it should be mechanically supported to prevent board flexure.

• Standardize the size of PCBs according to the company practices and available enclosures.

• PCBs should be rectangular in shape and free from angles and cutouts, etc. If the design does not allow this, breakaway portions that can be removed after the assembly should be provided.

• It is recommended that similar components be orientated on the PCB so that common pins or polarity are located in the same direction.

• Components should be located so they may be replaced by normal servicing without removing other components and wires.

• Adequate clearance required for manufacturing, testing, and servicing must be provided for insertions equipment such as tooling footprints, test jigs/fixtures, automatic test equipment, and tools.

• It is recommended that all components and jumpers to be on one side of the board only.

• If multiple boards are stacked in a normal mounting position, the serviceability of individual boards, component clearance, and circuits that may be affected by adjacent circuitry should be observed.

• Controls mounted on boards should be accessible and clearly marked. In order to avoid ergonomic hazards, the identifying information on boards should be oriented to be readable from the normal servicing position or according to end user's position when operating or working with the equipment.

- All ferrous metal parts should be protected against corrosion by plating, painting, or the equivalent.

The effectiveness of a serviceability program developed by the manufacturer is proved during the use of the product. The manufacturer needs to provide end users with relevant information and instructions for estimation of the product status during the normal use. Such information and instructions should refer primarily to a periodic visual inspection.

To carry out a visual inspection end users do not need to be experts, but they need to know what to look for, and they must also have sufficient knowledge to avoid danger to themselves and others. Simple training can equip end users (or a member of staff) with some basic knowledge to enable them to carry out a visual inspection competently.

Generally, the installation instructions and the user's manuals can include checklists that end users or service personnel who provide the maintenance and the repairs should check at regular intervals.

The following checklist is recommended for simple periodical verification (visual inspection).

- Is the electrical equipment being used in accordance with the manufacturer's instructions?
- Is the equipment suitable for the job?
- Have there been any changes in normal use conditions?
- Has the user reported any issues related to safety?
- Has integrity been maintained for earthing and bonding, the power cord (the cover and bent pins), the enclosures, and the power outlet?
- What is the condition of the interconnections cables and connectors?
- Are adequate identification labels and notices on accessible areas that can present hazards of electrical shock or excessive heating being maintained?
- Are there any signs of overheating (such as burn marks or staining on the plug, lead or piece of equipment), wear and tear, damage or other mechanical deterioration (to the outer cover of the equipment itself, including loose parts or screws)?
- Was the correct functionality of switches and indicator lights verified?
- Were identified cables trapped under furniture or in floor boxes?

The above list does not replace the periodical maintenance activities recommended by the manufacturer.

References

[1] Slee, D., et al., "Introduction to Printed Circuit Board Failures," *IEEE Symposium on Product Compliance Engineering,* Toronto, CA, 2009.

[2] Swart J., et al., "Case Studies of Electrical Component Failures," *Failures 2006,* South Africa, 2006.

[3] https://en.wikipedia.org/wiki/IPC_(electronics), 2017.

[4] IEC 60601-1, "Medical Electrical Equipment—Part 1: General Requirements for Safety and Essential Performance," Geneva, 2005 and 2012.

Selected Bibliography

Bolintineanu, C., and S. Loznen,*"Product Safety and Third Party Certification,"* The Electronic *Packaging Handbook,* edited by G. R. Blackwell, Boca Raton, FL: CRC Press, 2000.

ECMA-287, European Association for Standardizing Information and Communication Systems, "Safety of Electronic Equipment," Geneva, 2002.

Harris, K., and C. Bolintineanu, "Electrical Safety Design Practices Guide," *Tyco Safety Products Canada Ltd,* Rev 12, March 14, 2016.

Hasan, R., et al., "Integrating Safety into the Design Process: Elements and Concepts Relative to the Working Situation," *Safety Science 41,* 2003, pp.155–179.

IEC 60529+A1+A2, "Degrees of Protection Provided by Enclosures (IP Code)," Geneva, (1989-2013).

IEC 60950-1+AMD1+AMD2, "Information Technology Equipment—Safety—Part 1: General Requirements," Geneva, 2005–2013.

IEC/TR 62296:2003, "Considerations of Unaddressed Safety Aspects in the Second Edition of IEC 60601-1 and Proposals for New Requirements," Geneva 2003.

Lamothe, M., "Safety Approvals: Selecting the Right Components for IT Equipment," Lamothe Approvals Inc, Georgetown, Canada, 2002.

Underwriters Laboratories Inc., *"PAG 60950-1,"* 2008, Northbrook, IL.

12

Markings, Indicators, and Accompanying Documents

12.1 Marking/Safety Labels/External Marking

Marking/safety labels represent the information provided on or in connection with electrical equipment in order to identify all the characteristics of that product related to product safety. Electrical equipment should bear markings that are necessary to identify the equipment and to ensure that the equipment is suitable for the intended application.

The contents of the marking labels affixed on the equipment are specified within the applicable standard(s). Sometimes more than one standard must be used in order to ensure that the marking is fully compliant. Symbols used in marking should conform to dedicated standards where the appropriate symbol exists (e.g., ISO 7000, ISO 7010, ISO 3864, ISO 15223, IEC 60417, and IEC/TR 60878). The symbols used for marking should be found and explained within the installation/user's manual.

Generally, the marking labels affixed on equipment and/or within the installation/user's instructions manuals include the following main categories of information (a sample of the structure of a label is shown in Figure 12.1):

- The manufacturer's name, trademark, or other recognized symbol of identification (with a means of contact such as address and/or Internet site, if applicable);

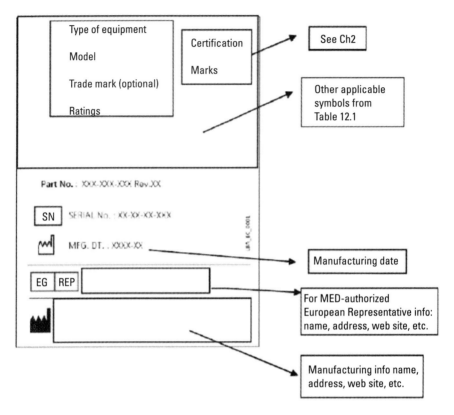

Figure 12.1   Structure of a label.

- Catalog, part number, and serial number or type of equipment, classification of the equipment, degree of protection of the equipment, and level of energy efficiency;
- Type of power supply (AC, DC, or both), with outlet voltage and current marked accordingly;
- Ratings, including applicable characteristics such as voltage, current consumption or power consumption, frequency, number of phases, rated load, and environmental conditions;

Note: With regard to the current consumption (power consumption), it is important to know that equipment should be rated by taking into account the allowable ampacity of the branch circuit to which it will be connected. It is recommended that the continuous load should not be rated for more than 80% of the branch circuit ampacity. (e.g., a plug-connected load intended to be connected to a 15-A branch circuit should not be rated for more than 12A.)

- Evidence of approval, such as certification mark/listing mark (e.g., CSA, UL, cULus, ETL, TUV, VDE, SEMKO, and CCC), inspection label, and self-declaration mark (e.g., CE mark and FCC), etc.;

- Other markings as may be required to ensure the safe and proper installation, operation, and maintenance of the equipment (e.g., short-circuit interrupting capacity of the overcurrent protective devices, diagram number, adjustment of the input voltage, mode of operation, cooling conditions, references to accompanying documents, disposal recommendations, and type of radiation);

1. Medical equipment (MED) is expected to be marked with regard to the type of applied part (B, BF, CF, defibrillator proof), the physiological effects (symbols and statements), potential equalization terminal, if present, mechanical stability in the case of equipment with limited stability, and contact information referring to EU authorized representative.

2. Audio/video equipment that involves laser radiation hazards must ensure that the appropriate marking as per the standard for safety of laser products is affixed on it.

3. Equipment that presents accessible hot surfaces should be marked accordingly.

4. Marking related to fuses should be located on or adjacent to each fuse holder or in another location provided that it is obvious to which fuse holder the marking applies and must contain the following information: fuse-rated current, fuse-rated voltage (where fuses of different rated voltage values could be fitted), special fusing characteristics (symbol denoting the relative prearcing time/current characteristic as given in the relevant standard that was used for the fuse certification of the fuse). For fuses located in an operator area a step further should be taken to provide an unambiguous cross-reference to accompanying documentation.

5. Products that include a laser source, except for laser class 1, should have affixed labels according to the standard for laser products (the IEC 60825 series of standards). These labels should be present at each connection, each panel or protective housing, and each access panel of a protective enclosure, which, when removed or displaced give human access to laser radiation in excess of the accessible emission level (AEL) for Class 1.

• Warning labels, which are used to bring supplementary information to users and are designed to provide or to supplement some safety features of the equipment. These are used mainly when MOP(s) are not feasible to be used or when a hazardous situation is not obvious to the end user. Warning labels are a redundant means of protecting the user from hazards that may arise during the functionality of the equipment. Please note that not all regulatory bodies accept the warnings as risk control means (Table 12.1).

Additional markings on the affixed labels are permitted, provided that they do not give rise to any misunderstanding. Markings should be durable, legible, indelible, and plainly visible to the user, as the equipment is installed and operated. In considering the durability of the marking, the effect of normal use and the life span of the equipment should be taken into account (considering factors such as corrosive agents and environmental conditions, for example). The marking text can be ink-stamped, silk-screened, or painted. If stickers are used, they should be suitable for the temperatures and humidity to which they are exposed and for the surfaces used. The product safety standards normally request a durability marking test to be conducted. After this test the markings should be clearly legible, and an adhesive label should not have worked loose or become curled at the edges [1]. Regarding the warning labels, the symbol color is very important and should be respected.

When an equipment is certified/listed, the testing laboratory that evaluated the equipment will approve the complete contents of the marking label including all the required cautions and warnings. The marking should not be placed on any removable parts that can be replaced.

Each particular product safety standard has specific requirements for different warning labels that must appear on the equipment, related to the specific designation of the equipment.

The warnings should be placed closed to the subject, and if there is not enough room on the equipment they may be placed in the operator/user's manual (e.g., hazardous voltages, replaceable batteries, fuses, moving parts, and radiation hazards). Except on handheld equipment or where space is limited, markings should not be on the bottom of the equipment.

12.2 Internal Markings

Internal markings that will be accessed by service personnel—or even end users within the limits of the access gained without the use of a tool—should be legible, durable ,and appropriately placed. Normally, for such markings, durability

Table 12.1

Samples of Symbols Used on Labels [2]

Symbol	Explanation
	Environmental conditions: Humidity, atmospheric pressure, temperature
	MED—Type B, BF, CF Applied part (adjacent to applied part)
	Refer to instruction manual/ booklet MED—"Follow instructions for use"
	Operating instructions
	MED—Do not reuse
IPN₁N₂	IP classification
	Symbol requested by EU WEEE directive
	ESD sensitivity (adjacent to connectors)
	Nonionizing radiation
	Class II equipment
	Caution

of marking tests are not performed, since safety is not involved for the end user, due to being in an enclosure.

Generally, internal markings should include information such as the following:

- All the fuses inside the equipment that are accessible with the aid of a tool should be identified by type and ratings or with a number that is connected to the accompanying documentation where it is identified.

- When heaters or lamp holders designated to be used with heating lamps are within the equipment, the maximum power loading of each element should be marked near the heater/lamp-holder.

- The presence of high voltage (hazardous voltages) should be marked with the symbol for dangerous voltage ⚡.

- The type of battery/batteries (if used within the equipment) and the mode of replacement showing the correct insertion should be provided.

- Protective earth terminal(s) and the functional earth terminals should be identified using the adequate symbol. This requirement applies to equipment using appliance inlets. Terminals provided within permanently connected equipment, exclusively for the connection of the neutral supply conductor should be marked with the appropriate symbol (see Figure 12.2).

- Unless no safety is involved, the correct method of connection of the supply conductors should be marked adjacent to the terminal block.

Figure 12.2   Symbol showing neutral supply conductor.

Note: For permanently connected equipment, when any point of the terminal block or the conductor that is connected within the equipment attains during the maximum temperature test a high temperature (e.g., over 75 °C), then the equipment should be marked within that area of connection with a statement that will indicate the necessity of wiring materials suitable for that temperature. Such decisions should be carefully considered, taking into account the upper limit of the operating temperature range for the equipment.

• Depending on the accessibility, equipment with moving parts may require warnings close to the area that might generate a hazardous situation, in order to protect the service persons.

12.3 Marking of Controls and Instruments

Control devices, visual indicators, and displays (particularly those related to safety functions) should be clearly marked with regard to their functions and should be identified with the appropriate symbols. All control devices and components should be plainly identified with the same designation as in the technical documentation (installation/user's manual). All the controls and indicators with safety functions (e.g., presence of the hazardous voltages, risk of an increased level of radiation, and alarms) should be clearly identified.

For controls intended to be adjusted during installation or in normal use, an indication should be provided for the direction of adjustment to increase or decrease the value of the characteristic being adjusted. The user should be able to observe without any effort, how adjustments are performed. The following need to be considered [3]:

The mains switch (means of disconnection of the power) should be clearly identified by appropriate marking of the ON and of the OFF position, using "O" and "I" symbols or other acceptable markings specified within the product standard; these two states should be indicated adjacent to the switch, using along with the symbols a light or other unambiguous means.

Note: For each piece of equipment, the accompanying documentation should specify the means of disconnection and how the power is removed completely if the equipment has more than one power supply or a battery.

For all the devices that are adjusted during normal use and that have switches or other means of adjustment, analog or digital, the adjustments and/ or different positions of switches available on the equipment should be indicated by figures, letters, numbers, or any other visual means, using icons and symbols that are acceptable under the product standard(s). For any setting change that in normal use could generate a hazard as per the applicable standard(s), their controls and indicators should be equipped with a reliable indication (e.g., instrument) and/or an indication of the direction in which the magnitude of the adjustment function changes. Explanatory text and figures should be supplied within all of the accompanying documents;

12.4   Color of Indicators and Lights

The human perception of the color red is that it indicates a warning or danger, and thus, this color should be used within electrical equipment exclusively to indicate a warning of danger and/or the need for urgent action.

The emergency shutoff switches and emergency stop buttons should be red to be visible and should be mounted ergonomically so that they are accessible in case of danger.

Electrical equipment safety standards recommend the following colors of indicator lights [3]:

• Red, which means warning of danger or urgent action;
• Yellow, which means caution or attention required;
• Green, means ready for action;

These colors have these specific universal meanings; any other colors have different meaning.

The nonilluminated push buttons should follow the same code of colors, and all of them should be described in detail within the accompanying documents.

12.5   User's Manual and Installation Instructions

With each piece of supplied equipment, it is the responsibility of the manufacturer to provide the necessary information for transport, storage, installation, operation, and maintenance of the equipment. The accompanying documentation should be regarded as a component part of the supplied equipment.

The required information should be supplied in the form of instructions, schematics, diagrams, charts, and tables. The documentation should be in the language acceptable by the end user or in a language agreed upon by the end user and supplier. When the equipment is designed to be installed by service persons, English is generally acceptable.

Due to some potential safety hazards, the functionality of the equipment, or performance aspects that may be involved, some of the equipment may be installed only by persons who have received appropriate training and are able to install/operate some equipment (service persons). Information regarding the prerequisites of installation should be mentioned in the manuals. The manufacturer, the supplier (the representative) of the equipment, or a recommended external organization can provide the required training by offering specific information as follows:

- Familiarization with the installation of the equipment and operating procedures;

- Description of proper use of such functions as the control procedures and interlocks;

- Basic requirements for personal protection-identification of the potential hazards;

- Accident-reporting procedures and first aid.

For each piece of equipment, depending on the type of equipment, the applicable standard may ask for specific details. (For example, for laser equipment, the instructions must explain in detail the warnings and must state information such as the following: precautions needed to avoid possible exposure to hazardous laser radiation, the pulse duration and the maximum output, the locations of laser apertures, the maximum permissible exposure, the conditions for ventilation, the relevant national regulations, and the safety classification of each laser product.

For medical electrical equipment, instructions should provide clear guidance and the appropriate cautions regarding the danger that may be encountered during the use of the equipment—for the operator and for the patient).

12.5.1 User's Manual: Operating Instructions

The complexity of the equipment defines the characteristics of the user's manual. The instructions for use (IFU) should include all information necessary to operate the equipment as it was designed and intended to perform within its specifications. The operating instructions should detail proper procedures for the installation that falls under the user's duty, and operation of the equipment. All necessary details must be provided as follows [2, 4]:

- A clear indication about the intended use of the equipment;

- Complete instructions for safety associated with the hazards that may occur during the normal use of the equipment;

- Identification of detachable components and part identification and a list of accessories recommended to be used with the equipment;

- Any expiration date of the consumable parts expressed in the order year, month, day;
- Instructions for transportation after the delivery to the user;
- Connections to the supply;
- Ventilation requirements;
- Requirements for special services (i.e., air and cooling liquid) including pressure limits;
- Identification and explanation of the function of controls and displays;
- Description of all input and output connection;
- Instructions for interconnection with accessories and other equipment;
- Illustrations showing the proper connection of all parts forming the system and the location and function of all controls;
- Specifications of limits for intermittent operation, where applicable;
- Explanation concerning all symbols and warnings marked on the unit;
- Step-by-step operation of the equipment;
- Instructions for the replacement of consumable materials;
- For equipment using batteries, the specific battery type(s);
- Instructions for the use and maintenance of the rechargeable (secondary) batteries, protective devices, and the recommended charging means;
- Details about the cleaning and the recommended cleaning agents;
- Instructions for the disposal of waste;
- Instructions for any actions to be taken by an operator in case of malfunction;
- A statement advising that the equipment may be impaired if it is used in a manner that is not specified by the manufacturer;
- Specification of any parts that are required to be examined or supplied only by the manufacturer or its agent (if applicable);
- Recommendations for users concerning preventive inspection and maintenance, including the frequency of such maintenance;
- Instructions for the regular testing of the equipment and the accessories (if applicable);
- Guidance on tests to permit the user to check the correct functioning of alarms and the operational safety of the equipment;
- Methods for programming the equipment using a clear algorithm that can be followed by users with no issues;

- Instructions for transportation and storage;

- Instructions regarding the suitable precautions that should be taken to protect against hazards that might be experienced during transportation or in conditions of storage for long and short periods, for example;

- An address/contact to which end users can refer in case of assistance.

Note: We recommend that manufacturers include with each operator/user's manual the classic statement "Read and save these instructions. Follow all warnings and instructions specified within this manual and/or on the equipment." It not only represents a matter of liability; it shows care and respect for the user who will use the equipment.

Special attention is needed for *technical specifications* that are part of the user's manual. Technical specifications should consist of the following [2, 4]:

- Electrical ratings (voltage, frequency, current, or power);
- Functional parameters (features);
- Interfaces (e.g., interconnections such as cable and Wi-Fi) ;
- Physical properties (weight, dimension, and color);
- Accessories;
- Operating environment (temperature range, humidity range, altitude range);
- Storage environment (temperature range and humidity range);
- Standards with which the product complies (including report number and date and name of the testing house).

12.5.2 Installation Instructions

The installation instructions may provide redundant information to the user's manual. The provided instructions should provide the following information:

- Normal operating conditions of the equipment (e.g., normal position and means of fixing).

- Methods of installation, location, and mounting requirements (spacing).

- Clear warnings on equipment that can generate hazards of excessive heat and/or sparks that it should be installed in nonhazardous locations only (ordinary locations). (It is strongly recommended that any electrical equipment that is not compliant with all of the applicable requirements of a hazardous location should not be installed in such locations.)

- Electrical supply requirements and the method of connection to the electrical supply (adjustments to the power supply if applicable; protective earthing requirements; and for on permanently connected equipment, requirements for any external switch or circuit-breaker and external overcurrent protection devices and a recommendation that the switch or circuit breaker be near the equipment).

- Information on the physical environment (e.g., operating temperature, humidity, vibration, noise, and type of location);
- Operating instructions for the installer should include the following:
- Block diagram, circuit diagram, and schematics;
- Programming instructions;
- Sequence of operation;
- List of the critical components;
- Specific instructions for the connection and disconnection of detachable parts and accessories and for the replacement of material that is consumed during operation.
- Precautionary instructions if a cover is removed and this condition can affect safety related to access possible hazards such as moving parts, hazardous voltages, or excessive radiation.
- Instructions for replacement of fuses and other parts [e.g., suitable warning(s) for service persons regarding a possible hazard when fuses are employed in the neutral of single-phase class I equipment connected to a polarized supply or, where after the operation of the protective device, parts of the equipment that remain under voltage might present a hazard during servicing].
- Warning statements and the explanation of warning symbols (marked on or within the equipment).

Note: The block diagram must represent the electrical equipment together with its functional characteristics with symbols (e.g., waveforms and test prints) without necessarily showing all the interconnections. Circuits must be shown in such a way as to facilitate the understanding of their function as well as maintenance and fault location. Characteristics related to the function of the control devices and components that are not evident from their symbolic representation must be included on the adjacent diagrams or referenced by a footnote or by some equivalent notation.

12.6 Safety Instructions, Cautions, and Warnings

The safety instructions should cover the steps starting with the storage of the equipment and continuing with the unpacking, installation, and operation of the equipment. Product standards cover almost all the necessary safety instructions for a piece of equipment. All the precautions that should be observed during the installation should be provided [5].

The manufacturer should understand that the safety instructions should be regarded as CAUTIONS. The purpose of safety instructions should be considered to be educational and not something that would scare users from using electrical equipment.

It is recommended that all the amendments to the instructions be provided in written form.

The manufacturer must keep accurate records of all the revisions of the instructions in order to ensure that each end user receives the updated version. It is recommended that, as far as possible, all the documents be included in only one book; where this is not feasible, it is recommended that a numeration of volumes be provided. The end user should be aware that there is more than one volume of the user's manual (the instructions). Each document should carry a cross-reference number to all the rest of the documents belonging to the equipment.

The safety instructions should be provided in writing. When the installation manual is supplied on a CD or DVD, the minimal safety instructions should be printed on the envelope in which it is delivered.

Manufacturers should ensure that their instructions convey the following information.

- The storage instructions should address aspects regarding the environment in which the equipment may be stored and operated, the values of the storage temperature range, and the acceptable maximum relative humidity that is imposed (if it may or may not be acceptable to be condensed).

- The safety instructions for installation of the equipment should offer wiring instructions and, where necessary, make reference to the local rules and regulations and national electrical codes.

- It is important that a clear recommendation for the correct protective earth terminal connection be made.

- It is mandatory to include information regarding the means of connection and disconnection from the supply mains and all the precautions regarding the proper position of the equipment in regard to the connection to the supply mains.

- For equipment that is included within metallic enclosures and has knock-outs (KOs), a method for safe removal of the KO and a recommendation for preserving the required IP after the KO removal should be provided.
- Equipment that includes batteries should have a detailed description regarding them.

Specific foreseeable hazards should be described, and appropriate warnings and cautions should be provided for each piece of equipment according to the product standard and engineering judgement.

The warnings should be used for those imminent situations when the danger is present if the warning is not respected.

Some examples follow:

- For equipment that contains lithium batteries—and these are extremely common today—at least the following warnings/instructions should be included within the installation/user's manual: "This product uses lithium batteries. Improper handling of lithium batteries may result in heat generation, explosion, or fire, which may lead to personal injuries."
- (If appropriate) this warning should follow: "Danger of explosion if batteries are installed incorrectly; replace only with the same or equivalent type recommended by the manufacturer."
- "Keep away from small children: If swallowed promptly see a doctor."
- "Do not try to recharge these batteries."
- "Disposal of used batteries must be made in accordance with the waste recovery and recycling regulations in your area."

Warning statements for class I equipment can include the following:

- "WARNING: To avoid the risk of electric shock, this equipment must only be connected to supply mains with protective earth."
- Adjacent to the fuse holder a warning of the type, "WARNING: For continued protection against risk of fire, replace only with fuse of the specified type and current ratings," can be affixed.
- If operators can gain access with a tool to a part that is hazardously live in normal use, there should be a warning marking stating that the equipment must be disconnected from the hazardous live voltage before access.

Warning notices should be prefaced with an uppercase signal word "CAUTION," "WARNING," or "DANGER." "DANGER" should be used for product functions representing the most serious risks. "WARNING" and "CAUTION" should be used in decreasing order of severity of the foreseeable risks. The letter height of all cautionary markings must be a minimum of 1.5 mm, and the signal word should be in letters at least 2.75 mm with good contrast maintained between the lettering and the background material. If molded or stamped in a material, the text should be at least 2.0 mm high and, if not contrasting in color, a depth or raised height of at least 0.5 mm.

References

[1] Bolintineanu, C., and S. Loznen, "Product Safety and Third Party Certification," *The Electronic Packaging Handbook,* edited by G. R. Blackwell, Boca Raton, FL: CRC Press, 2000.

[2] IEC 60601-1, "Medical Electrical Equipment—Part 1: General Requirements for Safety and Essential Performance," Geneva, 2005 and 2012.

[3] IEC 60073, "Basic and Safety Principles for Man-Machine Interface, Marking and Identification—Coding Principles for Indicators and Actuators," Geneva, 2002.

[4] IEC 60950-1+AMD1+AMD2, "Information Technology Equipment—Safety—Part 1: General requirements," Geneva, 2005–2013.

[5] UL 969, "Standard for Marking and Labeling Systems," Underwriters Laboratories, Inc., 2001.

Selected Bibliography

Harris, K., and C. Bolintineanu, "Electrical Safety Design Practices Guide," Tyco Safety Products Canada, Ltd., Rev 12, March 14, 2016.

https://ec.europa.eu/growth/single-market/ce-marking_en

Kirwan, B., "Safety Informing Design," *Safety Science 45,* 2007, pp.155–197.

IEC 60417-1, "Graphical Symbols for Use on Equipment," Geneva, 2002.

IEC 60878, "Graphical Symbols for Electrical Equipment in Medical Practice," Geneva, 2003.

ISO 7000:2004, "Graphical Symbols for Use on Equipment," Geneva, 2004.

13

Human Factors and Product Safety

13.1 Introduction

The main purpose of this chapter is to provide a general reference to key human factor questions and human-product interface design suggestions. Human factors and ergonomics principles have been applied in high-hazard industries for many years to minimize the risks from human error and ensure that these industries are designed to promote safe practices and take advantage of technology that anticipates and mitigates human mistakes.

Human factors and ergonomics principles are, therefore, employed by many companies in design for customer loyalty and marketing purposes.

13.2 Operator and Service Personnel

The *operator* is defined as the person who handles the product, destined for industry, research, or home.

This person could be one of the following:

- A professional using the product in context of his or her work;
- A private person or a layperson using the product in the home environment;
- A person using the product to compensate or alleviate the effects of disease, injury, or disability.

The operator is also the person expected to install, assemble, clean and move the product. The term *operator* is the same as the term *user,* and the two terms can be interchanged.

The operator should follow the information provided by the manufacturer in user manuals, information for use, installation instructions, and safety instructions about the special skills and knowledge required to safely handle the product and to learn about the locations or environments in which the product can be used.

The operator must be knowledgeable of the human factor characteristics of a product and the facility, sensitivities, or potential actions that can become hazardous.

It is important for an operator to be able to determine the functional status of the product. In normal use, the operator needs to be able to distinguish between the product in standby and the product in a fully functional state. Some products have extended warm-up periods or battery charging modes. It can be hazardous for products to be left unattended in the wrong state.

Operators are presumed to be competent to use the product but are not necessarily competent to avoid risks that can arise during servicing. This is the reason that service activities should be conducted by experienced service personnel. Operators might not be as well-trained or experienced in good safety practices as service personnel. Therefore, extra safety precautions are needed to prevent operators' accidental contact with hazardous areas. Based on this, parts such as lamps, fuses, and fuse holders that can be removed without the use of a tool should *not* be removed before determining which parts inside the product are to be considered nonhazardous accessible parts.

Fuse holders, where the fuse link is held in a cap that can be removed without the use of a tool, are a special concern. If the fuse link does not come out when the cap is removed, operators could be inclined to try to remove it by gripping the end of the fuse link with their fingers. In another situation, the operator could try to insert a new fuse link into the fuse holder without first inserting it in the cap. Both cases can be considered reasonably foreseeable misuse. This should be taken into consideration when assessing what parts are accessible.

For products where operators are allowed to perform restricted maintenance, they (the operators) become service personnel.

The term *service personnel* describes an individual, a firm, a corporation, or a company that, either in-person or through a representative, is involved with and responsible for installing, assembling, adjusting, maintaining, or repairing a product.

Qualified service personnel must be experienced in such work, be familiar with all necessary precautions, and have complied with all requirements of state or local authorities having jurisdiction.

The minimum qualifications for service personnel may be designated by manufacturers in their technical description.

However, service personnel, who are often engineers or engineering technicians, are expected to have certain competencies and be able to understand the technical description.

Therefore, in certain circumstances the safety of service personnel depends partly on their knowledge and training to take appropriate precautions when gaining access to hazardous parts of the product.

Service personnel are confronted with the same residual risk as those who use products for their intended use. They must know how to isolate the product from the supply mains and to be able to determine when the product is energized.

In particular, the following activities are done by the service personnel:

- Installation of electrical wiring from a main control box or from the service outlet of a product;

- Grounding of a class I permanently installed product, in accordance with local codes or regulations;

- Changing of components (i.e., lithium batteries, heating elements or lamp holders designed for use with heating lamps, and nondetachable power supply cords) specified by manufacturers in the accompanying documents to be changed with the use of a tool;

- Replacement of protective devices, and interchangeable or detachable parts as specified by the manufacturer;

- Preventive inspection and maintenance at the periods specified by the manufacturer;

- Reparation of those parts of the product that are designated by the manufacturer as repairable by service personnel.

13.3 Human Factors

A variety of operators' inherent capabilities can be compromised, affecting task performance and illustrating why *human error* occurs using modern technology—error that is "human" because the demands exceed human capabilities. For example, the ambient condition of light can compromise the visual acuity of the operator; the increased workload resulting from reduced staffing causes fatigue and stress; and size of the footprint of sophisticated equipment restricts workspace. The cost constraints of the organization cause changes in suppliers that provide different types of equipment, which can generate confusion.

A reasonable approach to reducing human errors is the implementation of the *human factors engineering* (HFE) principles [1].

HFE is the discipline that takes into account human strengths and limitations in the design of interactive systems that involve people, tools, technology, and work environments to ensure safety, effectiveness, and ease of use. The most important criteria are represented by an understanding of variability in humans and human performance.

Human factors engineers evaluate new systems and equipment under real-world conditions as much as possible, in order to identify potential problems and unintended consequences of new technology. Then, they examine a particular activity in terms of its component tasks and assess the physical demands, skill demands, mental workload, team dynamics, conditions of the work environment (e.g., adequate lighting, limited noise, or other distractions), and device design required to complete the task optimally. In essence, HFE focuses on how systems work in actual practice, with real—and fallible—human beings at the controls and attempts to design systems that optimize safety and minimize the risk of error in complex environments.

An axiom of HFE refers to necessity to have equipment and processes standardized whenever possible, in order to increase reliability, improve information flow, and minimize cross-training needs. Table 13.1 summarizes the key features of the principal HFE techniques [1, 2].

Table 13.1
Key Features of Principal HFE Techniques

HFE Techniques	Features	Suited for
Observation (sometimes called "ethnography")	Observing people working and using products	Gaining an understanding of what people really do in practice
Semistructured interviews	Interviewing people about their work, their experiences of technology, and their requirements for future technology	Gathering people's perceptions and experiences
Focus groups	A group interview, most commonly between people with similar backgrounds, about the work or product(s) of interest	Gathering perceptions and experiences, often with greater breadth but less depth than interviews
Contextual inquiry	Combining observations and interviews to understand work and the use of product	Gaining insights for design based on information flow, how current artifacts are used within work
Working with existing sources	Using existing sources (e.g., incident reports and academic literature) as data for understanding needs and practices	Building understanding based on existing information

Table 13.1 (continued)

HFE Techniques	Features	Suited for
Questionnaires/surveys	A set of questions to be answered, most commonly by selecting between options, with free-form entry also possible	For gathering perceptions and attitudes from a large number of people
FMEA	Analysis team brainstorms likely causes and consequences of failures, including human error	Reasoning about likely causes and consequences of product failure and human error
Task analysis	Systematically decomposing tasks (that the device supports) into subtasks to analyze the sequence and performance criteria for tasks	Supports systematic thinking about user tasks and how they are achieved with the product
Personas	Rich descriptions of a few typical users of the product	Helping the design team to keep the intended users in focus while developing the product
Scenarios	Rich descriptions of key and typical scenarios of use of the product (from a user perspective)	Helping the design team to think about how the product will be used in practice
Think-aloud	Users articulating thoughts while interacting with/using a product (as part of user testing)	Understanding how people perceive and experience a product and how they use it to support their work
Heuristic evaluation	A checklist approach to checking the product interface for usability and safety based on rules of thumb	Checking for obvious problems at early stages of development
Cognitive walkthrough	An expert review approach that involves walking through the steps of an interaction between user and product, reasoning about possible user errors	Early review, focusing on user cognition
User testing	Testing the product with representative users in a simulated-use environment	Identifying which product features people find easy to use and which cause problems

To limit human errors it is essential to identify workarounds represented by the bypassing of policies or safety procedures by frontline workers. Workarounds frequently arise because of flawed or poorly designed systems that actually increase the time necessary for workers to complete a task. As a result, frontline personnel work around the system in order to get work done efficiently.

Another way to mitigate human errors is represented by forcing functions, a design aspect that prevents an unintended or undesirable action from being performed or allows its performance only if another specific action is performed first.

The attitude of accommodating problems in using a product by jerry-rigging or developing workarounds must be replaced with the mission to document such problems so they can be avoided in future. Without documentation, identification of problems may be considered idle complaints; clear documentation can become a mandate for change—change that reduces the likelihood of human error in modern technology with the ultimate goal of technology that is compatible with the human characteristics of the user.

It is generally agreed that human factors principles are underutilized in examination of safety problems and in designing potential solutions. The ever-lengthening list of unintended consequences of a particular piece of equipment or system can, in part, be viewed as a failure to appropriately design such equipment or systems without considering the human factors.

13.4   Ergonomic Hazards

The term *ergonomics* can simply be defined as the study of work. It is the science of fitting jobs to the people who work in them. Adapting the job to fit the worker can help reduce ergonomic stress and eliminate many potential ergonomic disorders.

Ergonomics (or human factors as it is referred to in North America) is a branch of science that aims to learn about human abilities and limitations, and then apply this learning to improve people's interaction with products, systems, and environments. Ergonomics, the process of designing or arranging workplaces, products, and systems so that they fit the people who use them, takes into account features of the intended user population, such as age, size, strength, cognitive ability, and training.

The ISO Technical Committee 159 develops standards referring to ergonomics in the following four areas: general ergonomics principles, anthropometry and biomechanics, ergonomics of human-system interaction, and ergonomics of the physical environment.

The aims of ergonomics are [3] described as follows:

- To create safe, comfortable, and productive workspaces by bringing human abilities and limitations into the design of a workspace, including the individual's body size, strength, skill, speed, sensory abilities (vision and hearing), and even attitudes;

- To improve workspaces and environments to minimize risk of injury or harm. So as technologies change, so too does the need to ensure that the products we access for work, rest, and play are designed for the human body's requirements.

- To achieve best practice design, ergonomists use the data and techniques of several disciplines:

- Anthropometry: Body sizes and shapes and populations and variations

- *Biomechanics:* Muscles, levers, forces, and strength;

- *Environmental physics:* Noise, light, heat, cold, radiation, vibration body systems (hearing, vision, and sensations);

- *Applied psychology:* Skill, learning, errors, and differences;

- *Social psychology:* Groups, communication, learning, and behaviors.

Ergonomic hazards refer to workplace conditions that pose the risk of injury to the musculoskeletal system of the worker. Ergonomic hazards include repetitive and forceful movements, vibration, temperature extremes, and awkward postures that arise from improper work methods and improperly designed workstations, tools, and equipment [4].

Ergonomics focuses on the work environment and items such as the design and function of workstations, controls, displays, safety devices, tools, and lighting to fit the employee's physical requirements, capabilities, and limitations.

Ergonomic injuries occur at workstations due to reaching, bending, awkward postures, and applying pressure or force. If workstations are designed properly, most ergonomic hazards can be reduced if not eliminated. In some situations, the interaction between workers, the equipment, and their environment can actually increase the risk of disastrous errors.

Workstations that include display monitors should be ergonomically designed for both computer and noncomputer work. Display monitors at workstations should be adjustable so that users can easily change their working postures, and they should be equipped with the following:

- Adjustable and detachable keyboards;
- Display screens that tilt up and down;
- Brightness and contrast controls;
- Flexible copyholders that reduce the distance between the screen and source material;

When a product has armrests, they should be large enough to support most of the lower arms but small enough so they do not interfere with equipment positioning. Armrests should support operators' lower arms and allow operators' upper arms to remain close to the torso; further, they should be made of soft material and have rounded edges.

References

[1]   ANSI/AAMI HE 74, "Human Factors Design Process for Medical Devices," 2001.

[2]   MIL-HDBK-759C, "Human Engineering Design Guidelines," Washington, D.C.: U.S. Department of Defense (DOD), 1998.

[3]   ISO 18529, "Ergonomics—Ergonomics of Human-System Interaction – Human-Centred Lifecycle Process Descriptions," Geneva, 2000.

[4]   Ramsey, J., "Ergonomic Factors in Task Analysis for Consumer Product Safety," *Journal of Occupational Accidents 7,* 1985, pp.113–123.

Selected Bibliography

Bogner, M. S., "Human Error in Health Care Technology," *Biomed. Instrum Technol.,* 2003.

Fadier, E., and J. Ciccotelli, "How To Integrate Safety in Design: Methods and Models," *Journal of Human Factors and Ergonomics in Manufacturing 9,* 1999, pp.367–380.

Greatorex, G. L., and B. C. Buck, "Human Factors and Systems Design," *GEC Review,* 1995, 10 (3), pp. 176–185.

Nielsen, J., *Usability Engineering,* San Diego, CA: Academic Press, Inc., 1993.

Reason, J., *Human Error,* Cambridge, England: Cambridge University Press, 1990.

Sagot, J.-C., V. Gouin, and S. Gomes, "Ergonomics in Product Design: Safety Factor," *Safety Science 41,* 2003, pp.137–154.

Sanders, M. S., and E. J. McCormick, *Human Factors in Engineering and Design* Seventh ed.), New York: McGraw-Hill, 1993.

Vicente, K., *The Human Factor: Revolutionizing the Way People Live with Technology,* Toronto: Knopf Canada, 2003.

Wickens, C. D., *Engineering Psychology and Human Performance,* New York: Harper Collins, 1992.

14

Testing for Compliance and Safety

14.1 Introduction

This chapter is intended to familiarize the products safety practitioner with the tests that need to be conducted to support the compliance of electrical and electronic equipment in accordance with standards requirements. These refer to product basic safety, EMC, and software testing. The chapter describes types of tests, work safety during testing, and the kinds of equipment used in testing and briefly discusses primary basic safety, EMC and software testing issues.

Test laboratories often see products in the development stages before their official release to production and the market. Their advice can be invaluable in assisting manufacturers to consistently achieve compliance and improve the safety of products.

The following checklist outlines issues to consider when a product needs to be submitted for tests:

- Is the test laboratory you wish to use accredited in quality assurance and management systems, and does it have the capability to conduct specific tests for the products you provide according with standard ISO/IEC 17025?

- Do you know and understand the safety testing standards (e.g., basic safety, EMC, and environment) that apply to your particular products?

- Have you established a regular quality policy to ensure that future product batches continue to meet the relevant requirements?

- Do you have a means of monitoring changes in standards and regulatory requirements?

14.2   Kinds of Product Basic Safety and EMC Tests

Product safety and EMC testing at the design and development states as well as at the production stage is important to ensure that all products are safe before reaching the end user. The product safety and EMC tests need to be conducted to evaluate the right selection of the components and the correct construction in accordance with the requirements of the standards. Compliance with a specific test provides the presumption of the acceptability of the residual risk due to a specific hazard covered by the specific test.

To help ensure safety, it is important to test products at various stages of development and distribution. The stages when testing is essential are listed as follows:

- Initial design—type tests, conducted on models of new or modified products that are intended to be manufactured.

- Production—tests conducted on 100% of products to ensure the correctness of manufacturing;.

- Ongoing testing—test samples of products to ensure stock complies; conduct these tests in accordance with the types of products you supply and the quality assurance regime established.

- Following design, material, or production changes—major product safety legal cases have occurred because manufacturers failed to retest products after making a design, material or production change.

- To define the types of tests to perform on a given product, three items must be considered:

- Tests required for approval and certification (includes type tests and production line tests);

- Optional tests needed by the manufacturer to ensure quality of the product and the manufacturing process;

- Cost/benefit analysis of each optional test.

Usually the "type tests" are required for verifying basic safety of the product design and "production line tests" (routine production tests) for ensuring that the approved product continues to meet the safety standards as long as it is manufactured. (For details see Section 15.5 [1].) Since the type tests are intended to verify safety of the design of a product, they are usually much more stringent than routine production tests performed on every unit as it emerges from the assembly line.

In addition to type tests, a manufacturer of equipment can establish the testing intervals and the extent of testing for periodic inspection. In establishing the testing intervals, the following considerations should be taken into account:

- The risk level of the equipment;
- The frequency of its use;
- The operating environment;
- The frequency of occurrence of equipment failures.

The testing intervals for periodic inspection can be set in the range of six to 36 months.

In the event of the necessity for repairs or modifications after a failure or the likelihood of a failure during the sequence of tests, the testing laboratory and the manufacturer can agree either upon the use of a new sample on which all relevant tests are to be carried out again or, preferably, upon making all the necessary repairs or modifications after which only relevant tests are repeated.

14.2.1 Type Tests

For type tests, a product is subjected to tests and evaluations in accordance with dedicated specifications or a specific product safety standard. (For details about Standards see Chapter 3.) Table 14.1 summarizes the main IEC product safety standards applicable for different categories of products.

Table 14.1
Main IEC Product Safety Standards Applicable for Different Categories of Products

Product Category	IEC Standard	
	Basic Safety	EMC
Information and communication technology	60950;62368	CISPR 22; CISPR 32; CISPR 24
Laser	60825	N/A
Batteries	60086;62133;62620	N/A
Medical electrical	60601;80601	60601-1-2
Measurement	61010	61326
Control	61010;60730	61326
Laboratory	61010	61326
Household	60335;62301	CISPR 14; 61543
Industrial machinery	60204	ISO 13766; ISO 14982; EN 13309
Audio	60065;62368	CISPR 13; CISPR 20; CISPR 32
Video	60065;62368	CISPR 13; CISPR 20; CISPR 32
Lamp control	62347;60598; 61347	CISPR 15; 61547; 62493
Power supplies—low power	61204	61204-3
Tools (portable)	60745;61029; 62841	CISPR 14
Toys (electrical)	62155	CISPR 14
Luminaries	60598	CISPR 15; 61547; 62493
Cathode ray tubes	61965	N/A
LED (lamps)	62560	CISPR 15; 61547; 62493
UPSs	62040	62040-2
Electricity metering	62052;62053; 62054	62052; 62053
Railway	62278; 62279; 62425	62236
Programmable controllers	61131	61326; EN 61131-2
Electromagnetic interference suppressor	60938;60939	N/A
Circuit-breakers	60934	N/A
Fuses	60127;60269; 60282	N/A
Transformer	61558;61869; 60076	62041

Table 14.1 (continued)

Product Category	IEC Standard	
	Basic Safety	**EMC**
Low-voltage switchgear and control gear	60947	N/A
Surge protection	60099;61643	N/A
Rotating electrical machines	60034	N/A
Plugs, socket-outlets, vehicle connectors, and vehicle inlets	62196	N/A
Cables	60227;60245; 62821	62153
Capacitors	60252;60384; 60143;61049; 61071	N/A
Relay	61812	N/A

The above standards can be individual or series.

Table 14.2 summarizes the main IEC EMC standards applicable for different categories of measurements and tests.

Table 14.2

Main IEC EMC Standards Applicable for Different Categories of Measurements and Tests

EMC Category	IEC Standard
Emissions (radiated and conducted)	CISPR 11 ; CISPR 14-1 ; CISPR 15 ; CISPR 22 ; CISPR 32
Harmonic distortion (equipment input current ≤ 16A)	61000-3-2
Voltage fluctuations and flicker (equipment input current ≤ 16A)	61000-3-3
Voltage fluctuations and flicker (equipment input current ≤ 75A)	61000-3-11
Harmonic distortion (equipment input current ≤ 75A)	61000-3-12
Immunity test to electrostatic discharges	61000-4-2
Immunity test to radiated RF electromagnetic field	61000-4-3
Immunity tests to electrical fast transients and bursts	61000-4-4
Immunity test to surges	61000-4-5
Immunity to conducted disturbances, induced by radio-frequency fields	61000-4-6
General guide on harmonics and interharmonics measurements and instrumentation for power supply systems and equipment connected thereto	61000-4-7
Immunity test to power-frequency magnetic fields	61000-4-8
Pulse magnetic field immunity test	61000-4-9

Table 14.2 (continued)

EMC Category	IEC Standard
Damped oscillatory magnetic field immunity test	61000-4-10
Immunity test to voltage dips, short interruptions, and voltage variations on power supply input lines	61000-4-11
Ring wave immunity test	61000-4-12
Harmonics and interharmonics including mains signalling at AC power port, low-frequency immunity tests	61000-4-13
Voltage fluctuation immunity test for equipment with input current not exceeding 16A per phase	61000-4-14
Test for immunity to conducted, common mode disturbances in the frequency range 0 Hz–150 kHz	61000-4-16
Damped oscillatory wave immunity test	61000-4-18

14.3   Information Typically Required for Product Basic Safety and EMC Testing

Before starting to perform basic safety or EMC testing it is useful that the following information be prepared by the manufacturer and provided to the test house.

Basic Documentation

- User manual, sales brochures, drawing of markings (sample of final markings and labeling);
- Risk analysis, when applicable (i.e., medical electrical equipment, machinery, and household equipment);
- Usability information (if applicable);
- Software validation and software life-cycle information (if applicable).
- Description of Unit Under Test (UUT)
- Brief description of function and intended use of the equipment that will be tested, including the name and model number;
- Description of differences between models;
- Status of UUT (e.g., prototype, production, and postmarketing);
- Number of modes;
- Dimensions (W x D x H) and weight.

Example: "The UUT is a product family of general-purpose PCs mains supplied. Depending on the model, the UUT differs in the CPU, memory module, and HDD as shown in the table below. The tests will be performed on the two typical models. The UUT are in prototype status."

Model Name	CPU	Memory	HDD	Weight	Dimensions (W)x(D)x(H) mm
X1	1 GHz	2 GB	500 GB	10 kg	125 x 240 x 320
X2	2 GHz	4 GB	1 TB	11Kg	125 x 240 x 320

Power Requirements

- What are the power requirements (e.g., line voltage, current, frequency, and number of power cords) for the UUT and auxiliary equipment?
- What types of power connection is used?

Example: "Rating of the UUT:

Model X1 100-240 Vac, 2.5 A, 50/60 Hz
Model X2 100-240 Vac, 4 A, 50/60 Hz
Power supply cord detachable"

Grounding

- List any special grounding requirements.

Modes of Operation; Configurations

- How to operate the equipment in its maximum loading condition within the specified duty cycle (if applicable)?
- Which is the worst-case operating mode?
- How many line voltages are required to be tested?
- How many UUT configurations will be tested?
- How many I/O ports are present and how will they be used?

Failure Modes

- Define what constitutes a failure for performance, and describe how errors are identified and monitored.

Use Environment

- Where (in what environments) will the UUT be installed and used?

Example: "The UUT will be used indoors only."

Construction Details

- Structure and mechanical assembly of UUT including cables to/from UUT (of the recommended type and maximum length for the use), and peripherals;

Number	Description of Cable	Length (m)	Shielding Present?	Ferrite Core present?	Observation
1	LAN	10	No	Yes	-
2	AC mains	1.5	Yes	Yes	-
3	Keyboard USB	1.5	No	No	-
4	HDMI	1.0	Yes	No	Optional

- Block (connection) diagram (including the safety conception: insulation diagram), as in Figure 14.1.

The schematics need to be a complete set of electrical schematics and wiring diagrams, including the system flow (wiring) diagram, showing mains components and all-over current-protection devices.

The insulation diagram (for details see Section 7.2) needs to show the equipment and all points of isolation as in following example (Figure 14.2):

- Accessories;

- PCB layouts, shown in Figure 14.3

This needs to represent 1:1 color-coded PCB artwork or color-coded artwork and a PCB, identifying the following voltages:

- SELV voltages (< 60 VDC and < 25 VAC);

- Hazardous voltages (> SELV voltages);

- High voltages (> 1,000 VAC or VDC or 1,500-V peak value);

- Ground (signal);

- Ground (protective ground);

- If applicable, manufacturers may need to supply the testing house with any auxiliary equipment that is needed for testing, including any special

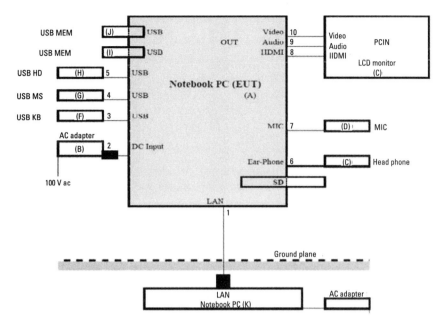

Figure 14.1   Example of a block diagram.

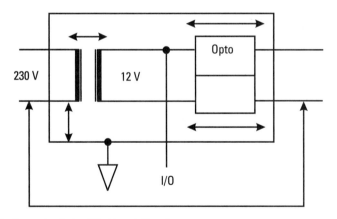

Figure 14.2   Example of simplified insulation diagram.

tools required to open up the product and as well as spare fuses or other needed replaceable parts.

Example: "The connection diagram should present the modular construction of the UUT and connections with peripheral devices. On this diagram are included the supply paths."

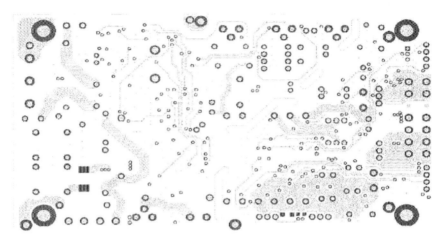

Figure 14.3 Example of a PCB artwork.

List of Safety-Critical Components and Relevant Approvals

- A list of all safety-critical components (For details see Chapters 8 and 10). This list will need to include the name of the safety-related (critical) component, type or model, manufacturer name, ratings, applicable standard, and the name of testing house(s) that has approved the component, including the relevant objective evidence of approval (i.e., certificate number). For all these components, copies of relevant approvals and licenses from established test houses and certification bodies are very useful (just copies of data sheets are not reliable). Table 14.3 provides a list of safety-critical components generally used in electrical equipment.

Special attention should be given to any condition of acceptability and applicable limitation of component approval (considering tests which were not conducted on the component approval, but need to be conducted on the end product containing the subject component). The conditions of acceptability should be included for power supplies, transformer, motors, and so forth.

Example: Condition of acceptability included in a power supply test report:

"When installed in an end-product, consideration must be given to the following:

The end-product Electric Strength Test is to be based upon a maximum working voltage of: *Primary: 304 Vrms, 429 Vpp*

The following secondary output circuits are SELV: *All outputs;*

Table 14.3
Example of Safety-Critical Components

Mains cords and cord sets
Mains inlets
Mains outlets
Mains switches
Fuses and fuse holders (mains circuit)
Capacitors and resistors across the mains poles or contacts of mains switches
Capacitors and resistors between "live" and "accessible parts"
PTCs
Optocouplers (if bridging reinforced or double insulation)
Mains filters
Protective devices such as fuses, solid-state fuses, and thermal cutouts
Wiring materials (double insulation)
Mains plugs
Contactors
Batteries
DC-DC converter
Protection circuit for a lithium battery
Isolation amplifier
Safety devices for mechanical systems
Emergency switch
Separating mains transformers
Connectors in mains circuits
High-voltage parts such as line-output transformers, deflection coils, picture tube sockets, and high-voltage cables
Voltage-setting devices
Lasers
Materials and dimensions of enclosures
Printed board materials (dependent on power)
Picture tubes
Barriers (extra flammability requirements)
Interlock switches
Mains relays
Capacitors (high-voltage)

Table 14.3 (continued)

Isolation foil and sleeves
Push-on connectors
Lamps
Power supplies
Motors
Pressurized systems, including safety valves
Foot switch
Strain relief (cord anchorage)
Storage devices (USB, CD-ROM, HDD, FDD)
Keyboard
Mouse
Motherboard
Modem
Bluetooth module
Sensing devices and transducers

The following secondary output circuits are at hazardous energy levels: *Main output V₁;*

The following secondary output circuits are at nonhazardous energy levels: *Auxiliary;*

The power supply terminals and/or connectors are: *Suitable for factory wiring only;*

The maximum investigated branch circuit rating is: *20A;*

The investigated pollution degree is: *2;*

Proper bonding to the end product's main protective grounding termination is: *Required;*

An investigation of the protective bonding terminals has: *Not been conducted;*

The following end-product enclosures are required: *Fire and Electrical;*

The maximum continuous power supply output (watts) relied on: *13 CFM of forced air cooling while mounted in a 37" long wind tunnel with a 4.25" (108mm) x 1.75"(44.5mm) air inlet."*

When the subject power supply is included in the UUT, all the above conditions need to be considered by a testing house.

For the components recognized by UL, this testing house provides *conditions of acceptability* (COA) service, which allows manufacturers to request conditions of acceptability for recognized components.

Software

- Validation information (including software version, software specification requirements, software development requirements, and software test plan with results of the tests).

If the product is controlled, monitored, or programmed from remote software, a laptop or PC with the software preinstalled should be provided.

Auxiliary Equipment

- List any equipment required to operate or serve as loads for the UUT (if applicable).

Transformers and Chokes

- Installation schematic with rated voltage, current, resistance, colors/numbers of leads, wire diameters, and integrated fuses.
- Constructional drawing (cross-section) with all parts numbered (e.g., core, core insulation, and spacer).
- Part list with description of: material, manufacturer, type/model, flame class, and approvals.
- Test samples: potted and unpotted.

14.4 Work Safety in a Product Basic Safety and EMC Testing Laboratory

14.4.1 Safe Working with Test Instruments

Guidelines for working with test instruments are outlined as follows [2, 3]:

- Read all safety and operating instructions before operating the instruments.
- Retain all safety and operating instructions for future reference.
- Adhere to all warnings on the instruments and in the operating instructions.
- Follow all operating and use instructions.
- Do not use the instruments near water and/or heat sources.

- Use the instruments only with a cart or stand that is recommended by the manufacturer or included as a part of the testing system by the manufacturer.

- Mount the instruments on a wall or ceiling only if is recommended by the manufacturer

- The instruments should be situated so that their location or position does not interfere with proper ventilation. Do not install in a cabinet or other situation that may impede the flow of air through the ventilation openings.

- Connect the instruments only to the type of power source described in the operating instructions or as marked on the instruments.

- Take precautions to ensure that the grounding means of the instruments is not defeated.

- Position power supply cords so that they are not likely to be walked on or pinched by items placed upon or against them. Pay attention to cords at plugs, convenience receptacles, and the point where they enter and exit the instruments.

- Clean the instruments only as recommended by the manufacturer.

- Unplug the power cord of the instruments from the outlet when it will be left unused for a long time.

- Take care that objects do not fall and liquids are not spilled into the enclosure through openings.

- Do not operate instruments that have been dropped or whose enclosure has been damaged.

- Whenever it is likely that the normal operation of the equipment has been impaired, remove and segregate it to prevent future operation; consider tagging or marking the instrument as *damaged* or the equivalent (e.g., *not in service*).

- Have it properly repaired and recalibrated or replaced as appropriate.

- Normal operation is likely to be impaired if, for example, the instruments can be described as follows:
  - They fail to perform the intended functions;
  - Have visible damage;
  - They have been subjected to prolonged storage under unfavorable conditions;
  - They have been subjected to severe transport stress.

- The instruments should be serviced only by qualified service personnel.

- All leads and cables that can be energized at dangerous voltages should be robustly insulated and properly terminated.

- All connections of conductors that can be energized at dangerous voltage should be electrically and mechanically robust to prevent conductors from becoming accidentally exposed.

- Test equipment connecting leads, probes, and connectors should be sufficiently protected to prevent accidental contact when being applied to and removed from live parts.

- Where practicable, apply test leads while the equipment is isolated and then energize it.

- Provided adequate means to prevent the supply being switched on (inadvertently, mistakenly, or by an unauthorized person).

- Where applicable, test equipment should be approved to IEC 61010.

- The EMC measuring equipment should be as specified in CISPR 16 series and ANSI C63 series.

- If higher current levels are necessary, use test probes fitted with control switches, or use interlocked enclosures to prevent access to the dangerous parts.

- The connecting leads of test equipment must provide adequate protection from electric shock.

- The tips of the high voltage probes should be covered by retractable insulated sleeving.

- The test voltage may be applied by a switch built into the probe's insulated handles.

- It may be necessary to discharge safely any stored energy that may remain in the equipment after the test has been carried out before allowing any further contact with the equipment.

- Each item of equipment under testing should be provided with its own test supply. These supplies should be from designated sockets or terminals provided with covers interlocked with the supply isolator. The supplies should have suitable system protection against overload and overcurrent in the event of faults (e.g., fuses or circuit breaker).

- A separate isolating transformer should be used at every test bench.

- The supply from the isolating transformer should be provided from a single socket outlet and clearly marked "only for use for making live equipment under test." The ground terminal of the socket outlet should be connected to a floating secondary of the isolating transformer (ungrounded) such that an artificial ground (common) connection is made. The faceplate of the socket should be made of insulating material.

- If isolation transformers are used to supply power to fixed-socket outlets as part of a distribution system for test supplies, the sockets should be of a different type to standard sockets, or of the polarized type, to ensure they are only used for the purpose intended.

- Connect oscilloscope(s), digital multimeter(s), and equivalent test equipment that are ground grounded, through isolation transformers with floating (ungrounded) ground (common). Connecting test equipment in this manner removes any protection against internal breakdown to the chassis.

- Don't try to fix electrical equipment if you don't thoroughly understand how it was supposed to work before it malfunctioned and if you don't know what voltage levels should and might be present.

- Never try to fix anything electrical when you are alone, even if you are familiar with what you are doing.

- Don't stretch electrical cords across aisles or doorways even in an "emergency."

- Don't use extension cords as substitutes for wiring additions or changes.

- Think—before you act. Never work alone when conducting tests where lethal voltages are present.

- Don't try to go it alone. If you are unsure that something is correct or safe and you do not feel you can resolve it yourself—*get help.*

14.4.2 Safe Working When Performing Product Basic Safety and EMC Tests

Guidelines for performing safety and EMC tests are outlined as follows [2, 3]:

- Do not make any connections to a UUT unless you have verified that high voltage is off.

- Never touch a UUT or its connections during a test.

- When connecting leads to the UUT, always connect the ground clip first.

- Never touch the metal of a high-voltage probe directly. Only touch the insulated parts.

- Use interlocked test fixtures only for all hazardous tests.

- Verify all UUT connections before starting a test. Make sure that no other objects are near the UUT or the tester.

- The integrity of the protective ground conductor of class I UUTs must be evaluated before all testing to ensure that no ground faults are present before the equipment is used on normal supply mains.

- Keep the area neat and uncluttered and avoid crossing test leads.

- Follow the prescribed procedure for each test exactly as written.

- Verify all setup conditions before starting a test and examine all leads for signs of wear.

- When performing a DC test, provide means to discharge any connection or device that may become disconnected during a test. This is necessary because unexpected, dangerous charges can build up during a test if a connection comes loose.

- If the test was DC, after tests discharge the UUT for the prescribed time.

- Protective gloves and face shields should be used when handling samples that present a chemical hazard (i.e., polychlorinated biphenyl-PCB- in transformers and capacitors, beryllium oxide and selenium in semiconductors, and free bromine)

- Do not use asbestos or parts containing asbestos.

- Use proper protective wear, such as breathing apparatuses, face guards, eyewear, gloves, and protective clothing where appropriate.

- Ensure that *no one* touches the UUT immediately after the test until mains power to the UUT has been turned off.

- Check the conductivity of painted surfaces before use—for example, in black painted test corners, where there is the likelihood of live wires or thermocouples coming into contact with paint.

- Do not use carbon-tetrachloride for removing grease (it is toxic). Use a less harmful liquid (i.e., trichlorethane).

- The smell of ozone is a warning that precautions should be taken. Avoid staying in rooms where ozone is present for long periods. Testing of equipment producing ozone should be carried out in large and well-ventilated rooms.

- When cutting cables with glass fibers, use personal protective gear (breathing apparatuses, face guards, eye wear, gloves, and protective clothing). For that matter, personal protective gear should be worn when doing any work such as cutting, sawing, drilling, and machining.

- When conducting tests during simulated fault conditions (short circuits, open circuits) of components or insulation, protective wear and appropriate guards are necessary.

- Use protective shields if tests under simulated fault conditions can cause component explosion or cracking

- When introducing faults inside the equipment, use an isolating transformer that is toroidally wound to reduce additional mains impedance or other problems. The transformer must be somewhat "over-dimensioned" as a rule.

- Do not try to charge any primary (not rechargeable) cell or batteries.

- Do not crush, puncture, open, dismantle, or otherwise mechanically interfere with or abuse cells or batteries.

- Do not store cells or batteries at temperatures above + 60 °C.

- Do not short-circuit cells or batteries unless under controlled test conditions and in an explosion-proof environment.

- Protect cell or battery terminations whenever they are not connected to a circuit.

- Unless cells or batteries are suitably insulated, they should not experience the following conditions:
    - Placement in pockets with keys, coins, or other metal objects;
    - Placement in metal storage such as drawers or filing cabinets;
    - Mixing with other batteries; or
    - Exposure to any other situation that may lead to a short circuit.

- Do not flow solder without the cell or battery manufacturer's permission.

- Do not connect cells to form a battery except where the arrangement has been approved by the cell manufacturer.

- Do not dispose of cells or batteries by burning;

- Do not encapsulate cells or batteries without approval of the cell or battery manufacturer.

- Do not replace ordinary primary or rechargeable cells or batteries with similar lithium cells or batteries of a different voltage.

- Do not install lithium cells or batteries next to a source of heat.

- Remove the battery if testing without the battery is possible.

- Do not remove the battery when the UUT is connected to the supply mains or when the supply mains have recently been disconnected.

- Wear a face shield or eye wear and a protective guard.

- Avoid the possibility of incorrect connections.

- If a battery remains in the UUT during normal testing, do not work with the battery with your face unprotected!

- When conducting abnormal condition tests, where there is a hazard of the battery overheating, outgassing, leaking, or exploding, due to overcharging, fast charging, fast discharging, or reverse charging or discharging, perform the test in a room void of staff and fitted with proper guards.

- If there is a fire, use a graphite-based, dry powder extinguisher or a suitable extinguisher designed for alkali metal fire, or drench with a fine spray of water. Avoid inhalation of fumes. Stay out of the contaminated area.

14.4.3 Guidelines Regarding Test Personnel and Testing Areas

Guidelines regarding test personnel and test areas are outlined in the following [4, 5]:

All test personnel must:

- Understand that the hazard of electric shock injury will still remain during the testing process, even with the use of ground-free test areas and/ or isolating transformers;

- Understand the scenarios in which these electric shock injury hazards can arise in the particular workplace(s);

- Be given adequate first-aid training, including cardiac pulmonary resuscitation (CPR) skills;

- Be trained on the safety procedures to be used in emergency situations;

- Be given training in the basic theory of electrical circuits—voltage, current, resistance, AC versus DC, Ohm's Law, and impedance;

- Fully understand the importance of safety interlocks;

- Fully understand the hazards of wearing metallic jewelry around electrical equipment and show how to interrupt power quickly in emergency situations;

- Hold regular meetings to review and update safety procedures and regulations;

- Be trained in the specific test procedures, using actual test setups wherever possible;

- Fully understand the object of each test, how it should be executed, and how to handle every normal and off-normal situation that may occur;
- Understand how much he or she can handle alone and when supervisory personnel should be called in for help.

The testing areas must:

- Be under the control of a responsible person;
- Be in an area set apart by barriers to prevent entry;
- Have suitable warnings provided at the entrance;
- Be accessible during testing only to authorized staff or people working under their direct supervision;
- Have suitable warning lights indicating that testing is in progress and other warning lights to indicate when it is safe to enter the area (duplicate red and green lights are often used);
- Have emergency-stop push buttons or equally effective means to cut all test supplies in the event of emergency;
- Have emergency controls prominently identified (the emergency controls should not remove supplies to the general lighting in the area);
- Display an electric shock poster with first-aid procedures at prominent locations, showing emergency arrangements, especially telephone numbers;
- Have good housekeeping arrangements, including adequate clear working space;
- Use a test bench made of insulating material with shrouded legs and framework to prevent the possibility of contact with ground while testing;
- Have removed all metallic parts (e.g., pipes, radiators, structural steelwork, metal conduits, grounded electrical appliances, and metallic socket outlets) from within reach of the test bench, or permanently shroud them with insulating material to prevent contact;
- Use soldering irons and task lighting to extra low voltage, supplied by an isolating transformer;
- Have insulating rubber matting provided on the floor, kept clean and dry and regularly tested and large enough for the test operator to remain on it whether standing or seated during testing (note that chair legs may damage the matting);

- When appropriate, use electrostatic discharge wrist straps incorporated with a suitable resistance (1 M Ω or more); the use of a wrist strap that directly connects the wearer to ground is not permissible;

- Have guards or enclosures around a UUT made of nonconductive material and equipped with safety interlocks that interrupt all high voltages when open;

- Have arranged the interlocks so that test operators are never exposed to high voltages under any conditions;

- Have arranged the power line connections so that, except for emergency lighting, all power is interrupted by a single, well-marked, palm operated emergency switch located at the outside edge of the test area;

- Be kept clean and neat, with equipment arranged so that it is easy and safe for the operator to use.

14.4.4 Contents of a Documented Safe Environment for Working in a Testing Laboratory

The contents of a documented safe environment for working in a testing laboratory should minimally include the following [5]:

- Designation of those authorized to undertake testing and those *not authorized* to access the test area and where appropriate, the proper method to access and utilize a test area.

- Rules for isolating equipment and how the isolation is secured.

- The correct use of additional protection measures (e.g., flexible insulation) that have to be applied to the equipment under test while its covers are removed.

- Designation of the form of power supply that should be used to energize the equipment under test, particularly where use of the wrong method would compromise safety.

- Expectations of test personnel regarding the inspection of test equipment before use and how defects are to be reported.

- The correct use of any warning devices that form part of the safety system at designated test areas.

- Instructions about what action should be taken in an emergency situation.

14.5   Equipment Used on Product Basic Safety and EMC Testing

In general, the test equipment should comply with requirements of the IEC 61010 series of standards or other applicable standards and should not expose the person doing the testing or other individuals to unacceptable risks. The accuracy of the measuring functions used in the test should be specified in the test result sheet. The usual accuracy [6] of the test equipment measurement range is indicated in Table 14.4.

For the tests, protective ground connections can be interrupted in the measuring devices, if protection against electric shock is guaranteed by another means of IEC 61010-1.

In the measurement equipment, an electrical separation of the measurement circuits, including measuring device, from the supply main including its protective ground conductor should be guaranteed. Any connection to ground of the UUT can result in wrong measurement data. Therefore, the setup of the measurement equipment should ensure a galvanic separation from ground, or attention should be drawn to the necessity of isolated positioning of the UUT by an automatic warning or by a clearly visible marking.

It is recommended that manufacturers use dedicated test equipment (e.g., dielectric withstand tester and ground bonding and continuity tester). The test equipment should be capable of providing all voltages and currents needed for the range of tests to be performed (e.g. for dielectric testing: voltage and current; for ground bond: current and impedance).

The test equipment should be easily adaptable to different test requirements. Most modern testers provide this flexibility through programmability plus an ability to recall previously stored test setups on demand. The test equipment should be designed so that normal variations in line voltage and connected load do not cause the output voltage and current measured at the UUT to rise above or fall below the levels required for the test. This improves test repeatability and greatly reduces inconsistencies in measurements.

The test equipment should have a well-designed front panel with easily read digital displays of measurements, settings, and pass/fail indicators. Audible alarms are also desirable. An ability to hold an alarm condition after operator acknowledgment can be useful for later analysis of the fault. All panel items should be clearly marked so that the function of each is readily apparent to anyone looking at the test equipment for the first time.

The *start test* button, where applicable, should be large, well-marked, and protected in a way that prevents accidental activation of a test. The stop-test button, where applicable, should also be easily identified (preferably bright red) and placed so as to be quickly found in an emergency. Similarly, pushbuttons for setting, storing, or recalling test values, alarm limits, and test sequences should be clearly marked and easily operated by test personnel.

Table 14.4
Usual Accuracy of the Test Equipment

Measurement of:	Accuracy
Voltage up to 1,000V (DC up to 1 kHz)	±1.5 %
Voltage, 1,000V and above (DC up to 20 kHz)	±3 %;
Current up to 5A (DC up to 60 Hz	±1.5 %;
Current, 5A and above (DC up to 5 kHz)	±2.5 %;
Power above 1W and up to 3 kW	±3 %;
Power factor	±0.05 %;
Frequency	±0.2 %;
Resistance	±5 %;
Temperature (thermocouple not included) below 100 °C	±2 °C;
Temperature (thermocouple not included) 100 °C up to 500 °C	±3 %;
Time, 1s and above	±1 %;
Linear dimensions up to 1 mm	±0.05 mm;
Linear dimensions, 1 mm up to 25 mm	±0.1 mm;
Linear dimensions, 25 mm and above	±0.5 %;
Mass, 100 g up to 5 kg	±2 %;
Mass, 5 kg and above	±5 %;
Force	±6 %;
Torque	10 %;
Angles	±1 degree;
Relative humidity	±6 % RH;
Barometric air pressure	±0,01 MPa;
Gas and fluid pressure (for static measurement)	±5 %.

Modern test equipment is equipped with some type of standard data communication interface for connection to remote data processing, computer, or control equipment. The typical interfaces are an IEEE-488 general-purpose interface bus and an RS232 serial communication line.

14.5.1 Selection of Test Equipment

The test equipment should be selected so that the test operator cannot be accidentally subjected to hazardous voltages and currents such as those used for a dielectric strength test, a line voltage leakage test, or a protective grounding connection and continuity test. It is recommended that manufacturers use test equipment that includes safety interlocks that provide protection by automatically shutting down the output whenever a safety switch on the UUT is opened. Cables used for output and ground clips should be flexible, well-insulated, and able to be repeatedly plugged into and removed from the front panel over a long period of time without becoming frayed, worn, or ineffective.

14.5.2 Calibration

The measurement equipment used for the tests should be tested and calibrated at regular intervals [7] according to the information given by its manufacturer. Calibration should be performed by a calibration laboratory with a quality management system in accordance with ISO/IEC 17025. The reference standards (e.g., voltage, current, and impedance) used for calibrating test equipment should be certified and traceable to national or international standards. This ensures sustained integrity of calibration accuracy and compliance with IEC/ISO 17025.

14.5.2.1 Traceability of Calibrations

Calibrations should be regarded as being traceable if the calibrations are done by following the requirements of ISO/IEC 17025—General requirements for the competence of testing and calibration laboratories [8]. In addition, the following are true [8]:

- The instrument may be calibrated by a national metrology institute.
- An external calibration laboratory that is not accredited should only be used in the event that an accredited calibration laboratory is not available or practical to use.
- The instrument may be calibrated by an ISO/IEC 17025–accredited calibration laboratory.
- The instrument may be calibrated by an internal or external calibration laboratory assessed on an annual basis, by the testing laboratory, and found to comply with the requirements of ISO/IEC 17025. The assessments should be conducted by a qualified ISO/IEC 17025 assessor or metrologist.

For specialized instruments where no accredited calibration laboratory is available, the instrument may be calibrated by the instrument manufacturer provided that the calibration standards used are traceable to national or international units of measure, the traceability chain is identified, and an estimation of uncertainty of measurement is included on the calibration certificate.

14.5.2.2 Calibration Intervals for Test Equipment Requiring Calibration

All test equipment requiring calibration should undergo an initial calibration before being put into service. Thereafter, the maximum calibration interval should be the following [7]:

- One year for electrical, electronic, and mechanical test equipment;
- Three years for mechanical test equipment made of solid materials not subject to deterioration;
- As recommended by the manufacturer of the instrument.

Test equipment that is fail-safe, in that failure would be evident to a user (with laboratory procedures requiring the user to check the equipment before use), may be assigned the status of initial calibration only (ICO). Examples of the equipment that can be placed on ICO status are: steel rules, tape measures, weights 4.5 kg or more calibrated to ± 1 % tolerance, single-piece steel probes greater than or equal to 3 mm diameter with blunt ends, graduate cylinder, thermometers, steel impact balls, and steel or plastic probes with no moving parts and sufficient structural integrity so as to not deform.

Weights do not need to be calibrated if verified with a calibrated scale before each use. The verification must be documented.

Test equipment that is delicate, subject to frequent usage or severe use conditions should be assigned shortened calibration intervals (e.g., six months, three months, weekly, or before each use). Infrequently used test equipment may be assigned the status of "calibrate before use" instead of a periodic calibration.

Calibration intervals may be extended based on the following if the reasons are documented:

- Passive electrical test equipment, such as current shunts, current transformers, potential transformers, may be extended to three years with good results for the initial calibration period and if not subject to severe use conditions.
- Weights may be extended to five years if there is a laboratory procedure that takes into account usage and has a provision for physical examination and/or intermediate checks of the weights.
- Where there is sufficient calibration data to statistically establish a trend or based on experience of use of the test equipment to assure good measurement results for a longer period.

It is recommended that each testing house implement quality control methods to evaluate the test equipment between calibrations.

14.5.3 Recommended Features for Specific Test Equipment

14.5.3.1 Dielectric Withstand Test Equipment

Dielectric withstand (hipot) test equipment should be provided with the following features [9]:

- The ability to detect minimum current in a dielectric withstand test guards against a false positive indication when the ground circuit is open. Without this feature, a ground fault might be missed by the tester, causing an unsafe product to be released for shipment to customers.

- To avoid damage to components in a UUT, the high-voltage output of the tester should be increased smoothly over the test range rather as an abrupt step change. A quality tester should provide this feature without introducing spikes or distortion in the AC waveform. The tester should provide easily programmable ramp and hold times for each test step.

- When a UUT fails a test, the tester should automatically save the test result and interrupt the test immediately to avoid potential damage to the UUT.

- In production environments, the ability to subtract leakage current due to test leads and test fixtures automatically from the instrument reading (automatic offset) can be a great convenience.

- Arc detection is an anticipatory tool that can be used to detect an impending fault before it occurs. The testers provide this feature by detecting the presence of high-frequency transients in the current waveform. If such variations exceed a specified level and persist for more than 10 μs, the tester should instantly alarm and interrupt the test. The UUT can then be examined offline to find and correct the cause of the problem (rather than being scrapped after a failure occurs).

- The accessories typically needed for a dielectric withstand test are listed as follows:
  - High-voltage probes with various lengths of cable including probe guns (trigger-operated);
  - A corded product adapter fixture (to accept two-prong or three-prong line cords);
  - A foot switch to start/stop tests.

- A 120-kΩ resistance is specified to check operation of a dielectric withstand tester. This requirement is based on a maximum current flow of 10 mA when a voltage of 1 250V is applied between the circuit of a UUT and ground. Using Ohm's Law, a voltage of 1,250V divided by a current of 10 mA gives a resistance of 125 k Ω.

To verify that a given dielectric withstand tester meets this standard for leakage impedance, the user sets the output voltage to the desired value and then connects a 120-kΩ resistor across the output terminals. To be accepted, the tester should indicate a fault within 0.5s. If it does not, the tester is not acceptable. The 120-kΩ value is the minimum value at which the tester should indicate a fault.

14.5.3.2 Ground Bond Test Equipment

Four-terminal Kelvin connections ensure maximum accuracy by preventing errors caused by measurement lead resistance. This feature is typically used to ensure accuracy of a ground bond test. The tester accessories typically needed for a ground continuity test are: ground continuity lead set and power entry adapter cable for ground continuity tests.

14.5.3.3 Leakage Currents Test Equipment

The measurement equipment for the direct measurement is to measure the current as true RMS and guarantee that during the measurement, protection against electric shock is effective by suitable means based on IEC 61010-1.

14.5.4 Preventive Maintenance

All measuring and test equipment should be appropriately maintained by a technically competent person. Maintenance comprises a range of activities including:

- Preventive maintenance of the measuring and test equipment and accessories;
- Calibration of the main characteristics.

14.5.4.1 Preventive Maintenance Checklist

The manufacturer of the measuring and test equipment will normally provide a checklist for preventive maintenance that generally includes the following:

- Inspect and clean safety-related components;
- Check and replace or replenish consumables;

- Verify the correct operation of the measuring and test equipment;
- Verify that the measuring and test equipment is electrically safe;
- Check the condition of the interconnection cables and power cables for obvious signs of wear;
- Check the protective means for availability and integrity;
- Inspect the accessories for signs of damage;
- Check the emergency-off switch operation (if applicable).

14.5.5 Testing and Measuring Equipment and Material Needed for Product Safety Tests

Table 14.5 lists the most common tests for product basic safety and the associated testing/measuring equipment and materials needed for conducting the tests. More detailed description for conducting a few of these tests will follow in Section 14.7.

14.5.6 Testing and Measuring Equipment for EMC Tests

Table 14.6 lists the most common tests for EMC and the associated testing/measuring equipment/materials needed for conducting the tests. Section 14.8 provides a more detailed description for conducting a few of these tests.

Table 14.5
Tests and Test Equipment for Product Basic Safety

Measurement/Test	Testing/Measuring Equipment/Material Needed
Ambient temperature, humidity, atmospheric pressure	Thermometer, hygrometer and barometer with recording capabilities
Humidity preconditioning treatment	Climate chamber (93 ± 3)% RH, (20...40 ± 2)°C with controlled and recorded humidity and temperature
Power input	Voltmeter, ammeter, watt meter, and frequency meter; one-phase and three-phase variac
Accessible parts	Force gauge (30 N), standard test finger, straight unjointed test finger, test hook, test pin (Ø4mm/Ø3mm/15 mm long), test rod Ø 4mm/ Ø 12 mm/100 mm long; oscilloscope with leads, suitable instruments for measuring voltage, current, capacitance
Legibility of markings	Illuminance meter
Durability of markings	Distilled water, ethanol (96% pure), isopropyl alcohol, petroleum spirit (aliphatic solvent hexane or reagent grade hexane), timer/stopwatch, cloth

Table 14.5 (continued)

Measurement/Test	Testing/Measuring Equipment/Material Needed
Limitations voltage and energy	Oscilloscope recorder /setup (measuring instrument with input impedance 100 MΩ in parallel with an input capacitance of 25 pF or less); RCL meter
Impedance and current-carrying capability (ground resistance)	Current source (40-A minimum, 50 or 60 Hz, 12-V maximum)
Test for operating voltages generated externally	Test generator (120V or 230V± 2V AC, 50 or 60 Hz, 1,200Ω ± 2%)
Power source circuit classification	Watt meter, variable resistor load, stop watch
Limited current circuits, limit values	Resistor 2,000Ω ± 10%, capacitance measuring device
Connection of TNV circuits to other circuits	Noninductive resistor 5,000Ω ± 2%
Leakage currents	Measuring device as specified in specific standards, mains isolation transformers, variac, voltmeter, millivoltmeter, aluminium foil, diverse switching circuits as specified in specific standards
Dielectric strength	High-voltage tester, isolating transformer for high-voltage tests, stopwatch/timer
Ball pressure test	Test equipment according to IEC 60695-10-2: Ball pressure test apparatus, micrometer/callipers, force gauge, multimeter, oven at least 125°C
Creepage distances and air clearances	Oscilloscope with leads, callipers, micrometer, spacing gauges, force gauge (2 N & 30 N), standard test finger; microscope
Thermal cycling and thermal ageing	Full draught oven (± 2°C) Cooling facility (0° C)
Cord anchorage	Force gauge (at least 100 N), torque gauge (at least 0.35 Nm)
Cord guards	Weights, angle gauge, radius gauge
Stability	5° and 10° inclined planes or inclinometer or trigonometric calculation, force gauge (at least 220 N), 20 cm by 20 cm test surface, weights, test threshold (10-mm-high and 80-mm-wide), 7-cm strap, stopwatch/timer
Pressure vessels	Hydraulic pressure test apparatus
Support systems	Weights or load cell, 0.1 m² test surface, stopwatch/timer, human body test mass as specified in standard IEC 60601-1
Equipment mounted to a wall or ceiling	Several weights, timer, torque gauges
X-radiation (Ionizing)	Radiation monitor, ionizing chamber type with an effective area of 1 000 mm²
Microwave radiation	Radiation meter

Table 14.5 (continued)

Measurement/Test	Testing/Measuring Equipment/Material Needed
High pressure lamps	Dark sticky mat, magnified glass with a resolution of 0,1 mm
Excessive temperatures	Temperature indicator/recorder, thermocouples, four-wire resistance unit, black test corner, variac, cheesecloth (bleached cotton cloth 40g/m^2)
Overflow	15° inclined plane or inclinometer or trigonometric calculation, stopwatch/timer, high-voltage tester
Spillage	Flask or graduated cylinder, stopwatch/timer
Hazardous situations and fault conditions	stopwatch/timer, voltmeter, ammeter, temperature indicator/recorder, thermocouples, 4 wire resistance unit, cheesecloth (bleached cotton cloth 40g/m^2)
Covering of ventilation openings	Piece of card with 200 g/m^2 density
Mechanical strength	Force gauge (250 N minimum), circular plane surface 30 mm in diameter, 50-mm-thick hardwood board (hardwood > 600 kg/m^3), 40-mm step, hardwood doorframe (40 mm^2), circulating air oven, balance
Impact test	Φ 50mm/500g± 25g steel ball
Drop test	Hardwood 13 mm on 18 mm ± 2 mm plywood, two layers, ruler up to 1,000 mm ± 10 mm
Carts, stands, and similar carriers	Force up to 440 N with a circular plan surface ± 30 mm, stopwatch
Actuating parts of controls, handles	Force gauge (at least 100 N), torque gauge (at least 6 Nm), stopwatch/timer
Cord-connected handheld and foot-operated control devices	Force gauge (minimum 350 N), 30-mm diameter test tool, stopwatch/timer
Transformers	Winding tester for transformers, temperature indicator/recorder thermocouples, variac, loads, 5x voltage/5x frequency source, stopwatch/timer
Insulated winding wires for use without interleaved insulation	Sample is prepared according to IEC 60851-5, dielectric according to 60601-1; flexibility and adherence test of IEC 60851-3; mandrels of specific diameters; heat shock test of IEC 60851-6:1996; 2 mm diameter shot of stainless steel, nickel or nickel plated iron
Insulation material groups classification (tracking index)	Test equipment according to IEC 60112
Mechanical strength of CRTs and protection against the effects of implosion	Test equipment according to IEC 61965, scale, diamond stylus, cooling liquid, timer
Audible acoustic energy	A-weighted sound pressure level according to ISO 3746, ISO 9614-1 or IEC 61672-1
Hand-transmitted vibration	Test equipment according to ISO 5349-1
Lasers	Test equipment according to IEC 60825-1

Table 14.5 (continued)

Measurement/Test	Testing/Measuring Equipment/Material Needed
Human exposure to UV radiation	Test equipment according to IEC 60825-14
Constructional requirements for fire enclosures	Test equipment according to IEC 60695-11-10
Ingress of water or particulate matter	Test equipment according to IEC 60529
Temperature and overload control devices	Test equipment according to IEC 60730-1
Primary lithium batteries	Test equipment according to IEC 60086-4
Secondary lithium batteries	Test equipment according to IEC 62133
LEDs	Test equipment according to IEC 62471
Prevention of electrostatic charges	Test equipment according to ISO 2882
Partial discharge test (on semiconductors)	Test equipment according to IEC 60747-5-5
AC power supply cords	Test equipment according to IEC 60227
Mould stress relief	Test equipment according to IEC 60695-10-3: Oven at least 125°C
Defibrillation protection	5 kV test circuit & oscilloscope interface circuit as specified in standard IEC 60601-1, oscilloscope
Energy reduction test	Test circuit as specified in standard IEC 60601-1, oscilloscope with leads
Effect of UV radiation on materials	Test equipment according to ISO 178, 179, 180, 527, 8256, and 4892 series
Materials used in high-voltage components	Needle flame test according to IEC 60695-11-5
Insulating winding wires	Test equipment according to IEC 60851-3, -5, and -6
Component flammability	Needle flame test according to IEC 60695-11-5
Mandrel test	Test equipment according to IEC 61 558
Thermoplastic parts on which conductive metallic parts are directly mounted	Vicat test B 50 of ISO 306 and ball pressure test apparatus according to IEC 60695-10-2; oven at least 125°C
Tubing and fittings compatibility test	Tensile strength test device according to ISO 527 series
Vibration test sinosoidal	Vibration test according to IEC 60068-2-6
Protection against internal ignition from external spark sources—spark test	Equipment according to IEC 60896-21

An EMC test site [10] should permit disturbances from the UUT to be distinguished from ambient noise. The suitability of the site in this respect can be determined by measuring the ambient noise levels with the UUT inoperative and ensuring that the noise level is at least 6 dB below the limits specified.

Table 14.6

Tests and Test Equipment for EMC

Measurement/Test	Testing/Measuring Equipment/Material Needed
Emission of simple electrical components (CISPR 14-1)	EMI receiver, artificial mains network (AMN)—known also as line impedance stabilization network (LISN), pulse limiter, voltage probe, clickmeter, absorbing clamp
Emission of lighting equipment (CISPR 15)	Test receiver, AMN, pulse limiter, signal generator, dummy lamps, symmetric/asymmetric transformers, triple loop antenna
Emission of industrial scientific and medical equipment (CISPR 11): Measurement of conducted disturbances on the mains, in the frequency range 150 Khz–30 Mhz Measurement of radiated disturbances between 30 MHz and 1 Ghz and between 1 Ghz and 18 Ghz Measurement of conducted disturbances on the mains when the AMN cannot be used	CISPR 16-compliant receiver or spectrum analyzer with quasipeak (QP) adapter and preselector, AMN, pulse limiter, artificial hand, current probe, semianechoic chamber and absorber or open area test site (OATS) (for f < 1 GHz), anechoic chamber (for f > 1 GHz), biconical antenna and log-periodic antenna or bilog antenna, double ridge horn antenna, RF amplifier, RF coaxial cable, high-pass filter, attenuator; triple-loop antenna, loop antenna, LPDA antenna or standard gain horn or double ridge horn antenna, band reject filter, voltage probe
Emission of information technology equipment (ITE) (CISPR 22)	Test receiver or spectrum analyzer with quasipeak adapter and preselector, AMN, pulse limiter, current probe, semianechoic chamber or OATS (for f < 1 GHz), biconical antenna and log-periodic antenna or bilog antenna, double ridge horn antenna, RF amplifier, anechoic chamber (for f > 1 GHz)
Emission of multimedia equipment (CISPR 32): Conducted emissions from the AC mains power ports Asymmetric mode conducted emission on wired network ports and optical fiber ports with metallic shield or tension members Measurement of radiated disturbances up to 1 GHz and above 1 GHz	Receiver or spectrum analyzer + preselector + QP adapter (CISPR 16-1-1-compliant), AMN, asymmetric artificial network (AAN), RF coaxial cable, high-pass filter, attenuator, capacitive voltage probe, current probe, 150- –50- adaptor (substitutes for AAN), broadband linearly polarized antenna (e.g., biconical antenna, log-periodic antenna, hybrid antenna, standard horn, or double ridged guide antenna,), OATS, or full anechoic chamber (FAR), RF amplifier
Harmonic distortion (IEC 61000-3-2)	Power source, harmonic meter
Voltage fluctuations and flickers (IEC 61000-3-3)	Power source, flicker meter, impedance network, voltage fluctuation meter
Emission-limitation of voltage changes, voltage fluctuations and flicker in public low-voltage supply system-equipment with rated current < or equal 75A and subject to conditional connection (IEC 61000-3-11)	Power source, flicker meter, reference impedance network

Table 14.6 (continued)

Measurement/Test	Testing/Measuring Equipment/Material Needed
Emission limits for harmonics currents produced by equipment connected to public low-voltage systems with input current > 16A and inferior or equal to 75A per phase (IEC 61000-3-12)	Power source, harmonic meter
Immunity test to electrostatic discharges (ESDs) (IEC 6100-4-2)	ESD simulator, horizontal coupling plane, vertical coupling plane, discharge electrode (for air discharges and direct discharges), discharge return cable, bleeder resistors, insulating support
Immunity test to Radiated disturbances due to RF, electromagnetic field (IEC 61000-4-3)	Signal generator, RF power amplifier, function generator, biconical antenna and log-periodic antenna or bilog antenna, horn antenna, millivoltmeter (or power meter with power sensor), isotropic field probe, directional coupler, power amplifier, anechoic chamber or semianechoic chamber (SAC), RF coaxial cable, controller (e.g., PC and controller software)
Immunity tests to electrical fast transients and bursts (IEC 61000-4-4)	Burst generator, coupling/decoupling network (CDN), capacitive clamp, 33-nF capacitor probe for direct injection, reference ground plane, interconnection cable (for clamp to generator)
Immunity test to surges (IEC 61000-4-5)	Surge generator, coupling/decoupling network, reference ground plane
Immunity test to Conducted disturbances, induced by RF fields (IEC 61000-4-6)	Signal generator, RF power amplifier, continuous wave generator, attenuator, EM clamp, ferrite decoupling tube, CDN, millivoltmeter, RF probe, coupler, RF coaxial cable, power meter with power sensor, sinusoidal generator, current clamp,100Ω–50Ω adaptor and direct injection device, Artificial hand, 50Ω termination, EMI filter
Immunity test to power frequency magnetic fields (IEC 61000-4-8)	Test generator, square coil and/or rectangular coil and/or another inductive coil (e.g., Helmholtz coil), magnetic field probe, magnetic field tester, decoupling network, back filter
Immunity test to pulsed magnetic field (IEC 61000-4-9)	Test generator, square coil
Immunity test to voltage dips, short interruptions, and voltage variations on power supply input lines (IEC 61000-4-11)	Test generator, three-phase selectors
Emission and immunity testing in transverse electromagnetic (TEM) waveguides (IEC 61000-4-20)	Receiver or spectrum analyser + preselector + QP adapter (CISPR 16-1-1-compliant), RF coaxial cable, TEM (substitutes for SAC, OATS, or FAR)

Table 14.6 (continued)

Measurement/Test	Testing/Measuring Equipment/Material Needed
Emission tests for residential, commercial and light-industrial environments (IEC 61000-6-3): Measurement of conducted disturbances on the mains Measurement of conducted common mode disturbance on telecom/network ports and DC ports Measurement of discontinuous disturbance (terminal voltage) Measurement of radiated disturbances up to and above 1 GHz	Receiver or spectrum analyzer + preselector + QP adapter (CISPR 16-1-1 compliant), AMN, RF coaxial cable, AAN, high-pass filter, attenuator, current probe, voltage probe, 150-–50- adaptor, CMAD (substitutes for AAN), clickmeter, receiver 150 kHz, receiver 500 kHz, receiver 1.4 MHz, receiver 30 MHz, oscilloscope, biconical antenna and log-periodic antenna or bilog antenna, OATS, FAR full anechoic chamber, common mode absorption device (CMAD), RF amplifier, broadband linearly polarized antenna (e.g., standard horn, or double-ridged guide antenna)
Emission tests for industrial environments (IEC 61000-6-4): Measurement of conducted disturbances on the mains Measurement of conducted common mode disturbance on telecommunications/network ports Measurement of discontinuous disturbance (terminal voltage) Measurement of radiated disturbances up to and above 1 GHz	Receiver or spectrum analyzer + preselector + QP adapter (CISPR 16-1-1-compliant), AMN, RF Coaxial Cable, AAN, high-pass filter, attenuator, current probe, voltage probe, 150Ω–50Ω adaptor, CMAD (substitutes for AAN), clickmeter, receiver 150 kHz, receiver 500 kHz, receiver 1.4 MHz, receiver 30 MHz, oscilloscope, biconical antenna and log-periodic antenna or bilog antenna, OATS, FAR full anechoic chamber, CMAD , RF amplifier, broadband linearly polarized antenna (e.g., standard horn, and double-ridged guide antenna)

It is not necessary that the ambient noise level be 6 dB below the specified limit where both ambient noise and source disturbance combined do not exceed the specified limit. Where the combined ambient noise and source disturbance exceed the specified limit, the UUT should be judged to fail the specified limit if it is demonstrated that, at any measurement frequency for which the limit is exceeded, one of the following two conditions is met:

1. The ambient noise level is at least 6 dB below the source disturbance plus ambient noise level.

2. The ambient noise level is at least 4.8 dB below the specified limit.

The OATS should be located on an open and plane area and satisfy the site attenuation value ±4 dB of the normalized site attenuation values in CISPR 16-1-4. The OATS should be free from any reflecting objects such as buildings, aerial cables, walls, trees, buried cables, and pipelines. (See Figure 14.4, where R represents the measuring distance.)

The electromagnetic wave semianechoic chamber is a shielded room surrounded with electromagnetic wave absorbing plates except on the floor. The chamber should satisfy the attenuation requirements as the OATS. Additionally,

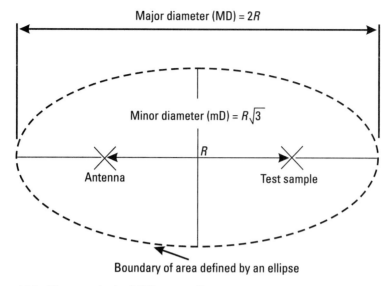

Figure 14.4 The range in the OATS surrounding, which should be free from any reflecting object above the ground. From [10].

the chamber should also provide no rapid change of the electromagnetic wave propagating characteristics in all the frequencies in the range 30 MHz–1 GHz within an area occupied by the UUT on the turntable.

For the specific purpose of making conducted emissions voltage measurements on the mains input of the product, CISPR 16-1 defines a transducer known as an AMN. The U.S. term LISN is in more general use and usually means the same thing. The AMN/LISN has three main purposes, listed as follows:

- To define the RF impedance seen by the UUT's mains port;
- To couple the interference signal from the UUT mains terminals to the measuring instrument and to prevent the mains voltage from being directly applied to the measuring instrument;
- To reduce the ambient noise that might be present on the incoming mains circuit.

An AMN should have as small a series voltage drop as possible at the mains frequency. In any case the voltage of UUT does not need to become lower than 95% of the rated voltage. The network should be capable of showing the maximum displayed current continuously. It is necessary to use an AMN/LISN of the 50-Ω, 50–μH type.

When using a LISN, consider the following characteristics:

- Common-mode termination impedance in the frequency range 0.15 MHz–30 MHz;
- The LISN should be calibrated together with all necessary adapters to connect the UUT and the auxiliary equipment (AE), if used;
- There should be attenuation of the LISN;
- There should be isolation (decoupling) against common-mode current or voltage disturbances originating from the AE;
- There should be longitudinal conversion loss (LCL);
- There should be a voltage division factor.

In order to obtain EMC test results that are accurate, and, moreover, repeatable, it is important to use measuring instruments that are subject to proper supervision. Measuring instruments must meet the important conditions set forth in CISPR 16-1. These instruments—for example, measuring receivers, spectrum analyzers, antennas, artificial mains networks, impedance stabilization network, current probe, and cables—must be periodically calibrated and checked as frequently as necessary. It is necessary that the certification standard referred to for calibration is either directly or indirectly traceable to the national standards of the country. It is recommended that antennas and measuring instruments incorporating active components be calibrated on an approximately annual cycle.

For traceability reasons and in accordance with the international standardization each test result should be accompanied by information related to the test equipment used (such as in the form shown by Table 14.7).

14.6   General Testing Conditions

When tests are conducted, the following general conditions should be applied [1]:

Table 14.7
List of the Test Equipment Used

Name of Test Equipment	Manufacturer	Model	Accuracy	Last Calibration
xxxxx				
yyyyy				
zzzzz				

- After the UUT has been set up for normal use conditions, tests are carried out under the least favorable working conditions, which are specified by the manufacturer in accompanying documents.

- Before testing, the UUT should be disconnected from the supply mains. If not possible, special precaution measures should be taken to prevent harm.

- Prior to the EMC immunity test, a means to monitor the UUT (i.e., CCTV) for its essential performance before, during, and after each exposure needs to be arranged.

- Cables and cords (e.g., mains cords, measuring leads, and data cables) should be positioned in such a way as to minimize their effect on the measurement.

- The UUT is to be shielded from other influences (for example, drafts) that might affect the validity of the tests.

- Considering the ambient temperature, humidity, and pressure described in the technical description, tests should be performed at the worst-case extremes depending on the test and the effects of these parameters on the test results. If the test is not impacted by these parameters, then the test can be conducted anywhere within the specified range.

- Equipment having operating values that can be adjusted or controlled by the operator is adjusted as part of the tests to values that are the least favorable for the relevant test, but in accordance with the instructions for use.

- Where test results are influenced by deviations in the supply voltage from its rated value, the effect of such deviations is to be taken into account.

- In cases where ambient temperatures cannot be maintained, the test conditions are to be consequently modified and results adjusted accordingly.

- The results of a risk analysis should be used to determine which combination(s) of simultaneous faults should be tested.

- Qualified personnel are to perform these tests. Qualifications include training on the subject, knowledge, experience, and acquaintance with the relevant technologies and regulations. The personnel should be able to assess safety and should be able to recognize possible consequences and hazards arising from nonconforming equipment.

- Accessories for the equipment, which can affect the safety of the UUT or the results of the measurements, should be included in the tests and should be documented.

- If the test results are influenced by the inlet pressure and flow or chemical composition of the cooling liquid, the test is to be carried out within the limits for these characteristics as prescribed in the technical description.

- A test need not be carried out if analysis shows that the condition being tested has been adequately evaluated by other tests.

- Covers and housings should be opened only if it is required in the equipment instructions for use

- Equipment for AC only should be tested with AC at rated frequency (if marked) ± 1 Hz for a rated frequency between 0 Hz and 100 Hz and ± 1 % for a rated frequency above 100 Hz. Equipment marked with a rated frequency range is to be tested at the least favorable frequency within that range.

- Equipment designed for more than one rated voltage, or for both AC and DC, is to be tested in conditions related to the least favorable voltage and nature of supply [for example, the number of phases (except for single-phase supply) and the type of current]. It might be necessary to perform some tests more than once in order to establish which supply configuration is the least favorable.

- Equipment for DC only is to be tested with DC. When performing the tests, the possible influence of polarity on the operation of the equipment is to be taken into consideration.

- If the instructions for use specify that equipment is intended to receive its power from a separate power supply, it is to be connected to such a power supply.

- All tests performed should be comprehensively documented. The documentation should contain as a minimum the following data:

    - Identification of the testing house (e.g., company and department);
    - Names of the persons who performed the testing and the evaluation(s);
    - Identification of the UUT (e.g., type, serial number, and inventory number) and the accessories tested;
    - Measurements (measured values, measuring method, measuring equipment, environmental conditions);

• Date and signature of the individual who performed the evaluation.

14.6.1 Supply Mains Used in Product Basic Safety and EMC Tests

Supply mains used for testing should have the following characteristics [11, 12]:

• Voltage dips, short interruptions, and voltage variations as described in applicable EMC standard;
• No voltage in excess of 110% or lower than 90% of the nominal value between any of the conductors of the system or between any of these conductors and ground;
• Voltages that are practically sinusoidal and forming a practically symmetrical supply system in case of polyphase supply;
• A frequency of not more than 1 kHz;
• The protective measures described in IEC 60364-4-41;
• A DC voltage (as measured by a moving coil meter or equivalent method) having a peak-to-peak ripple not exceeding 10% of the average value. Where peak-to-peak ripple exceeds 10% of the average value, the peak voltage has to be applied.

14.7 Product Basic Safety Testing

The product basic safety testing is conducted in the well-defined status of the UUT. Below are a few examples which contain the framework for performing tests that are required by product safety standards [1]. These are presented as a series of test procedures. They are divided into the following three categories:

• Tests performed by inspection of the UUT;
• Test performed with the UUT not energized;
• Tests performed with the UUT energized.

Each test procedure describes the following:

• Test category;
• Applicable standard;
• Scope of the test;

- Test/measuring equipment needed for the test;
- Work safety precautions during the test;
- Test sample preparation;
- Test conditions;
- Special recommendations;
- Test setup;
- Test procedure;
- Presentation of the test results;
- Observation.

14.7.1   Tests Performed by Inspection of the Product

14.7.1.1   Visual Inspection

Test Category: Performed by Inspection of the Product	Applicable Standard(s): All Basic Safety Standards
a) Scope of the test: To ensure that the equipment submitted for testing: 1) Consists of the parts specified by manufacturer and included in the user manual; 2) Has not suffered from any external damage and/or contamination; 3) Has components whose ratings are compatible with the ratings of UUT; 4) Has markings that conform with the product specification included in the user manual.	b) Test/measuring equipment needed for the test: Caliper Optical magnifying device
c) Work safety precautions during the test: N/A	d) Test sample preparation: One representative test sample. For power supply cord strip insulation for 5–7-mm to allow wire diameter measurement with the caliper.
e) Test conditions: Do not energize the UUT during this test Have provided adequate illumination	f) Special recommendations: Calculate the cross-sectional area (in mm^2) as πr^2
g) Test setup: The UUT should be in normal use conditions (power sources disconnected: mains switch OFF position; batteries removed)	

h) Test procedure: The following are typical visual checks that should be made:

- Housing enclosure—look for damage, cracks, etc;
- Contamination—look for obstruction of moving parts, connector pins, etc;
- Cabling (supply, interconnection, etc.)—look for cuts, wrong connections, etc;
- Power supply cord—check if the cross-sectional area of conductors of the power supply cord is in accordance with the standard requested values pending on the product ratings;
- Fuse rating—check correct values and markings;
- Markings and labeling—check the integrity of safety markings (if are legible and complete);
- Integrity of mechanical parts;
- Required documentation, such as instructions for use—check if is present and reflects the current revision of the equipment;
- Grounding—check the integrity of the ground connections;
- Examine the circuit diagrams for the UUT to identify any critical components that need to be included in the list of critical components. Identify the types and manufacturers of these components using the parts lists. Verify the approvals, data sheets, and/or drawings for each critical component and assess if these components are working within their specified ratings. If the operating conditions cannot be established from the circuit analysis, then determine these ratings based on other tests (e.g., heating tests). Verify the flammability rating of all plastics (i.e., PCBs, connectors, fans, insulators, bobbins, relay housings, plastic fuse holders, sleeving, insulated cables, and plastic enclosure). Only plastics of sufficient size to influence the spread of fire need be assessed. Where several small amounts of a plastic are in the same vicinity then the cumulative effect should be taken into account.

i) Presentation of the test results:

Environmental test conditions:
Temperature: xx °C
Relative humidity: yy %
Atmospheric pressure: zzz mmHg
Tested product:
Model_____ Manufactured by_____
Drafting a checklist that consists on the inspected issued and the acceptance status (pass/fail) for each.

j) Observations: N/A

14.7.2 Test Performed with the Product Not Energized

14.7.2.1 Ground Connection Bonding and Continuity

Test Category: Performed with the Product Not Energized	Applicable Standard(s): All Basic Safety Standards
a) Scope of the test: Proves the integrity of the low-resistance connection between the ground conductor and any metal conductive parts, which may become live in fault situations in a Class I equipment	b) Equipment needed for the test: 1) Adjustable AC current source with a frequency of 50 Hz, 60 Hz, or DC and with a no-load voltage not exceeding 6—12V, which is able to produce 25–40A or 1.5 times the highest rated current of the relevant circuit(s), whichever is greater (± 10 %) 2) Suitable voltmeter and ammeter 3) Assorted connectors and cables 4) Shunt Alternatively, the above can be replaced by a ground bond tester

c) Work safety precautions during the test:	d) Test sample preparation:
High current testing can cause excessive localized heating of conductive parts and possible burns.	A complete UUT should be used
e) Test conditions:	f) Special recommendations:
Do not energize the UUT during this test.	No special recommendations

g) Test setup (**Figure 14.5**):

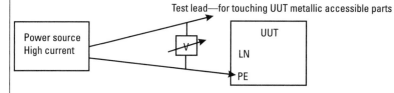

h) Test procedure:

1) A test current of 25–40A or 1.5 times the highest rated current of the relevant circuit(s), whichever is greater (± 10 %), from a current source with a frequency of 50 Hz, 60 Hz, or DC and with a no-load voltage not exceeding 6–12V, is passed for 5–10s through:
 The protective ground terminal or the protective ground contact in the appliance inlet or the protective ground pin in the mains plug and each protective grounded part
 Each protectively grounded part or the mains plug of detachable power supply cord (3-m-long) and any part of the equipment that is protectively grounded
2) The voltage drop between the ground terminal and the part to be grounded is measured, and the resistance between these two points is to be calculated.
3) The test instrument leads impedance should be considered.

i) Presentation of the test results (Table 14.8):

Environmental test conditions:
Temperature: xx °C
Relative humidity: yy %
Atmospheric pressure: zzz mmHg
Tested product:
Model_____ Manufactured by_____

Table 14.8 Impedance of PE Connection

Test Location	Test Current	Duration	Measured Voltage	Resistance
	(I)		(U)	(R = U/I)
	A	s	V	Ω

j) Observations:

1) Although many pieces of Class I equipment are supplied with an equipotential point, this equipment requires multiple ground bond tests to validate the connections of additional metal accessible parts on the enclosure.
2) Higher test currents—of 10A or more—might potentially be destructive to parts of the UUT that are connected to the protective ground but have a functional purpose, such as screening. As such, consideration should be given to the test current.
3) Low-test currents—of less than 8A—may not always overcome problems associated with contact resistance caused by constriction, pressure, or film-resistance factors and may therefore show a relatively higher reading than there is and indicate unnecessary failures.

14.7.2.2 Dielectric Strength

Test Category: **Performed with the Product Not Energized**	Applicable Standard(s): **All Basic Safety Standards**
a) Scope of the test: Proves the integrity of the solid insulation.	b) Equipment needed for the test: Dielectric strength AC and/or DC tester (HiPot) as appropriate. Note: In order to ensure standardized control of test voltage in time, testers with program-controlled test voltage are recommended. Manual adjustment of the test voltage in certain circumstances can be valuable. The test equipment should display the current measurement through the insulation. Alternatively, where needed, current can be measured using an ammeter in series providing it has sufficient protection against the high voltage of the test. Adding series-connected impedances can protect the ammeter from high voltage. For older dielectric strength test equipment, any means to measure ramp time (stopwatch, watch, or clock) can be used.
c) Work safety precautions during the test: The product, test equipment, test leads, and any auxiliary equipment and components should not be accessible upon commencement of the high voltage. Provide adequate markings and warnings at the testing location. Give special consideration to the possibility someone might come into contact with the high voltage. Design the test station so that accidental touching of parts at high voltage is not possible. Test operators should not be able to keep test probes in their hands during high-voltage activation. Put precautions in place to prevent conductive liquids from being near the test station. Take steps (including training) to ensure that the test operator is not distracted during the test (involved in conversations with others or telephone calls for example). Test operator(s) are properly trained, authorized and physically/mentally able to perform the test.	d) Test sample preparation: 1) The configuration(s) of the product must allow all solid insulations to be tested according to the insulation diagram. 2) Observe standard requirements that allow for short-circuiting of either circuit side of the electrical test node and the removal of specified components. 3) When testing across more than one solid insulation, give consideration to the effects different impedances have on the solid insulation involved and overvoltage stressing of particular solid insulation in the test circuit path. In such test situations, a separate test of each solid insulation using the applicable dielectric strength test voltage might be necessary. 4) Tightly cover enclosures or their parts made of nonconductive material with foil. Place foil so that it does not bridge the solid insulation under test but does test all applicable areas. 5) The surface of cables and lead wires connected to the UUT should be treated as parts of the UUT enclosure. 6) The surface of mains power cords can be exempt from wrapping with foil and inclusion as an electrical test node based on relevant analysis of the component.

e) Test conditions:	f) Special recommendations:
Connect test circuits (switches and relay contacts closed) and do not energize the UUT. If necessary (to prevent battery-powered UUTs from being energized), use a solid piece of insulation to block one pole of the battery. Perform testing immediately after humidity preconditioning treatment and after reaching the steady-state operating from the excessive temperature test.	No Special requirements

g) Test setup (**Figure 14.6**):

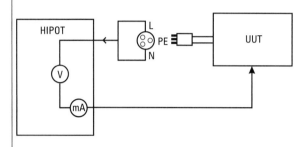

h) Test procedure:

1) Prior to the test, discuss the equipment design, insulation diagram, and appropriate test strategy with the manufacturer. Determine the dielectric strength voltage and waveform to be applied across each solid insulation and circuit arrangement including any components to be removed and any circuits to be short-circuited.
3) Perform the testing across the single mean of protection solid insulation prior to the two MOP solid insulation.
4) Perform each dielectric strength test in the sequence by applying not more than half the test voltage, then ramping the voltage over a 10-s period, holding for 1 min and ramping over a 10-s period to less than half the test voltage.
5) Breakdown (current that rapidly increases in an uncontrolled manner) constitutes a failure. Corona discharge or a single momentary flashover is not regarded as insulation breakdown.
6) Observing the linear relationship between a change in the dielectric strength test voltage to change in current through the solid insulation can provide useful information about the solid insulation.

i) Presentation of the test results (Table 14.9):
Environmental test conditions:
Temperature: xx °C
Relative humidity: yy %
Atmospheric pressure: zzz mmHg
Tested product:
Model_____ Manufactured by_____

Table 14.9 Dielectric Strength

Insulation Under Test (Area From Insulation Diagram)	Insulation Type (Functional, Basic, Double, Reinforced)	Working Voltage (V)	Test Voltage (V)	Remarks

j) Observations: N/A

14.7.3 Test Performed with the Product Energized

14.7.3.1 Maximum Input Current

Test Category: Performed with the Product Energized	Applicable Standard(s): All Basic Safety standards
a) Scope of the test: Determine the maximum input current of the product under maximum load operating conditions. The maximum input current should not exceed the rating limit specified in the product specifications.	b) Equipment needed for the test: 1) Adjustable regulated AC power supply 1–270V, 50/60 Hz, 15A or other similar voltage and frequency depending on input rating of the product. 2) Suitable true RMS-calibrated voltmeters, ammeters 3) Power analyzer (broadband digital complex waveform VAW meter) 4) Suitable load resistors and/or optional accessories 5) Assorted interconnection cables
c) Work safety precautions during the test: Use normal laboratory work safety procedures during this test. It is important to determine the correct type of power input circuit to use for the UUT.	d) Test sample preparation: One representative sample of the product and all optional accessories in such a way to enable maximum loading possible in normal use.
e) Test conditions: The testing configuration should simulate the worst-case conditions of normal use (max load) that might affect the test result.	f) Special recommendations: No special recommendations

g) Test setup (**Figure 14.7**):

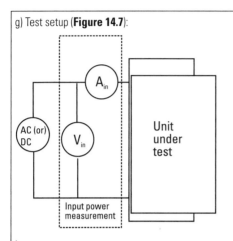

h) Test procedure:

1) Connect normal load to the UUT and operate the UUT under the most severe conditions of normal use until the input has reached a stable value.
2) Operate UUT under normal load and normal duty-cycle at the least favorable voltage between 90 % of the minimum rated voltage and 110 % of the maximum rated voltage.
3) Measure and record the input current, power (watts or volt-amperes) at the lowest and highest rated voltage (when provided as a range). Measure at each nominal marked setting when scalable.
   Measure at the nominal marked voltage when singular.
   The steady state or average current is measured with a true RMS reading instrument.
   Rated input power, if expressed in watts or volt-amperes (pending on the value of power factor; in watts if PF>0.9), is either measured with a volt-ammeter or determined as the product of the steady state current (measured as described above) and the supply voltage.

i)   Presentation of the test results (Table 14.10):
Environmental test conditions:
Temperature: xx °C
Relative humidity: yy %
Atmospheric pressure: zzz mmHg
Tested product:
Model_____ Manufactured by_____

Table 14.10   Input Maximum Current (Power Consumption)

Operating Condition	Voltage (V)	Frequency (Hz)	Current (A)	Power (VA or W)	Remarks
Maximum load					

j) Observations: N/A

14.7.3.2 Normal Heating

Test Category: Performed with the Product Energized	Applicable Standard(s): All Basic Safety standards
a) Scope of the test: Determine the temperature of the equipment parts under normal operating conditions. The temperatures should not exceed the temperature limit specified in material specifications or in applicable standards. To determine whether components and materials attain temperature high enough at which they would fail and where such failure would result in a fire or burning hazard.	b) Equipment needed for the test: 1) Temperature recorder (data logger); 2) No. 30 AWG (recommended) welded thermocouples (e.g., type K and T) compatible with the temperature recorder; 3) Voltmeter; 4) A dull black test corner with linear dimensions at least 115 % of the linear dimensions of the UUT; 5) Adjustable regulated AC supply or other similar voltage and frequency source depending on the input rating of product; 6) Load resistors and/or optional accessories; 7) Ohmmeter; 8) Material (glue) for fixing thermocouples; 9) Watch or any means to measure time; 10) Any means to verify frequency;
c) Work safety precautions during the test: Use normal laboratory work safety procedures during this test. Have accessible a suitable fire extinguisher When connecting thermocouples, and conducting the test, be careful when placing parts due to hazardous voltages.	d) Test sample preparation: One representative sample of the UUT and all optional accessories in such a way to enable maximum loading possible in normal use.

e) Test conditions:	f) Special recommendations:
1) Examples of places where temperatures might be measured include the point of separation of cores of a multicore cord and where insulated wires enter lamp holders. 2) Suspend a handheld UUT in its normal position in still air. 3) Operate a UUT having heating elements with all heating elements energized, unless prevented by switching interlocks, at a supply voltage equal to 110% of the maximum rated voltage. 4) Operate UUT under normal load and normal duty-cycle at the least favorable voltage between 90% of the minimum rated voltage and 110% of the maximum rated voltage. 5) When modules are tested separately, the testing configuration should simulate the worst-case conditions of normal use that might affect the test result. 6) Consider the effects of voltage and frequency on the temperature recorder in regards to thermocouple placement.	1) The black test corner = a corner with 20 mm plywood on the joining walls (at right angle), painted flat-black. A grid of holes, 7 mm in diameter, spaced 100 mm apart, covers the entire surface of the plywood making it resemble pegboard. Attach blackened copper or brass discs with thermocouples to the holes. Place these discs in enough holes to cover the surface area relative to the product being tested. The linear dimensions of the test corner must be at least 115% of the linear dimensions of the UUT. Attach thermocouples to wall surfaces in hottest area of UUT enclosure. If it is necessary to use copper or brass disks, then attach the thermocouple to a 15 mm ± 5 mm diameter, 1 mm ± 0,5 mm thick disk at hottest location. A UUT intended for installation in a cabinet or wall is built in as required by technical description, using dull black painted plywood walls, 10-mm-thick when representing cabinet walls if the technical description so specifies and 20-mm-thick when representing building walls. 2) When thermocouples are used to determine the temperature of windings, reduce the temperature limits by 10°C. In this case, the measurement is made by devices so chosen and positioned that they have a negligible effect on the temperature of the part under test. Determine the temperature of insulation, other than that of windings, on the surface of the insulation at places where failure could cause: • A short circuit; • Bridging of a means of protection; • Bridging of insulation; • Reduction of spacings (creepage distances or air clearances) below the values specified for the insulation type.

g) Test setup (**Figure 14.8**):

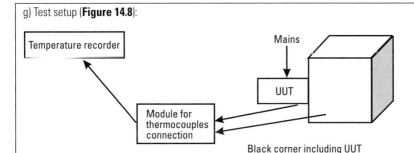

Figure 14.9   The use of the black corner. From [13].

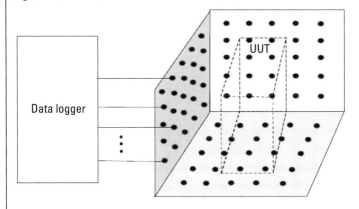

Black corner with built-in thermocouples

h) Test procedure:

1) In UUT place on the selected points the thermocouples and introduce the UUT in the black corner;
2) Operate at 110% of rated voltage the UUT at maximum load mode until thermal stability (difference of maximum 0.5°C for two consecutive, at minimum 10 minutes, readings of the temperature) is reached.
3) Record the maximum reached temperature for each measured point.
4) For windings, the preferred temperature measurement method is the change of resistance (COR) method. The value of temperature rise of a copper winding is calculated from the formula:
$\Delta T = R2 - R1/R1 \quad (234,5 + T1) - (T2 - T1)$
Where:
ΔT is the temperature rise in °C;
R1 is the resistance at the beginning of the test in ;
R2 is the resistance at the end of the test in ;
T1 is the room temperature at the beginning of the test in °C;
T2 is the room temperature at the end of the test in °C.
At the beginning of the test, windings are at room temperature.
Take the resistance measurement as soon as possible after switching off and then periodically thereafter so that a curve of resistance against time can be plotted to determine the value at the instant of switching off.
5) Determine the maximum temperature by making the measurement, calculating the temperature rise and adding it to the maximum permissible ambient temperature.

i) Presentation of the test results:
Environmental test conditions:
Temperature: xx °C
Relative Humidity: yy %
Atmospheric pressure: zzz mmHg
Tested product:
Model_____ Manufactured by_____

Table 14.11   Presentation of the Results for Measurement of Temperature by Thermocouple Method

Normal Temperature		
Supply voltage:		Test condition:
Ambient temperature: °C		Duration of test:
Measuring location	**Measured Temperature (°C)**	**Remarks**

Table 14.12   Presentation of the Results for Measurement of Temperature by COR Method

Temperature by Change of Resistance (COR) Method							
Winding designation	$T1$ °C	$R1$ W	$T2$ °C	$R2$ W	ΔT °C	$T = T2 + \Delta T$ °C	Remarks

j) Observations: N/A

14.7.4 Leakage Current

Test category: Performed with the Product Energized.	Applicable Standard(s): All Basic Safety Standards
a) Scope of the test: To evaluate the Leakage current that flows to ground from user-accessible parts of the product when is operating.	b) Test/measuring Equipment needed for the test: 1) Voltmeter 2) Digital storage oscilloscope with true RMS feature 3) Variable source of AC power supply with isolating transformer 4) Measuring device (as shown in j) Observation)

c) Work safety precautions during the test:	d) Test sample preparation:
Normal laboratory work safety procedures.	Place the UUT, including accessories (when present) on an insulating surface with a dielectric constant of approximately 1 (for example, expanded polystyrene). Position the supply circuit and the measuring device as far as possible away from unscreened power source leads. Avoid placing the UUT on or near a large grounded metal surface. If an isolating transformer is not used for this measurement (e.g. for very high input power), connect the reference ground of the measuring device to protective ground of the supply mains.
e) Test conditions:	f) Special recommendations:
-For single-phase products, the polarity of the supply is reversible and tests are conducted at both polarities. -Test the product provided with a power supply cord using this cord. -Test the product provided with an appliance inlet while connected to the supply circuit via a detachable power supply cord having a length of 3 m or a length and type specified by the manufacturer. -Test permanently installed products while connected to the supply circuit by the shortest possible connection. -If significant currents or current components with frequencies exceeding 1 kHz are likely to occur, measure these using other appropriate means such as a 1 kΩ non-inductive resistor and a suitable measuring instrument. -The measuring instrument (voltmeter) is to have an input resistance of at least 1 MΩ and input capacitance of no more than 150 pF. It should indicate the true r.m.s. value of the voltage, being d.c., a.c., or a composite waveform having components with frequencies from 0,1 Hz up to and including 1 MHz, with an indicating error not exceeding $\pm$ 5% of the indicated value. -The scale may indicate the current through the measuring device including automatic evaluation of components with frequencies above 1 kHz. -The UUT shall be in Normal Use Conditions. -Products specified for connection to a supply mains are connected to an appropriate power source as shown in Figure 14.10.	No special requirements

g) Test setup (**Figure 14.10**). From [12]:

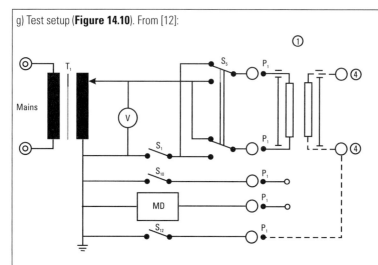

Measure in all possible combinations of positions of S_5, S_{10} and S_{12} with:
S_1 closed (normal condition), and S_1 open (single fault condition).

h) Test procedure:

The measurement of the leakage current is conducted in any combination of the following conditions:
At operating temperature following the humidity preconditioning treatment.
In normal and in the single fault condition (the interruption of one supply conductor at a time).
With the product energized in stand-by condition and fully operating and with any switch in the mains part in any position.
With the highest rated supply frequency.
With a supply, equal to 110% of the highest rated mains voltage.
The measurement reference point is switchable to the live, neutral, or ground wire of the power cord.
Current is measured through the ground connector from the case to one of the lines or from one point to another on the case.
If the product has more than one protective ground conductor (for example one connected to the main enclosure and one to a separate power supply unit) then the current to be measured is the aggregate current that would flow into the protective grounding system of the installation.
Measure the leakage currents that can flow in a functional ground conductor in nonpermanently installed products.

i) Presentation of the test results (**Table 14.13**):
Environmental Test Conditions:
Temperature: xx °C
Relative Humidity: yy %
Atmospheric Pressure: zzz mmHg
Tested Product:
Model_____ Manufactured by_____

Leakage Current

Type of Leakage Current and Test Condition (Including Single Faults)	Supply Voltage V	Supply Frequency Hz	Measured Maximum Value μA	Remarks

j) Observations:

The leakage current measurement is done using a measuring device (MD) while simulating the impedance of a human body. The structure of this MD differs in product safety standards. Follow two example for IEC 60601-1 (medical electrical equipment) and IEC 60950-1 (Information Technology Equipment). Same MD from IEC 60950-1 is used also for IEC 61010-1 standard for measuring, control and laboratory equipment.

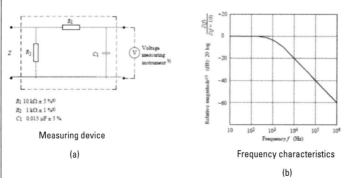

R_1 10 kΩ ± 5 %[i]
R_2 1 kΩ ± 1 %[i]
C_1 0.015 μF ± 5 %

Measuring device

(a)

Frequency characteristics

(b)

Figure 14.11   Measuring device for Medical Electrical Equipment (IEC 60601-1) leakage current measurement and its frequency characteristics. From [12].

Resistors should be of a noninductive type
The voltage measuring instrument should have a resistance minimum of 1 MΩ and capacitance maximum 150 pF
Z(f) is the transfer impedance of the network, e.g V_{out}/I_n, for a current of frequency f.

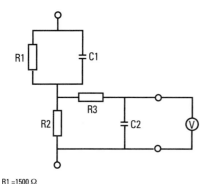

R1 =1500 Ω
R2 = 500Ω
R3 = 10 kΩ
C1 = 0.22 μF
C2 = 0.022 μF

Figure 14.12   Measuring decice used in IEC 60950-1 and IEC 61010-1 standards. From [14].

V – voltmeter or oscilloscope (r.m.s or peak reading)
Input Resistance >1 MΩ
Input Capacitance < 200 pF
Frequency Range 15 Hz – 1 MHz
This MD is used for a.c. with frequencies up to 1 MHz and for d.c.

14.8 EMC Testing

EMC, the ability of equipment to function satisfactorily in its electromagnetic environment without introducing intolerable electromagnetic disturbance to anything in that environment, differs from other aspects of safety because the electromagnetic phenomena exist, with varying degrees of severity, in the normal use environment of all equipment and by definition the equipment must "perform satisfactorily" within its intended environment in order to establish electromagnetic compatibility. This means that the conventional single-fault approach to safety is not appropriate for application here.

The electromagnetic disturbance (any electromagnetic phenomenon that may degrade the performance of a piece of equipment) environment can be compared to ambient temperature, humidity, and atmospheric pressure.

If the UUT consists of both AC power supply and a battery unit, its AC power should be used for measurements. If the battery is of secondary type (rechargeable), and UUT can operate while charging, measurement should be conducted also in this state.

The UUT should be operated within the rated operating voltage range and typical load conditions. In general, the product standards specify the operating voltage at which EMC tests need to be conducted.

If the UUT uses software, the test report should specify the revision of the software used during the tests.

Below are a few examples contain the framework for performing tests that are required by EMC emission and immunity standards. These are presented as a series of test procedures with the same structure as in Section 14.7. All EMC tests are conducted with UUT energized.

14.8.1 Emission Tests

14.8.1.1 Radiated Emission

Test Category: Performed with the Product Energized.	Applicable Standard(s): CISPR 11; CISPR 22; CISPR 16-1; CISPR 32; CISPR 16-2; ANSI C63.4
a) Scope of the test: To evaluate the performance of radiated emission from the enclosure port and interface cables of UUT	b) Equipment needed for the test: 1) EMI receiver + Preselector + QP adapter (CISPR 16-1-1 compliant), 2) Turntable, 3) Must and table control, 3) RF coaxial cable, 4) High pass filter, 5) Attenuator, 6) Broadband linearly polarised antenna (biconical antenna, log-periodic antenna, hybrid antenna, standard horn antenna, antenna must, double ridged guide antenna), 7) Open area test site and 8) Full anechoic chamber
c) Work safety precautions during the test: Use normal laboratory work safety procedures during this test.	d) Test sample preparation: One representative sample of the UUT and all optional accessories in such a way to enable maximum emission possible in normal use.
e) Test conditions: •The testing of equipment intended to be operated on a table top or desk will be performed on a 0.8 meter nonconductive table. •Floor standing equipment will be tested on a ground plane. •Testing will only be carried out if ambivalent environmental conditions are in the range of 8ºC–38ºC and 10%RH–90%RH, in accordance with ANSI C63.4. •Excess cable length beyond 1 meter will be bundled in the center into a 30-40 cm bundle. • each cable connected between UUT Port and Auxiliary Equipment Port (out of the OATS) will be placed in an absorbing clamp (for CISPR 22). • Additional information: Up to six points of radiated field strength within the frequency range of 30 to 1000 MHz should be shown. The measuring instrument should be set to the quasi-peak detection mode in 120 kHz bandwidth (-6 dB).	f) Special recommendations: An attempt shall be made to maximize the disturbance consistent with the typical applications by varying the configuration of the test sample. The effect of varying the position of the cables shall be investigated to find the configuration that produces maximum disturbance. The configuration shall be precisely noted in the test report. To reduce the measurement time, a peak detector receiver can be used instead of a quasi-peak detector receiver or an average detector receiver. • Measurement uncertainty needs to be specified Conversions: Emission level (dBµV/m) = 20 log emission level (µV/m). When limits are measured in dB (µV/m) than 1 µV/m is regarded as 0 dB

g) Test setup (Figure 14.13):

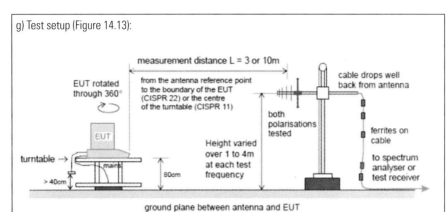

Figure 14.13 From [15].

h) Test procedure:

1) A preliminary measurement to characterize the UUT will be performed inside a full anechoic room with a distance of 3 meters between the UUT and the receiving antenna, using peak detection mode and broad-band antennas.

2) Test and comparison to the limits will be performed in the open area test site (OATS), with the UUT placed on a remotely controlled turntable.

3) The specification limits and applicable correction factors will be loaded to the EMI receiver

4) The readings will be maximized by adjusting the antenna height between 1–4 meters, the turntable azimuth between 0–360°, and antenna polarization.

5) Evaluation of the UUT emissions will be based on the following methods:
• Turning the UUT on and off
• Using a frequency span of less than 10 MHz.
• Observation of the signal level during the rotation of the turn table. Background noise should not be affected by UUT rotation.
• Reducing the test distance to 3 meters.
• Where applicable, test results will be normalized to the limit specified distance, using an inverse proportionality factor of 20 dB per decade. Minimum test distance will be 3 meters.
6) Emission Level = Reading Value + Ant. Factor + Cable Loss.
7) The output of the preliminary measurement will be a list of the highest emissions, their frequencies, and antenna polarization.
8) Using the information obtained in the preliminary measurement, the emissions levels on the frequency range of 30–1000 MHz will be recorded in form of tables and spectral plots.

i) Presentation of the test results (Table 14.14):

Environmental Test Conditions:
Temperature: xx °C
Relative Humidity: yy %
Atmospheric Pressure: zzz mmHg
Tested Product:
Model_____ Manufactured by_____

Table 14.14

Horizontal Polarization (QP)							
No.	Frequency (MHz)	Reading (dBuV)	c.f. (dB[1/m])	Result (dB[uV/m])	Limit (dB[uV/m])	Margin (dB)	Height (cm)	Angle (°)
1	364.50	41.3	-6.5	34.8	47.0	12.2	100	124
2	728.74	37.7	0.2	37.9	47.0	9.1	135	179
Vertical Polarization (QP)							
1	62.21	45.8	-16.7	29.1	40.0	10.9	100	280
2	65.66	43.7	-17.5	26.2	40.0	13.8	100	230
3	69.12	39.1	-17.9	31.2	40.0	8.8	100	254
4	121.99	38.9	-10.5	28.4	40.0	11.6	100	232
5	780.00	34.8	0.8	35.6	47.0	11.4	100	133

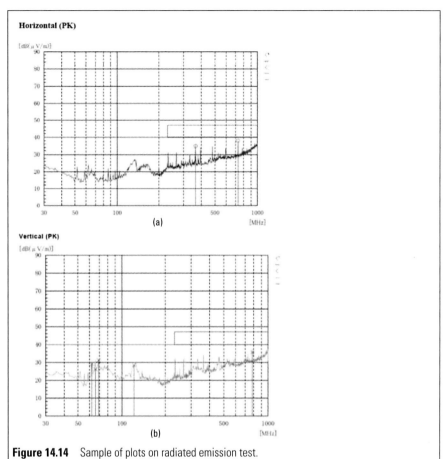

Figure 14.14 Sample of plots on radiated emission test.

j) Observations: N/A

14.8.1.2 Conducted Emission

Test Category: Performed with the Product Energized.	Applicable Standard(s): CISPR 11; CISPR 22; CISPR 16-1; CISPR 32; CISPR 16-2; ANSI C63.4
a) Scope of the test: To evaluate the performance of conducted emission from the UUT on the mains circuit in the frequency range 150 kHz–30 MHz. .	b) Equipment needed for the test: EMI receiver, AMN (artificial mains network – former line impedance stabilization network - LISN) for UUT and for AE (additional-peripheral equipment) 50 Ω, 50 μH), Termination 50 Ω Ground plane (2.4 m (H); 2.4 m (W)), Current probe, Coaxial cable 3 m, Isolation transformer, Filter 2 line, 30A
c) Work safety precautions during the test: Use normal laboratory work safety procedures during this test.	d) Test sample preparation: One representative sample of the UUT and all optional accessories in such a way to enable maximum load possible in normal use.
e) Test conditions: •In order to minimize background noise interference, the conducted emission testing should be performed inside a shielded room •The UUT will be set up on a nonconductive (wooden) table 0.8m high above the reference ground plane and 0.4 m away from reference ground plane	f) Special recommendations: • Measurement uncertainty needs to be specified • If the quasi-peak (Q.P.) measured value also meets average limit required, the measurement with the average detector (AV) is unnecessary. When limits are measured in dB (μV) than 1 μV is regarded as 0 dB

g) Test setup (Figure 14.15):

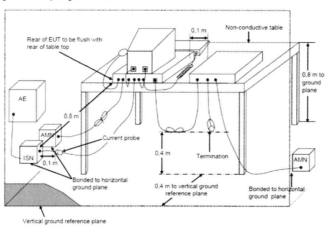

Figure 14.15   From [10].

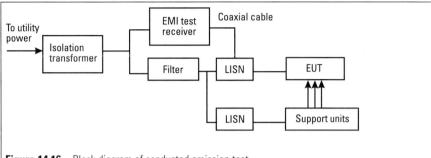

Figure 14.16   Block diagram of conducted emission test.

h) Test procedure:

• Emission level = Reading value + Correction factor
• Correction Factor = Cable loss + Insertion loss of LISN
• Margin value = Emission level - Limit
• The frequency spectrum from 0.15 MHz to 30 MHz should be investigated. The
LISN used is of 50Ω/50μH type. All readings are quasi-peak and average
values with 10 kHz resolution bandwidth of the test receiver. The UUT system shall be operated in all
typical methods specified by manufacturer. Both lines of the power mains of UUT shall be measured
and the cables connected to UUT and support units (AE-peripheral) shall be moved to find the
maximum emission levels for each frequency.
• All interface ports shall be connected to the appropriate peripheral units via specific cables and
shall be recorded (especially the cables information: length, if are shielded or unshielded).
• The emissions levels on the frequency range of 150 kHz–30 MHz will be recorded in form of tables
and spectral plots.

i) Presentation of the test results (Table 14.15):
Environmental Test Conditions:
Temperature: xx °C
Relative Humidity: yy %
Atmospheric Pressure: zzz mmHg
Tested Product:
Model_____ Manufactured by_____

Table 14.15

Power Line Measured : Line

Freq. (MHz)	Correct. Factor (dB)	Reading Value (dBμV)		Emission Level (dBμV)		Limit (dBμV)		Margin (dB)	
		Q.P.	AV.	Q.P.	AV.	Q.P.	AV.	Q.P.	AV.
0.171	0.30	57.58	41.66	57.88	41.96	64.89	54.89	-7.01	-12.93
0.174	0.30	58.92	45.01	59.22	45.31	64.75	54.75	-5.53	-9.44
0.773	0.20	23.38	15.18	23.58	15.38	56.00	46.00	-32.42	-30.62
1.230	0.14	26.40	23.77	26.54	23.91	56.00	46.00	-29.46	-22.09
2.032	0.16	23.70	21.06	23.86	21.22	56.00	46.00	-32.14	-24.78
21.868	0.39	29.70	24.70	30.09	25.09	60.00	50.00	-29.91	-24.91

Power Line Measured : Neutral

Freq. (MHz)	Correct. Factor (dB)	Reading Value (dBμV)		Emission Level (dBμV)		Limit (dBμV)		Margin (dB)	
		Q.P.	AV.	Q.P.	AV.	Q.P.	AV.	Q.P.	AV.
0.171	0.30	56.42	37.83	56.72	38.13	64.89	54.89	-8.17	-16.76
0.174	0.30	57.26	41.07	57.56	41.37	64.75	54.75	-7.19	-13.38
0.524	0.24	38.52	22.58	38.76	22.82	56.00	46.00	-17.24	-23.18
1.230	0.14	26.68	23.76	26.82	23.90	56.00	46.00	-29.18	-22.10
2.032	0.16	24.26	21.56	24.42	21.72	56.00	46.00	-31.58	-24.28
21.868	0.29	29.84	24.80	30.13	25.09	60.00	50.00	-29.87	-24.91

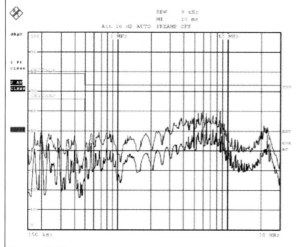

Figure 14.17

j) Observations: N/A

14.8.1.3 AC Line Fluctuation and Flicker

Test Category: Performed with the Product Energized.	Applicable Standard(s): IEC 61000-3-3
a) Scope of the test: To evaluate the UUT if produce fluctuating load in the branch circuit causing r.m.s voltage fluctuations with effect of variation in light output as perceived by the human observer as flicker.	b) Equipment needed for the test: 1) Power source, 2) flicker meter, 3) impedance network, 4) Voltage fluctuation meter
c) Work safety precautions during the test: Use normal laboratory work safety procedures during this test.	d) Test sample preparation: One representative sample of the UUT and all optional accessories in such a way to enable maximum load possible in normal use.
e) Test conditions: -The UUT will be set up on a wooden table 0.8m high above the ground plane.	f) Special recommendations: • Measurement uncertainty needs to be specified.

g) Test setup (Figure 14.18):

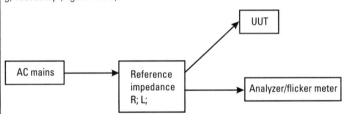

Figure 14.18   Block diagram of AC line fluctuation and flicker test

h) Test procedure:

Limit acceptable values:
Short-team flicker (P$_{st}$): 1.0
Long-term flicker (P$_{lt}$): 0.65
Relative steady-state voltage change (Dc): ≤ 3%
Relative voltage change characteristics:
(D (t)) > 3% ; (T$_{D(t)}$) : ≤ 200 ms
Maximum relative voltage change (Dmax): ≤ 4%
For voltage changes that are caused by manual switching of equipment or that occur less frequently than once per hour, Pst and Plt are not applicable.
The measurement of the rms voltage fluctuations on the ac mains caused by the equipment under test is the basis for flicker measurements. There are different methods of evaluating flicker severity (Pst) that range from direct measurement via a device called flickermeter to the use of mathematical analysis or a Pst graph provided by the standard. The direct method using the flickermeter is the reference method for true compliance-level testing. This instrument must comply with the specifications given in the IEC 61000-4-15 reference standard.
Measurement of voltage fluctuations is also a critical part of determining if electrical equipment causes excessive voltage disturbances on the ac mains. While flicker measurements provide an accurate assessment of the effect of continuous voltage changes, the voltage fluctuation measurements provide a better indication of the effect of sudden large voltage changes.
The relative voltage changes must be measured with a total accuracy better than ±8%.

i) Presentation of the test results (Table 14.16):

Environmental Test Conditions:
Temperature: xx °C
Relative Humidity: yy %
Atmospheric Pressure: zzz mmHg
Tested Product:
Model_____ Manufactured by_____

Table 14.16

Test Parameter	Measurement Value	Limit	Test Result
P_{st}	0.07	1.0	Pass
P_{lt}	0.07	0.65	Pass
$T_{D(t)}(ms)$	0	200	Pass
D_{max} (%)	0%	4%	Pass
D_C	0%	3%	Pass

P_{st} means short-term flicker indicator
P_{lt} means long-term flicker indicator
$T_{D(t)}$ means maximum time that D(t) exceeds 3%
D_{max} means maximum relative voltage change
D_C means relative steady-state voltage change

j) Observations:

Pst = 1 is the conventional threshold of irritability, and therefore the limit.
Plt = 0.65 is the conventional threshold of irritability, and therefore the limit.
Dc is the difference between two adjacent steady-state voltages relative to the nominal voltage.
(D(t)) is the change in rms voltage, relative to the nominal voltage, as a function of time and between periods when the voltage is in a steady-state condition for at least 1 second.
(Dmax) is the difference between maximum and minimum rms values of the voltage change characteristic relative to the nominal voltage.

14.8.2 Immunity Tests

The manufacturer should provide a functional description and a definition of performance (pass-fail) criteria of the product, during or as a consequence of the immunity testing. The pass-fail criteria should be based on the following:

The equipment should continue to operate as intended during and after the test. No degradation of performance or loss of function which generate an unacceptable risk of harm is allowed.

Temporary degradation or loss of function is allowed, when the function is self-recoverable or can be restored by the operation of the controls.

14.8.2.1 Electrostatic Discharge Immunity

Test Category: Performed with the Product Energized	Applicable Standard(s): IEC 61000-4-2; MIL-STD-1686C
a) Scope of the test: To evaluate the performance of the immunity to electrostatic discharges at the enclosure, accessible ports, and similar areas of the UUT.	b) Equipment needed for the test: 1) ESD simulator 2) Oscilloscope 3) Horizontal coupling plane (HCP) 1.6 x 0.8 m, 4) Vertical coupling plane (VCP) 0.5m x 0.5m 5) Discharge electrode (for air discharges and direct discharges) 6) Discharge return cable 7) Bleeder resistors, 8) Insulating support
C) Work safety precautions during the test: Special attention for the presence of the ESD high-voltage Refer to paragraph 14.6.2.2. C)	D) Test sample preparation: One representative sample of the UUT and all optional accessories in such a way to enable maximum load possible in normal use
e) Test conditions: (1) Discharge impedance (R-C Network): 330, 150 pF (2) Kind of discharge: air, contact (direct and indirect) (3) Test levels: air discharge: ±2kV, ±4kV, ±8kV, ±15kV Contact discharge: ±2kV, ±4kV, ±6kV, ±8kV HCP discharge: ±2kV, ±4kV, ±6kV, ±8kV VCP discharge: ±2kV, ±4kV, ±6kV, ±8kV (4) Discharge mode: Single discharge (5) Discharge period: At least 1 s (6) Discharge polarity: Positive and negative (7) Number of discharge: Minimum 50 times at each test point of contact discharge at least 200 times of discharge to UUT in total. Minimum 10 times at each test area of air discharge selected. (8) Pass/fail criteria: Normal performance during test and temporary degradation or loss of function or performance that is self-recoverable. In the case of table-top equipment, the UUT will be set up on a wooden table 0.8m-high on an insulating support 0.5 mm thick above the reference ground plane. In the case of floor-standing equipment, the UUT and cables will be set up on an insulating support 0.1m above the reference plane. The VCP must be parallel to the UUT at a distance of 0.1m. It is not generally permitted to mix contact and air discharges when testing to conductive surfaces. The HCP and VCP must be connected to the GRP via a cable with a 470-k resistor located at each end.	f) Special recommendations: Under normal operation, discharges are applied to those points and surfaces that are accessible to personnel during the normal operation of the equipment. Under installation and maintenance conditions, discharges are applied to those points and surfaces that are accessible to personnel installing the equipment or performing maintenance operations. The UUT should be tested to both the immunity criteria for normal operation and to the immunity criteria for installation and maintenance. The results reported should list all test points that are selected for normal operation. Measurement uncertainty needs to be specified

g) Test setup (Figure 14.19):

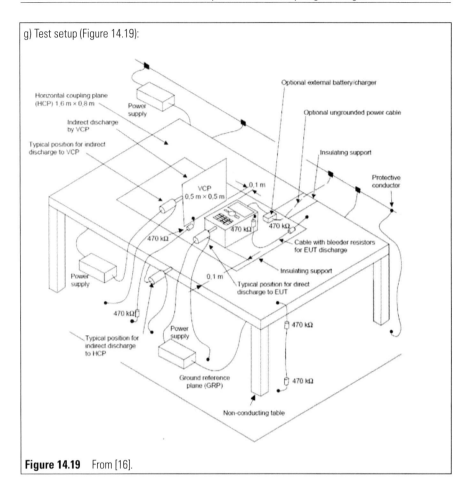

Figure 14.19   From [16].

h) Test procedure

1) Air discharge:
Potentials of ±2 kV, ±4 kV, ±8 kV, and ±15 kV (or others specified on product standards) will be applied near each applicable test point (air discharges are applied to insulating surfaces). At places where discharge occurs, the potential will be applied 20 times; 10 times negative and 10 times positive.
2) Contact discharge:
Potentials of ±2 kV, ±4 kV, ±6 kV, and ±8 kV (or others specified on product standards) will be applied to each applicable test point (contact discharges are applied to conductive surfaces and to coupling planes). In places where discharge occurs, the potential will be applied 20 times; 10 times negative and 10 times positive.
3) Indirect discharge (vertical and horizontal coupling plane):
This should be performed using the direct contact ESD test tip.
Potentials of ±2 kV, ±4 kV, ±6 kV, and ±8 kV (or other specified on product standards) will be applied to the center of the vertical edge of the coupling plane at a distance of 0.1m from the outer casing of the UUT to each applicable test point.
The potential will be applied ten times for each polarity to each location of the coupling plane. All four faces of the UUT will be completely illuminated.
An ESD of the same characteristics as for the vertical coupling plane will be applied to the horizontal coupling plane, at each side of the UUT, at a distance of 0.1m from its outer casing.
Test points selected should include all surfaces that may be contacted during the normal operation of the equipment. Test points should include (but not be limited to) wriststrap jacks, any area near a wriststrap jack that personnel may inadvertently contact while connecting the wriststrap, user-accessed components such as tape and disk drives, outer surfaces of doors and panels enclosing the UUT, edges and inner surfaces of doors (at least 5 cm from the hinge axis), and normally exposed equipment frames and shelves.
Discharges must be applied directly only to those points and surfaces of the UUT accessible to personnel during normal use. This includes areas accessible to maintenance personnel. For contact discharges, the discharge electrode tip must touch the UUT before the discharge switch is operated. For air discharges, the round tip of the electrode must approach the UUT as quickly as possible without causing mechanical damage. After each discharge, the ESD generator must be removed from the UUT so that it can be retriggered. This procedure must be repeated until all discharges are completed.

i) Presentation of the test results (Table 14.17):

Location of discharge: see below
Environmental test conditions:
Temperature: xx °C
Relative humidity: yy %
Atmospheric pressure: zzz mmHg
Tested product:
Model_____ Manufactured by_____

Table 14.17

Contact Discharge Location	Positive Polarity (kV)				Negative Polarity (kV)			
	Level 1	Level 2	Level 3	Level 4	Level 1	Level 2	Level 3	Level 4
	2	4	6	-	2	4	6	-
Indirect Mode								
Vertical Coupling Plane								
Front	1	1	1	-	1	1	1	-
Left	1	1	1	-	1	1	1	-
Rom	1	1	1	-	1	1	1	-
Right	1	1	1	-	1	1	1	-
Horizontal Coupling Plane								
Front	-	-	-	-	-	-	-	-
Direct Mode								
Front Panel	1	1	1	-	1	1	1	-
Left	1	1	1	-	1	1	1	-
Right	1	1	1	-	1	1	1	-
Top	1	1	1	-	1	1	1	-

Air Discharge Location	Positive Polarity (kV)				Negative Polarity (kV)			
	Level 1	Level 2	Level 3	Level 4	Level 1	Level 2	Level 3	Level 4
	2	4	8	15	2	4	8	15
Switch Red	2	2	2	-	2	2	2	-
Switch Power	2	2	2	-	2	2	2	-
DC Cable Connector	2	2	2	-	2	2	2	-

Comments:
1) Discharge observed, no response observed from UUT.
2) No perceived discharge, no response observed from UUT.

j) Observations: N/A

14.8.2.2 Radiated RF Electromagnetic Immunity

Test Category: **Performed with the Product Energized.**	**Applicable Standard(s):** **IEC 61000-4-3**
a) Scope of the test: To evaluate the performance of the immunity of UUT to radiated RF, electromagnetic field disturbances, for simulating the interference of transmitted electromagnetic waves.	b) Equipment needed for the test: 1) Signal generator, 2) RF power amplifier, 3) Function generator, 4) Biconical antenna and log periodic antenna or bilog antenna, Horn antenna, 5) Millivoltmeter (or power meter with power sensor), 6) Isotropic "E" field probe, 7) Dual directional coupler, 8) Power amplifier, 9) Field sensor 10) Anechoic chamber or semi-anechoic chamber (SAC), 11) Absorbers 12) RF coaxial cable, 13) CCD 14) Monitor for CCD

c) Work safety precautions during the test:	d) Test sample preparation:
Use normal laboratory work safety procedures during this test	One representative sample of the UUT and all optional accessories in such a way to enable maximum load possible in normal use.
e) Test conditions:	f) Special recommendations:
(1) Source voltage and frequency: 230V/50Hz, single phase (2) Sweeping frequency: 80MHz–1 GHz (3) Test level: 3V/m or 10V/m, the frequency step is 1% (4) The four sides of UUT are tested: front, rear, left, right (5) Modulation: 80% AM, 1k Hz dwell time (time spent in the same position) for each frequency is 3 sec. (6) Antenna polarization: horizontal and vertical (7) Pass/fail criteria: normal performance during test and temporary degradation or loss of function or performance which is self-recoverable. • In the case of tabletop equipment, the UUT will be set up on a wooden table 0.8m high on an insulating support 0.5 mm thick above the reference ground plane. • In the case of floor-standing equipment, the UUT and cables will be set up on an insulating support 0.1m above the reference plane. • This test is usually done in an anechoic chamber. Special absorbent material (2 m in length) compensates for standing waves and reflections.	• It is recommended to have a uniform field of 1.5 x 1.5 m at a distance of 3 m for more reliable test results. • Measurement uncertainty needs to be specified

g) Test setup (**Figure 14.20**):

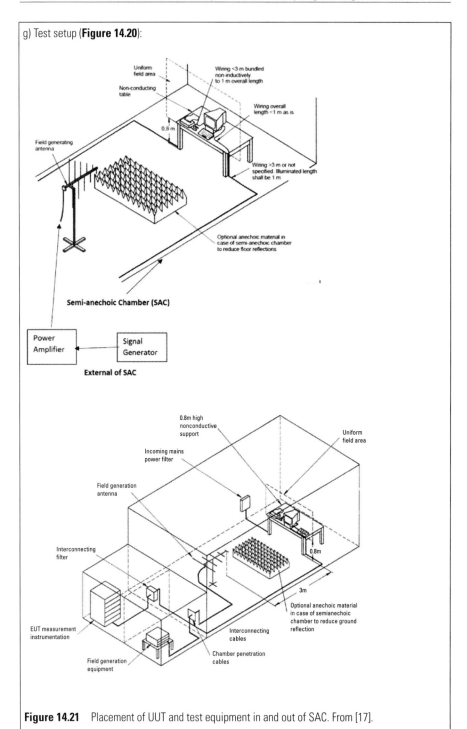

Figure 14.21   Placement of UUT and test equipment in and out of SAC. From [17].

h) Test procedure:

The UUT is subjected to a field of 3V/m, amplitude modulated 80% by a 1-kHz sinusoidal signal. The radiated Field is applied in vertical and horizontal polarization using Biconilog antenna in the frequency range of 80-1000 MHz and horn antennas in the frequency range 1000–2500 MHz. The frequency is swept using discrete increments having a value less than 1% of the fundamental frequency.
The test is carried out in a shielded room (semi-anechoic chamber).
Is recommended to conduct a preliminary radiated emission test in the frequency range 80–1000 MHz inside the semi-anechoic chamber using an E-field probe and spectrum analyzer. The surface with the maximum radiation level should be selected as the most sensitive surface.
When a degradation in the performance of the UUT is observed, the radiated field intensity level should be reduced to the threshold level, and its value should be recorded.

i) Presentation of the test results (Table 14.18):
Environmental Test Conditions:
Temperature: xx °C
Relative Humidity: yy %
Atmospheric Pressure: zzz mmHg
Tested Product:
Model_____ Manufactured by_____

Table 14.18

Frequency (MHz)		Antenna Polarity	Specification (V/m)	Pass/Fail	Imunity Threshold (V/m)
From	To				
80	1,000	Horizontal	3.0	Pass	
80	1,000	Vertical	3.0	Pass	
1,000	2,500	Horizontal	3.0	Pass	
1,000	2,500	Vertical	3.0	Pass	

j) Observations: N/A

14.8.2.3 Electrical Fast Transient (EFT) Immunity

Test Category: Performed with the Product Energized.	Applicable Standard(s): IEC 61000-4-4
a) Scope of the test: To evaluate the performance of the immunity of UUT to electrical fast transient (ETF) disturbances.	b) Equipment needed for the test: 1) Burst generator, 2) Coupling/decoupling network, 3) Capacitive clamp, 4) 33 nF capacitor probe for direct injection, 5) Reference ground plane, 6) Interconnection cable (for clamp to generator)
c) Work safety precautions during the test: Use normal laboratory work safety procedures during this test.	d) Test sample preparation: One representative sample of the UUT and all optional accessories in such a way to enable maximum load possible in normal use.

e) Test conditions:	f) Special recommendations:
(1) Source voltage and frequency: 230V/50Hz, single phase (2) Pulse rise time and duration: 5ns / 50ns (3) Pulse repetition: 5 kHz (or other specified on product standard) (4) Polarity: positive polarization and negative polarization (5) Burst duration and period: 15 ms / 300 ms (6) Test duration: > 1 minute each line (7) Time between test: 10 sec (8) Severity levels: Power line ±1kV (or other specified on product standard) Signal/control line ±0.5kV (or other specified on product standard) (9) Pass/fail criteria: Temporary degradation or loss of function or performance which is self-recoverable. • In the case of tabletop equipment, the UUT will be set up on a wooden table 0.8m high on an insulating support 0.5 mm thick above the reference ground plane. • The bursts or EFTs should be coupled by using a coupling-decoupling network or by using a coupling clamp on the UUT cables. The coupling-decoupling network for an ac/dc main supply circuit allows the test voltage to be applied non-symmetrically to the UUT's power-supply input terminals. The capacitive coupling clamp enables coupling of the fast transients to the circuit under test without any galvanic connection to the circuit terminals, cable shielding, or any part of the UUT. The clamp should be placed on a ground plane with a minimum area of 1 m^2, and the ground reference plane should extend beyond the clamp by at least 0.1 m on all sides. The generator should be connected to the end of the clamp nearest to the UUT. • In the case of floor-standing equipment, the UUT and cables will be set up on an insulating support 0.1m above the reference plane. • The minimum distance between UUT with the coupling plates of the coupling clamps (if used) and all over conductive structures, except the ground plane beneath the coupling clamp and beneath the UUT should be more than 0.5m.	• Measurement uncertainty needs to be specified

g) Test set-up (Figure 14.22):

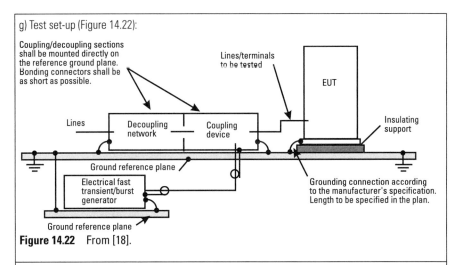

Coupling/decoupling sections shall be mounted directly on the reference ground plane. Bonding connectors shall be as short as possible.

Lines/terminals to be tested

EUT

Lines

Decoupling network

Coupling device

Insulating support

Ground reference plane

Electrical fast transient/burst generator

Grounding connection according to the manufacturer's specification. Length to be specified in the plan.

Ground reference plane

Figure 14.22 From [18].

h) Test procedure:

A EFT test signal is applied to the phase, neutral and ground lines of the UUT mains input, at a distance of 1 meter from the UUT. The test signal voltage is as specified in product standard and it is applied for 1 minute to each line, in negative and positive polarities.
The same test signal is applied to the signal lines, control and DC lines (as applicable), that are connected to the UUT. The voltage level is as specified in product standard.
Applicable signal and control lines should have a length greater than 3m.

i) Presentation of the test results (Table 14.19):

Environmental Test Conditions:
Temperature: xx °C
Relative Humidity: yy %
Atmospheric Pressure: zzz mmHg
Tested Product:
Model_____ Manufactured by_____

[x] Positive Polarity   [x] Negative Polarity

Test Point	Pass/Fail	Anomaly	Specification (kV)	Threshold (kV)
Phase	Pass	No anomaly	2.0	
Neutral	Pass	No anomaly	2.0	
Ground	Pass	No anomaly	2.0	

j) Observations: N/A

14.8.2.4 Surge Immunity

Test Category: Performed with the Product Energized.	Applicable Standard(s): IEC 61000-4-5
a) Scope of the test: To evaluate the performance of the immunity of UUT to surge (caused by over-voltages from switching and lightning transients) disturbances	b) Equipment needed for the test: 1) Surge wave generator, 2) Coupling/decoupling network, 3) Reference ground plane
c) Work safety precautions during the test: In addition to using the normal laboratory work safety procedures, during this test the following should be considered: Surge voltages and currents must be contained to insure they will not appear where they can cause damage to other instruments in the test area. The test pulses used for surge testing are of sufficient energy to cause components to fragment under fault conditions and become hazardous to personnel in unprotected environments.	d) Test sample preparation: One representative sample of the UUT and all optional accessories in such a way to enable maximum load possible in normal use.
e) Test conditions: (1) Test level: Common mode: ±0.5kV, ±1kV, ±2kV (or other specified on product standard) Differential mode: ±0.25kV, ±0.5kV, ±1kV (or other specified on product standard) (2) Number of pulses: 5 (3) Phase: 0°, 90°, 180°, 270° (4) Polarity: Positive and negative polarization (5) Repetition: max. 60 s (6) Waveform: 1.2/50 μs (open circuit voltage) 8/20 μs (short circuit current) (7) Pass/fail criteria: Temporary degradation or loss of function or performance which is self-recoverable. • The UUT will be set up on a wooden table 0.8m high above the reference ground plane. • The pulse is coupled via a coupling-decoupling network on the power line of the UUT.	f) Special recommendations: • Capacitive coupling via 9 μF (line to ground) or 18μF (line to line) capacitors is required for coupling surges to AC or DC power mains. These coupling capacitors are typically included as part of a coupler/dDecoupler (C/D) in the surge simulators. The C/D provides both coupling to the UUT power mains and a decoupler to prevent the surge from appearing on the ac mains connected to other equipment in the testing area. • Measurement uncertainty needs to be specified

g) Test set-up (Figure 14.23):

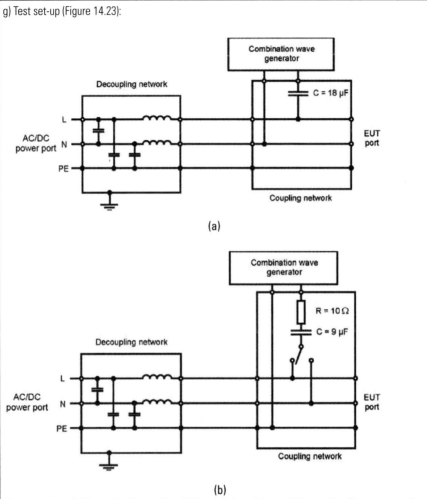

(a)

(b)

Figure 14.23 (a) Coupling line to line (differential mode), and (b) coupling line to ground (common mode) [19].

h) Test procedure:

Test voltages are applied synchronized to the voltage phase at zero-crossing and peak value of the A.C. voltage wave (positive and negative). The surges are applied line to line and line to ground. When testing line to ground the test voltage is applied successively between each of the lines and ground.

The surge is to be applied to the UUT power supply terminals via the capacitive coupling network. The power cord between the UUT and the coupling/decoupling network should be 2m in length (or shorter).

At least five positive and five negative discharges must be tested at selected points of the power supply. The pulse must be repeated at a rate of at least one per minute, and it is recommended to increase the test levels from 0.5–1 kV to 2 kV. The selected points should be 0°, 90°, 180°, and 270° of the sine wave.

i) Presentation of the test results (Table 14.20):

Environmental Test Conditions:
Temperature: xx °C
Relative Humidity: yy %
Atmospheric Pressure: zzz mmHg
Tested Product:
Model_____ Manufactured by_____
Table 14.20

Test Point	Polarity	0°/360°	90°	180°	270°	Specified Level	Remarks
Phase to ground	+	P	P	P	P	0.5, 1, 2 kV	
	−	P	P	P	P	0.5, 1, 2 kV	
Neutral to ground	+	P	P	P	P	0.5, 1, 2 kV	
	−	P	P	P	P	0.5, 1, 2 kV	
Phase to neutral	+	P	P	P	P	0.5, 1 kV	
	−	P	P	P	P	0.5, 1 kV	

j) Observations: N/A

14.8.2.5 Magnetic Field Immunity

Test Category: Performed with the Product Energized.	Applicable Standard(s): IEC 61000-4-8
a) Scope of the test: To evaluate the performance of the immunity of UUT to magnetic field disturbances.	b) Equipment needed for the test: 1) Test generator, 2) Square coil and/or rectangular coil and/or other inductive coil (e.g., Helmholtz coil); 3) Magnetic Field Probe, 4) Magnetic field tester, 5) Decoupling network, 6) Back filter
c) Work safety precautions during the test: Use normal laboratory work safety procedures during this test. Precautions must be taken if the test magnetic field may interfere with the test instrumentation and other sensitive equipment in the vicinity of the test setup. WARNING: People fitted with heart pacemakers and similar implanted or body-worn medical devices should not be exposed to the magnetic fields generated by this test.	d) Test sample preparation: -One representative sample of the UUT and all optional accessories in such a way to enable maximum load possible in normal use.

e) Test conditions:	f) Special recommendations:
(1) Test axis: X, Y and Z axes (2) Test time: 5 min / each axis (3) Field strength: 3 A/m – 30 A/m (or other specified on product standards) (4) Frequency: 50/60 Hz (5) Pass/fail criteria: Normal performance during test and temporary degradation or loss of function or performance which is self-recoverable. •-The UUT will be set up on a wooden table 0.8m high above the reference ground plane. •- The ground plane shall be a nonmagnetic metal sheet (copper or aluminium) of 0,25 mm thickness; other metals may be used but in this case, they shall have 0.65 mm minimum thickness. The minimum size of the ground plane is 1 m × 1 m. The UUT shall be placed on the ground plane with the interposition of a 0,1m thickness insulating support (e.g., dry wood). • The test generator shall be placed at less than 3m distance from the induction coil. • One terminal of the generator shall be connected to the ground plane as far as used. • The UUT and auxiliary test equipment shall be placed on the ground plane and connected to it. • The equipment cabinets shall be connected to the safety ground directly on the ground plane via the ground terminal of the UUT. • The cables supplied or recommended by the equipment manufacturer shall be used. In absence of any recommendation, unshielded cables shall be adopted, of a type appropriate for the signals involved. • All cables shall be exposed to the magnetic field for 1 m of their length. • The back filters, if any, shall be inserted in the circuits at 1 m cable lengths from the UUT and connected to the ground plane. •The induction coil, shall enclose the UUT placed at its centre. • Different induction coils may be selected for testing in the different orthogonal directions. • Induction coils used in the vertical position (horizontal polarization of the field) can be bonded (at the foot of one vertical conductor) directly to the ground plane, which represents the low side of the coil, as a part of it. In this case, 0,1m minimum distance from UUT to the ground plane is enough.	Conversion: 1A/m = 12.56mGauss = 1.26 µTesla 3A/m = 37.68mG, 10A/m = 125.6mG, • Measurement uncertainty needs to be specified

g) Test set-up (Figure 14.24):

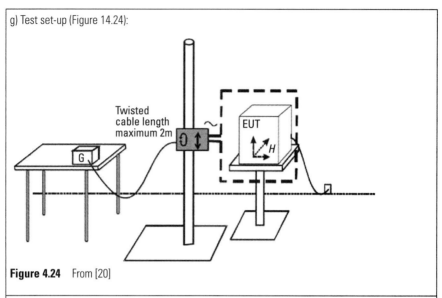

Figure 4.24   From [20]

h) Test procedure:

The UUT is subjected to a continuous magnetic field as specified in product standard by use of an induction coil of standard dimensions 1m x 1m. The induction coil is then rotated by 90° in order to expose the UUT to the test field with different orientations. Three orthogonal planes are tested. The dwell time at each frequency is not less than the time necessary for the UUT to be able to respond.

i) Presentation of the test results (Table 14.21):

Environmental Test Conditions:
Temperature: xx °C
Relative Humidity: yy %
Atmospheric Pressure: zzz mmHg
Tested Product:
Model_____ Manufactured by_____

Table 14.21

	Pass/Fail	**Strength of Magnetic Field (A/m)**
Vertical	Pass	3.0
Vertical at 90°	Pass	3.0
Horizontal	Pass	3.0

Immunity to Magnetic Field

	Background Noise Strength A/m	**Limit, A/m (-20dB for Specification)**	**Pass/Fail**
Vertical	0.03	0.3	Pass
Vertical at 90°	0.02	0.3	Pass
Horizontal	0.03	0.3	Pass

Background noise

j) Observations: N/A

14.9 Software Testing

Many of today's electrical and electronic products are provided with dedicated software for fulfilling functional requirements. In a large number of applications, the software play an important role in product basic safety with features that allow preventive and protective actions. Accordingly, software can be treated as a critical component when it is part of electrical and electronic product.

14.9.1 Why Is Software Tested?

The most challenging goal of software engineering is to find better techniques and methods for developing quality- and error-resistant software at a reasonable cost. Such software provides users with a great level of user convenience, quality, and utility.

In order to achieve high software quality, appropriate quality characteristics must be defined and taken into account. These characteristics should drive the significant architectural and design decisions. Software quality management should help to ensure that the required level of quality is reached.

To produce software that is accurate and reliable, effective testing is essential. Software testing helps to evaluate the quality of software. Executing tests in terms of the number of defects found, the tests run, and the system covered by the tests helps move toward improved quality of product [21].

Verification of the software provides information about whether the output of one phase of software development conforms to requirements of its previous phase (by examination and through the provision of objective evidence that specified requirements have been fulfilled). Additionally, the process of software validation determines if the fully developed product, using software, conforms to its requirements specification (intended use or application). Accordingly, verification is concerned with phase containment of errors, and validation aims to achieve final products that are error-free.

When testing software, each condition that violates a program's specification is called an incident. Incidents can be failures, and finding failures is the main aim of testing. However, for most real products, even after satisfactorily carrying out the testing phase, it is not possible to guarantee that the software is error-free. This is because of the fact that the input data domain of most software products is very large. It is not practical to test the software exhaustively with respect to each value that the input data may assume. Even with this practical limitation of the testing process, the importance of testing should not be underestimated. Rigorous testing includes looking for places in the user interface where a user might make a mistake in input of data or in the interpretation of the output and looking for potential weak points for intentional and malicious attack. Testing can be conducted for both the functional attributes of the software and for the nonfunctional software requirements and characteristics.

14.9.2 Which Standards Apply in Software Testing?

The software testing standards describe what testing is, how these should be organized, and which testing aims have to be met for distinct purposes of using software.

Many of ISO and IEEE standards that concern software development and software engineering are identified. Without focusing on software testing directly, applying these standards influences the software testing.

Quality characteristics of the software can be measured with a set of attributes defined for each characteristic. These characteristics help evaluate the quality of software, but they do not provide guidance in constructing high-quality software. Quality characteristics are defined in the standards ISO/IEC 9126 and ISO/IEC 25010.

Quality management system requirements are defined in the ISO 9001 standard. The main goal of these requirements is to satisfy customer needs, which is the measure of quality in software products.

The software testing steps and requirements are specified in the new ISO/IEC/IEEE 29119 series of software testing standards. The purpose of this standards series is to define an internationally agreed set of standards for software testing that can be used by any organization when performing any form of software testing. ISO/IEC/IEEE 29119-1 facilitates the use of the other ISO/IEC/IEEE 29119 standards by introducing the concepts and vocabulary on which these standards are built, as well as providing examples of its application in practice.

Table 14.23 summarizes the standards that are used for software testing. These standards refer to product, process, and technical sector of applicability. Product standards refer to software as a product and specify requirements such as those concerned with quality assurance and documentation . Process standards focus on life-cycle aspects. Sector-specific standards define requirements that have to be met in order to ensure the fail-safe or failure-tolerant operation of a particular sector product.

Further standards that influence software testing are IT frameworks such as the IT infrastructure library (ITIL) or control objectives for information and related technology (CobiT). The most notable testing-related process models are test management approach (TMap) and test process improvement (TPI).

14.9.3 What Is Software Testing?

The process of creating a program consists of the following phases:

1. Defining a problem;
2. Designing a program;
3. Building a program;
4. Analyzing the performance of a program;
5. Final arrangement of a product.

According to this classification, software testing means checking if a program for specified inputs gives correct and expected results.

A common perception of testing is that it only consists of running tests (e.g., executing the software). This is part of testing but not all of the testing activities.

Test activities exist before and after test execution; other testing activities include planning and control, choosing test conditions, designing test cases

Table 14.22
Software product quality characteristics according to ISO/IEC 25010 standard [22].

Software Product Quality							
Functional Suitability	Performance Efficiency	Security	Compatibik	Reliability	Portability	Useability	Mantainance
Appropriateness Completeness Correctness	Time behavior Resource utilization Capacity	Confidentiality Integrity Nonrepudiation Accountability Authenticity	Coexistence Inter-operability	Availability Fault tolerance Recoverability Maturity	Adaptability Installlability Replaceability	Accessibility Learnability Operability User error protection User interface aesthetics	Analyzablity Modifiability Modularity Reusability Testability

Table 14.23
List of Standards Used for Software Testing

Categories of Standard	Name of Standard
Product Standards	ISO 6592: Guidelines for the Documentation of Computer Based Application Systems
	ISO 9126: Software Product Quality Measurement
	ISO 14598: Software Product Evaluation.
	ISO 15026: System and Software Integrity Levels.
	ISO 15910: Software User Documentation Process.
	ISO 18019: Guidelines for the Design and Preparation of Software User Documentation.
	ISO/IEC 25010 Systems and Software Engineering - Systems and Software Quality Requirements and Evaluation (SQuaRE) System and Software Quality Models.
	ISO 25051: Requirements for Quality of Commercial Off-The-Shelf (COTS) Software Product and Instructions for Testing.
	ISO 90003- Guidelines for the Application of ANSI/ISO/ASQC 9001To The Development, Supply, Installation and Maintenance of Computer Software
	IEEE 730-2002 IEEE Standard for Software Quality Assurance Plans
	IEEE 829 Standard for Software Test Documentation.
	IEEE 1008 Standard for Software Unit Testing.
	IEEE 1012 IEEE Standard for Software Verification and Validation
	BS 7925-2 Software Component Testing.
	NASA-STD-8719.13 Software Safety Standard
Process Standards	ISO/IEC 12119: Software packages—Quality requirements and testing
	ISO/IEC 12207 Information Technology - Software life cycle processes.
	ISO 14102: Guidelines for the Evaluation and Selection of CASE Tools.
	ISO/IEC 15289 Content of life-cycle information products.
	ISO 15504: Software Process Assessment.
	ISO 15939: Software Measurement Process.
	ISO/IEC/IEEE 29119 - Software and systems engineering -- Software testing
	ISO/IEC 33063- Information technology — Process assessment — Process assessment model for software testing

Table 14.23 (continued

Categories of Standard	Name of Standard
Sector Standards	Automotive - MISRA
	Aviation-DO-178B: Software Considerations in Airborne Systems and Equipment Certification
	Defense – Def Stan 00-55
	Railway- DIN/EN50128 Railway applications. Communications, signaling and processing systems
	Healthcare-IEC 62304: Medical Device Software – Software life cycle processes
	IEC61508-3:Functional safety of electrical/electronic/programmable electronic safety-related systems

and checking results, evaluating completion criteria, reporting on the testing process and system under test, and finalizing or closure (e.g., after a test phase has been completed). Testing also includes reviewing of documents (including source code) and static analysis [23].

Both dynamic testing and static testing can be used as a means for achieving similar objectives and provide information in order to improve both the system to be tested and the development and testing processes.

There can be different test objectives, listed as follows:

• Finding defects;

• Gaining confidence about the level of quality and providing information;

• Preventing defects.

The thought process of designing tests early in the life cycle (verifying the test basis via test design) can help preventing defects from being introduced into code. Reviews of documents (e.g., requirements) also help to prevent defects appearing in the code.

Debugging and testing are different. Testing can show failures that are caused by defects. Debugging is the development activity that identifies the cause of a defect, repairs the code, and checks that the defect has been fixed correctly. Subsequent confirmation testing by a tester ensures that the fix does indeed resolve the failure. The responsibility for each activity is very different—testers test and developers debug.

The most visible part of testing is executing tests. However, to be effective and efficient, test plans should also take into account the time required to plan the tests, design test cases, prepare for execution, and evaluate status.

14.9.4 How Is Software Testing Done?

Software can be tested in three ways [21]:

- 1. Black box testing;
- 2. White box testing;
- 3. Gray box testing.

White box testing is highly effective in detecting and resolving problems, because bugs (manifestations of errors in a software, also known as faults) can often be found before they cause trouble. In brief, this method is defined as testing software with the knowledge of the internal structure and coding inside the program. White box testing is also called white box analysis, clear box testing, or clear box analysis. It is a strategy for software debugging (the process of locating and fixing bugs in computer program code or the engineering of a hardware device) in which the tester has excellent knowledge of how the program components interact. This method can be used for web services applications, but is rarely practical for debugging in large systems and networks. White box testing can be considered security testing (a process to determine that an information system protects data and maintains functionality as intended) method that can be used to validate whether code implementation follows intended design, to validate implemented security functionality, and to uncover exploitable vulnerabilities.

Black box testing is testing software based on output requirements and with knowledge of the internal structure or coding in the program. A black box is any device whose workings are not understood by or accessible to its user. For example, in telecommunications, it is a resistor connected to a phone line that makes it impossible for the telephone company's equipment to detect when a call has been answered. In data mining, a black box is an algorithm that doesn't provide an explanation of how it works. In film-making, a black box is a dedicated hardware device, equipment that is specifically used for a particular function, but in the financial world, it is a computerized trading system that doesn't make its rules easily available.

Gray box testing it is defined as testing software while already having some knowledge of its underlying code or logic. It is based on the internal data structures and algorithms for designing the test cases more than is black box testing but less than is white box testing. This method is important when conducting integration testing between two modules of code written by two different developers, where only interfaces are exposed for test. Also, this method can include reverse engineering to determine boundary values. Gray box testing is nonintrusive and unbiased because it doesn't require that testers have access to the source code.

14.9.4.1 Phases of Testing [21]

Testing is done in phases, referred to as staging by practitioners. There is no definite scheme for the phases used; but there is a typical layout that can be followed or become a corporation-wide standard. The partitioning of phases roughly resembles the classical V-model and is outlined as follows.

1. Component tests (also known as module test or unit test): Developers test modules they have coded, working both incrementally and iteratively.

2. *Central component tests:* In contrast to the first phase, these optional tests are usually not done on the developers' working stations. Components are tested on a system that is similar to the target system for the finished software product.

3. *Integration tests* (also known as product tests): These tests are usually not done on developers' working stations but on testing systems. Components developed by multiple developers are integrated, and their interplay is checked.

4. *Performance tests:* A first, optional performance test can be conducted during or shortly after the system test. It aims at getting a first idea of the system's performance and at finding possible performance problems.

5. *System tests:* The system test is a large-scale integration test that is less technically focused. Only black box tests are used. Testing commonly is done by dedicated testers who do not know the source code.

6. *Performance tests:* As soon as all main components are integrated, another optional measurement driven functionally can be done. Whereas the first performance test could reveal algorithmic limitations and general misconceptions, the system performance measures the program under realistic conditions.

7. *Acceptance tests:* During these test, almost finished programs re checked for compliance with the specification. If development follows an agile paradigm, acceptance tests are regarded as the key tests.

8. *Pilot tests:* The almost finished product is installed on a number of products. It is first tested and eventually can be used productively. Beta tests put the concept of pilot tests to a larger number of testers.

9. *Productive usage:* Software is put into regular operation

10. *Maintenance:* Optionally, the system is maintained. This is particularly important if development is a periodic process that leads to new releases of the program.

14.9.4.2 Test Tools

Several test tools [21]—also known as computer-aided software testing (CAST)—are listed as follows.

Tools for the management and control of testing (with a narrow technical focus, used to plan testing and measure the testing effort and results, among other functions);

- Test case generators;
- Analytic tools (automate static tests or enable static testing techniques that would not be feasible without tool support);
- Unit test tools such as JUnit or CppUnit.
- GUI testing tools;
- Tools to test web applications such as HtmlUnit or Selenium and mutation test tools;
- Computer-aided software engineering (CASE);
- Test execution tools (functional);
- Test harness/unit test framework tools;
- Test comparators;
- Coverage measurement tools;
- Security tools;
- Dynamic analysis tools;
- Performance testing/load testing/stress testing tools;
- Monitoring tools.

References

[1]   IEC TR 62354, "General Testing Procedures for Medical Electrical Equipment," Geneva, 2014.

[2]   Associated Research, Inc., "Safe Workstation Best Practice," Lake Forest, IL, 2016.

[3]   QuadTech, Inc., "Electrical Safety Testing Reference Guide," East Maynard, Massachusetts, 2002.

[4]   Baretich, M. F., "Electrical Safety Manual," *AAMI ESM4,* Association for the Advancement of Medical Instrumentation, Arlington, VA, 2015.

[5]   Brauer, R. L., *Safety and Health for Engineers,* New York: Van Nostrand Reinhold, 1990.

[6]   IECEE OD 5014, "Instrument Accuracy Limits," Geneva, 2016.

[7]   IECEE OD 5011, "Requirements for Traceability of Calibrations and Calibration Intervals," Geneva, 2015.

[8]   ISO/IEC 17025, "General Requirements for the Competence of Testing and Calibration Laboratories," Geneva, 2005.

[9]   Associated Research, Inc., "Hipot-Product Catalog," Lake Forest, IL, 2015.

[10]   CISPR 22, "Information Technology Equipment—Radio Disturbance Characteristics—Limits and Methods of Measurement," Geneva, 2008.

[11]   IECEE OD 5010, "Procedure for Measuring Laboratory Power Source Characteristics," Geneva, 2015.

[12]   IEC 60601-1, "Medical Electrical Equipment—Part 1: General Requirements for Safety and Essential Performance," Geneva, 2005 and 2012.

[13]   Begeš, G., I. Pušnik, and J. Bojkovski, "Testing of Heating in a Black Test Corner," *IMTC/2000: Proceedings of the 17th IEEE Instrumentation and Measurement Technology Conference,* Baltimore, Maryland, May 1–4, 2000.

[14]   IEC 61010-1, "Safety Requirements for Electrical Equipment for Measurement, Control, and Laboratory Use—Part 1: General Requirements," Geneva, 2010.

[15]   Schaffner-Chase EMC Ltd., *RF Emission Testing: A Handy Guide,* Luterbach, Switzerland, 2000.

[16]   IEC 61000-4-2, "Electromagnetic Compatibility (EMC)—Part 4-2: Testing and Measurement Techniques—Electrostatic Discharge Immunity Test," Geneva, 2008.

[17]   IEC 61000-4-3 +A1+A2, "Electromagnetic Compatibility (EMC)—Part 4-3: Testing and Measurement Techniques—Radiated, Radio-Frequency, Electromagnetic Field Immunity Test," Geneva, 2006–2010.

[18]   IEC 61000-4-4, "Electromagnetic Compatibility (EMC) Part 4-4: Testing and Measurement Techniques—Electrical Fast Transient/Burst Immunity Test," Geneva, 2012.

[19]   IEC 61000-4-5, "Electromagnetic Compatibility (EMC)—Part 4-5: Testing and Measurement Techniques— Surge Immunity Test," Geneva, 2014.

[20]   IEC 61000-4-8, "Electromagnetic Compatibility (EMC)—Part 4-8: Testing and Measurement Techniques—Power Frequency Magnetic Field Immunity Test," Geneva, 2009.

[21]   Majchrzak, T. A., "Improving Software Testing," *Springer Briefs in Information Systems,* 2012.

[22]   ISO/IEC 25010, "Systems and software Engineering—Systems and Software Quality Requirements and Evaluation (SQuaRE)—System and Software Quality Models," Geneva, 2011.

[23]   Pezze, M., and M. Young, *Software Testing and Analysis: Process, Principles and Techniques,* New York, NY: John Wiley and Sons, 2007.

Selected Bibliography

Agilent Technologies, "Cookbook for EMC Precompliance measurements" Application Note 1290-1.

Alberico, D., et al., *Software System Safety Handbook,* JSSSP and EIA, 1999

ANSI, "ANSI Essential Requirements," New York, 2017.

Armstrong, K., and T. Williams, "EMC Testing Part 1—Radiated Emissions," *EMC + Compliance Journal,* Feb. 2001, pp. 27–39.

Armstrong, K., Williams, T., "EMC Testing Part 2—Conducted Emissions," *EMC + Compliance Journal,* April 2001, pp. 22–32.

ASTM D149, "Standard Test Method for Dielectric Breakdown Voltage and Dielectric Strength of Solid Electrical Insulating Materials at Commercial Power Frequencies," 2013.

Bates, C., "Experiences with Test Automation," in *Software Test Automation: Effective Use of Test Execution Tools* (ed. By Fewster, M., and D. Graham, New York: ACM Press, 1999.

Black, R., *Pragmatic Software Testing,* Indianapolis: John Wiley and Sons, 2007.

Black, R., *"Managing the Testing Process,"* Indianapolis: John Wiley and Sons, 2009.

CISPR 11, "Industrial, Scientific and Medical Equipment—Radio-Frequency Disturbance Characteristics—Limits and Methods of Measurement," Geneva, 2015.

CISPR 16-1-1, "Specification for Radio Disturbance And Immunity Measuring Apparatus and Methods," Geneva, 2015.

CISPR 16-4-2, "Specification for Radio Disturbance and Immunity Measuring Apparatus and Methods—Part 4-2: Uncertainties, Statistics, and Limit Modeling—Uncertainty in EMC Measurements," Geneva, 2011.

CISPR 32, "Electromagnetic Compatibility of Multimedia Equipment—Emission Requirements," Geneva, 2015.

Ewing, P. D., and K. Korsah, "Technical Basis for Evaluating Electromagnetic and Radio-Frequency Interference in Safety-Related I&C Systems," NUREG/CR-5941, Lockheed Martin Energy Research Corp., Oak Ridge Nat. Lab., April 1994.

Gensel, R., "Immunity Testing for the CE Mark," Associated Research, 2006.

Hammer, W., *Product Safety Management and Engineering,* Des Plaines, IL: American Society of Safety Engineers, 1993.

Hammer, W., and D. Price, *Occupational Safety Management and Engineering,* Englewood Cliffs, NJ: Prentice Hall, 2001

IEC 60060-1, "High-Voltage Test Techniques. Part 1: General Definitions And Test Requirements," Geneva, 2010.

IEC 60065, "Audio, Video and Similar Electronic Apparatus—Safety Requirements," Geneva, 2014.

IEC 60601-1-2, "Medical Electrical Equipment, Collateral Standard: Electromagnetic Compatibility—Requirements and Tests," Geneva, 2014.

IEC 60950-1+AMD1+AMD2, "Information Technology Equipment—Safety—Part 1: General Requirements," Geneva, 2005–2013.

IEC 61000-3-2, "Electromagnetic Compatibility (EMC)—Part 3-2: Limits—Limits for Harmonic Current Emissions (Equipment Input Current ≤ 16A per Phase)," Geneva, 2014.

IEC 61000-3-3, "Electromagnetic Compatibility (EMC)—Part 3-3: Limits—Limitation of Voltage Changes, Voltage Fluctuations and Flicker in Public Low-Voltage Supply Systems, for Equipment with Rated Current ≤ 16A per Phase and Not Subject to Conditional Connection," Geneva, 2013

IEC 61000-4-1, "Electromagnetic Compatibility (EMC)—Part 4-1: Testing and Measurement Techniques—Overview of IEC 61000-4 Series," Geneva, 2014.

IEC 61000-6-1, "Electromagnetic Compatibility (EMC)—Part 6-1: Generic Standards—Section 1: Immunity Standard For Residential, Commercial and Light-Industrial Environments," Geneva, 2016.

IEC 61000-6-2, "Electromagnetic Compatibility (EMC)—Part 6-2: Generic Standards—Immunity Standard for Industrial Environments," Geneva, 2016.

IEC 62304, "Medical Device Software—Software Life Cycle Processes," Geneva, 2006.

IEC 62368-1, "Audio/Video, Information and Communication Technology Equipment—Part 1: Safety Requirements," Geneva, 2014.

IECEE OD 2048, "Utilization of Customers' Testing Facilities," Geneva, 2016.

IECEE OD 5012, "Laboratory Procedure for Preparation, Attachment, Extension and Use of Thermocouples," Geneva, 2015.

IECEE, OD 5013, "Leakage (Touch) Current Measurement Instruments," Geneva, 2015.

IEEE C62.41, "IEEE Recommended Practice on Surge Voltages in Low-Voltage AC Power Circuits," Institute of Electrical and Electronics Engineers, 2002.

IEEE 1044, "Standard Classification for Software Anomalies," IEEE, New York, 2010.

ISO 5725-1, "Accuracy (Trueness and Precision) of Measurement Methods and Results – Part 1: General Principles and Definitions," Geneva, (1994+1998).

ISO 9004, "Managing for the Sustained Success of an Organization—A Quality Management Approach," Geneva, 2009.

ISO/IEC 12119, "Information Technology—Software Packages—Quality Requirements and Testing," Geneva, 1994.

ISO/IEC 14598, "Information Technology—Software Product Evaluation," Parts 1–6 , Geneva, Switzerland, 1999–2001.

ISO/IEC 29119-1, "Software and Systems Engineering—Software Testing—Testing Concepts and Definitions," Geneva, 2013.

ISO/IEC 29119-2, "Software and Systems Engineering—Software Testing—Test Processes," Geneva, 2013.

ISO/IEC 29119-3, "Software and Systems Engineering—Software Testing—Test Documentation," Geneva, 2013.

ISO/IEC 29119-4, "Software and Systems Engineering—Software Testing—Test Techniques," Geneva, 2015.

ISO/IEC 29119-5, "Software and Systems Engineering—Software Testing—Keyword Driven Testing," Geneva, 2016.

LAB 34, "The Expression of Uncertainty in EMC Testing," UKAS—United Kingdom Accreditation Service, Feltham, Middlese 2002.

Mansdorf, S. Z., *Complete Manual of Industrial Safety*, Englewood Cliffs, NJ: Prentice Hall, 1993.

MIL-STD-461F, "Interface Standard Requirements for the Control of Electromagnetic Interference Characteristics of Subsystems and Equipment," U.S. Department of Defense, 2007.

MIL-STD-462D, "Measurement of Electromagnetic Interference Characteristics," U.S. Department of Defense, 1999.

NIS 81, "The Treatment of Uncertainty in EMC Measurements," National Physical Laboratory, United Kingdom.

Pol, M., R. Teunissen, and E. vanVeenendaal, *Software Testing: A Guide to the TMapApproach*, Boston, MA: Addison-Wesley, 2001.

Rashid, M. H., ed., *Power Electronics Handbook (Second Edition)*, San Diego, CA: Academic Press, 2007.

Rubin, J., and D. Chisnell, *Handbook of Usability Testing: How to Plan, Design, and Conduct Effective Tests*, Hoboken, NJ: John Wiley and Sons, 2008.

Slaughter Company, Inc., "Basic Facts About Electrical Safety Testing," Lake Forest, IL, 2005.

Watkins, J., *Testing IT: An Off-the-Shelf Software Testing Process*, New York: Cambridge University Press, 2001.

Wysopal, C., et al., *The Art of Software Security Testing: Identifying Software Security Flaws*, Boston, MA: Addison-Wesley, 2006.

Whitaker, J. C., ed., *The Electronics Handbook*, Boca Raton, FL: CRC Press, IEEE Press, 1996

Williams, T., *EMC for Product Designers*, Oxford, UK: Elsevier, 2006.

Williams, T., and K. Armstrong, *EMC for Systems and Installations*, Oxford, UK: Newnes, 2000.

15

Manufacturing a Safe Electrical Product

15.1 Responsibility of the Manufacturer

A *manufacturer* is any natural or legal entity that designs, manufactures, fabricates, assembles, or processes a finished product with a view to placing it on the market *under its own name* (or trademark).

The manufacturer is responsible and liable to its customers and employees as well to society with regard to all the electrical safety aspects of products it places on the market. These safety aspects are in fact the measure of willingness to remain in the business and to continue to compete in the market. The responsibilities of the manufacturer apply also to any natural or legal people who assemble, pack, process, or label ready-made products with a view to their being placed on the market under their own names. Where subcontracting takes place, manufacturers must retain the overall control for the product and ensure that they receive all the information that is necessary to fulfill their responsibilities. The manufacturer that subcontracts some or all of its activities may in no circumstances discharge itself from its responsibilities (e.g., to an authorized representative, a distributor, a retailer, a wholesaler, a user, or a subcontractor.

The liability that is involved in manufacturing the products, starting with design and ending with decommissioning is huge, and it can be protected by having in place a sound quality program with following elements that ensure the output of safe products [1]. Elements of a quality program include the following:

- Implementing safety design into products;
- Drawing up and keeping available the required technical documentation;
- Developing consistent production and postproduction processes;
- Managing risks;
- Complying with applicable standards and regulation of the target market;
- Obtaining third-party independent assessment and certification;
- Being cautious when advertising and marketing;
- Collaborating with customers;
- Monitoring product safety in the specific industry.

Regardless of the type of the manufactured equipment, or whether there is low or high volume, the first priority is an *ethical* approach and then, the responsibility and liability of placing safe equipment on the market.

To do this properly, each manufacturer should have, in addition to the above elements, very well trained personnel, a safe work environment, and a sound and well-developed supply chain.

15.2   Supply Chain

The *supply chain* is represented by the sequence of processes involved in the production and distribution of any products/equipment. That sequence starts from the manufacture of products and extends to the servicing of these products on the market.

The introduction of new products to manufacturing implies first some administrative aspects, and during those steps, the design team continues to closely assist the manufacturing by performing the following tasks [2]:

- Elaborating the bill of materials, including critical components, mandatory suppliers, and alternate components;
- Collaborating with the selected suppliers, which must appear on the list of approved manufacturers and suppliers;
- Managing the required audits at the selected suppliers;
- Reaching the targeted cost.

During this process, there are likely to be corrective actions that will regulate the new product's introduction to the market.

It is the manufacturer's responsibility to control, by inspection or otherwise, all subcontractors and suppliers with special attention to those that prepare assemblies or parts with safety implications; all purchased material and services should conform to specified requirements.

When ordering the *safety-critical components*, evidence (i.e., certificates) of the components' conformity with applicable standards should be requested. Reference to advertising data sheets or catalog pages are not relevant. Additionally, compliance with environmental requirements (i.e., RoHS, REACH, and WEEE) [3–5] need to be considered. Safety data sheets (formerly material safety data sheets [MSDSs]) are valuable sources of information regarding the hazards (i.e., chemical or biological), emergency responses, and protective measures pertaining to any hazardous material.

The presence of the requested characteristics, performance, and safety approvals for the procured components should be proven and documented (i.e., with CoCs, test reports, and routine tests performed by suppliers) and confirmed on a regular basis by the incoming inspections.

Implementing a *quality management* system within the manufacturing yields advantages that should be regarded by the manufacturer as an investment; having the manufacturing locations registered based on an ISO quality standard offers, at a minimum, the following advantages:

- Reduced errors and costly penalties;
- Increased confidence in the products and services that a manufacturer provides;
- The opportunity for manufacturers to make smarter and more organized decisions regarding production, remaining continuously within the set limits that define sustainability;
- Establishment of areas of responsibility across the organization;
- Improvement in communications within the supply chain;
- Highlighting clearly any deficiencies;
- Opportunities for continuous assessments and improvements;
- Opportunities to work in the public sector, where, lately, these criteria have become mandatory.

Dependable manufacturers are able to take better advantage of a quality management system and can rely on sound manufacturability due to its implementation.

15.3 Manufacturability

Design for manufacturability (DFM) is a means of proactively addressing product issues early in the design cycle. This is the method for creating robust product designs that are insensitive to long-term dynamic variation in the processes and materials used in manufacturing and that are immune to foreseeable misuse of products in the environments in which they are used.

DFM provides a means for integrating specific manufacturing concerns into a product's design to obtain a product that is easier to manufacture with excellent overall quality.

DFM must include a detailed understanding of the processes that will be used to build the product, how the processes are developed, how the processes are controlled, and how continuous improvement is accomplished. For this to occur one uses workmanship standards and DFM and assembly (DFMA) guidelines.

DFM includes, but is not limited to, the following aspects of manufacturing [6]:

- Optimizing the fabrication process;
- Material selection;
- Part cost estimation;
- Assembly time;
- The detailed assembly process;
- Tooling cost estimates and strategies to reduce cost.

ANSI/J-STD-001 classifies three levels of electronic assemblies based on end-item use. These classifications were established to reflect differences in producibility, complexity, functional performance requirements and verification frequency. They are described as follows:

- *Class 1 or general electronic products:* Consumer products, computer and computer peripherals, and hardware suitable for applications where the major requirement is a function of the completed assembly;
- *Class 2 or dedicated service electronic products:* Includes communication equipment, sophisticated business machines, and instruments, where high performance and extended life are required and for which uninterrupted service is desired but not critical;
- *Class 3 or high-performance electronic products:* Includes equipment for commercial and military products where continued performance or performance on demand is critical.

With respect to these classifications are established criteria to design the manufacturability of a product.

When discussing manufacturability, we consider the extent to which equipment can be manufactured within the targeted cost and with maximum reliability, and then maintaining it within the characteristics defined within the PDD.

It is well-known that using the "general engineering art of designing products" will lead to an easy way to manufacture a product. The capabilities of the manufacturing location, the machineries that are used to produce the product, and the implementation of all of the applicable *good manufacturing practice* (GMP) requirements will bring to the production line a product easy to be reproduced within the expected limits. All of the functional requirements of the product should be continuously monitored in different stages of manufacturing, when the integration of electrical safety is embedded within the manufacturing process.

15.4 Integration

There is no doubt that the integration of electrical safety with manufacturing is a result of having in mind from the design stage that a product has to be safe for everybody, not only for the end user.

Providing sound effective training to the people in manufacturing and integrating them as the first customers is necessary. Workplace safety represents a primary goal for manufacturers, and it is amplified by the culture that is found within each company.

Starting with all of the used materials and ending with the operation of the manufacturing equipment, from the first operation within the technologic flow of the process to packaging and preparation of equipment for its journey to customers, represents a goal that should be achieved with no unwanted events.

Providing the proper maintenance of the manufacturing equipment will ensure not only the functionality of it within the expected parameters. In addition, it will work safely, indirectly protecting workers during the process.

Respecting all of the regulatory documents that address the safety aspects integrated within the process of manufacturing imposed by the authorities with the jurisdiction to do so not only displays but educates the workers to maintain the same level of care during their activity.

The process of *integration* of electrical safety considerations during the manufacturing process represents in fact the ability of the manufacturer to address the requirements of the standards and regulations concerned with electrical safety-related work practices for employee workplaces. In fact, it is necessary to safeguard employees relative to the following:

- Hazards during activities such as the installation, inspection, operation, and maintenance of electric equipment, associated with electrical energy;
- Work practices for employees performing other work activities that can expose them to electrical hazards during manufacturing.

In the United States, these considerations are presented with detailed requirements in the standard for electrical safety in the workplace, NFPA 70E, which warn that treating these requirements superficially is "in the detriment of both: worker safety and a company's reputation." Using the concepts and strategies of the NFPA 70E can enhance a company's worker safety and productivity and, moreover, is certain to generate a positive image about the company.

Taking shortcuts by eliminating totally or partially preventive maintenance or other service to manufacturing equipment will lead to poor outcomes in the equipment manufactured by it. Further, it may lead to recalls or, even worse, to accidents that may be fatal. Understanding the regulatory framework, in terms of the safety and the efficiency of electrical equipment maintenance and modifications, is imperative. It facilitates the use of safe work practices under both OSHA regulations and NFPA 70E during installation, maintenance, use, and manufacturing of the electrical equipment. It is critical to understand that in any situation where OSHA regulations establish a more stringent guideline than NFPA, the OSHA regulations must take precedence; as federal regulations, they have the force of law.

Integrating electrical safety requirements into the design of a manufactured electrical system is important to ensuring that workplace safety is provided. Moreover, it will inspire workers to put their efforts into ensuring the safety of the manufactured equipment.

The life of the equipment, which starts with the end of its manufacture, begins with the process of the final inspection, which in numerous cases, ends with the routine tests in production. Then, the equipment is packaged and prepared to travel to the next destination, or it will be stored in the warehouse where the manufacturer defines and assumes conditions of storage, including environmental conditions and sometimes even intermediate processes to keep the equipment functional (e.g., charging the batteries at specified levels during specified time periods). Finally, the equipment is transported to the end user.

15.5   Routine Tests (Production Line Testing)

At the end of manufacture (or during the manufacturing) and before transportation, manufacturers must prove that the equipment is functional and safe. In general, safety measures should be applied exclusively for the purpose of safety and should not share any task with functionality.

To acquire the proof, which exists in records kept for each piece of equipment—according to the quality management system that the manufacturer has in place and to the applicable requirements of the *product standards* used and/or in conjunction with the requirements imposed by a surveillance program that is part of the *listing/certification* agreement with a NRTL, which provides the listing/certification of the equipment—a *set of minimal routine tests* are administered to the equipment.

These routine tests (production line tests) are tests to which each individual device (100% of the production line) is subjected after (or during) manufacture to detect failures and/or unacceptable tolerances in manufacturing (or materials) that may not be detected by functionality tests and that may create a hazardous situation. The purpose of these tests is to evaluate the safety parameters that could also be affected by the manufacturing process. (e.g., tightening torque of washers, missing a star-washer, wiring-related issues, grounding clips, insulation barriers, warning labels, insulation, rubber rings, and below-ring core transformers) These are performed in order to guarantee an acceptable level of safety for the equipment.

Therefore, each product must be verified for a number of essential parameters including the following:

- Dielectric strength;

- Grounding continuity;

- Leakage currents in normal condition.

In Europe, all of these requirements are defined within the factory inspection procedures under harmonized requirements issued by the *European Testing, Inspection and Certification System* (ETICS). In North America, the NRTL is involved in the process of listing/certification of equipment. In Europe, all of these requirements are defined within the factory inspections procedures harmonized requirements issued by the European Testing, Inspection and Certification System (ETICS) and in North America by the NRTL involved in the process of listing and certification of the listed/certified products. Routine tests are an important element of the follow-up inspections conducted at factory locations of certified products; they make it possible to ensure that the necessary routines and procedures are being maintained at an acceptable level.

15.5.1 Performing the Routine Tests

For setting up the routine tests (production line testing), the following standards can be used:

- EN 50106, for household appliances;
- EN 50116, for information technology equipment (ITE);
- EN 50144-1, for handheld motor-operated tools;
- EN 50514 and IEC 62911, for audio, video, and ITE;
- ENEC 303, for luminaries covered by the EN 60598 standard series;
- IEC/EN/UL 61010-1, for measuring, laboratory, and control equipment.

Routine tests should be made with equipment fully assembled. The equipment should not be unwired, modified, or disassembled for the test, but snap-on covers and friction-fit knobs may be removed if they would interfere with the tests. The equipment should not be energized during the tests, but the mains switch should be in the on position.

15.5.1.1 Dielectric Strength

Dielectric strength is a test of voltage as specified in the applicable product standard, or by a NRTL for the following:

- Basic insulation, applied between the mains terminals connected together on one side and grounded accessible conductive parts on the other.
- Double insulation, applied between the mains terminals connected together on one side and low-voltage (42.4-V peak or less) accessible conductive parts, including terminals, on the other. For this test, the contacts of any output terminal intended to be connected to circuits of other equipment that are not hazardous live are considered to be accessible conductive parts.

The test voltage is raised to its specified value within 10s and maintained for a maximum of 2s. No breakdown or repeated flashover should occur. Corona effects and similar phenomena are disregarded.

WARNING: Never perform a dielectric strength test on energized circuitry or equipment.

1. *Location:* Select an area away from the main stream of activity that employees do not walk through in the performance of their normal duties. If this is not practical because of production line flow, then the area should be roped off and marked for *high-voltage testing.* No employees other than the test operators should be allowed inside.

   If benches are placed back-to-back, be especially careful about the use of the bench opposite the test station. Signs should be posted such as:

"DANGER: High-voltage test in progress. Unauthorized personnel keep away."

2. *Work area:* Perform the tests on a nonconducting table or workbench, if possible. If use of a conductive surface cannot be avoided, be certain that it is connected to a good earth ground and that the high-voltage connection is insulated from the grounded surface.

There should not be any metal in the work area between the operator and the location where products being tested will be positioned. Any other metal in the work area should be connected to a good ground, never left "floating."

Position the tester so that the operator does not have to reach over the product under testing to activate or adjust the tester. Keep the area clean and uncluttered. All test equipment and test leads not necessary for the test should be removed from the test bench and put away. The difference between the product being tested and the product that is waiting to be tested should be apparent to both the operator and to any observers

Do not perform these tests in a combustible atmosphere or in any area where combustible materials are present.

15.5.1.2 Grounding Continuity

A continuity test is made between the earth pin of the appliance inlet or of the mains plug for nondetachable power supply cords on one side and all grounded accessible conductive parts that can be energized in a SFC on the other. (see Figure 15.1.) No value is specified for the test current. The test is conducted with a grounding continuity tester (i.e., an ohmmeter in the lower scale).

Evaluate the continuity between these points and the PE terminal from the appliance inlet or between the mains plug of the tested equipment.

Figure 15.1 Example of location for grounding continuity test.

Note: When testing a painted metallic surface make sure that the probe is penetrating the paint at hidden area.

To evaluate the integrity of the ground connection, during the test the ground wire should be flexed along its length. If during the flexing, changes in continuity indication are observed, it should be assumed that the ground connection is damaged.

15.5.1.3 Leakage Current

As specified in product standards, measurements of leakage current are taken with a MD that consists of resistive and capacitive networks designed to simulate the impedance of the human body. The placement of the MD determines the type of test. (See Section 14.2.6.)

For this test, the equipment is energized. Factors evaluated are the earth leakage, touch (enclosure) current and for medical equipment patient leakage current.

Note: Routine tests can cause damage to equipment if carried out incorrectly or inappropriately. In addition, where it is applicable, the standards define even the documentation that should be maintained by the manufacturer in respect to these routine tests in production. All the routine tests should be performed with calibrated equipment and records of the calibration should be available for factory inspections.

Table 15.1 contains a test record sheet example that is used to record test results produced by routine test electrical safety protocol.

Table 15.1
Test Record for Routine Tests

Safety—Production Line Test Report

Equipment Under Test:	Serial Number:	Supply Voltage	Class	Applied Part Type (If Applicable)

1. Dielectric strength test

Description	Expected Results	Results Breakdown (Yes/No)	Pass/Fail (Note P or F)
.........Vac or Vdc between............... and.................	Test should be completed with PASS result		

Equipment Used:

Description	Manufacturer and Model	Serial Number	Calibration Due Date

Tested by: _____ Signature: _____Date: _____

2. Earth continuity

Test Point No.	Description of Testing Points	Expected Results	Pass/Fail (Note P or F)
1		Continuity	
2		Continuity	
3		Continuity	
4		Continuity	
5		Continuity	

Equipment used:

Description	Manufacturer and Model	Serial Number	Calibration Due Date

Tested by: _____ Signature: _____Date: _____

3. Leakage Currents

Number	Description	Expected Results	Measured Current (mA)	Pass/Fail (Note P or F)
	Earth leakage current (normal condition)	$\leq$ ......mA		
	Touch current (normal condition)	$\leq$ ......mA		
	Patient leakage current (normal condition)—if applicable	$\leq$ ......mA		

Equipment Used:

Description	Manufacturer and Model	Serial Number	Calibration Due Date

Tested by: _____ Signature: _____Date: _____
Verified by: _____ Signature: _____Date: _____

_____
Notes: _____

QA Review Of Production Line Testing:
ACCEPTED/ REJECTED
QA: _____ Signature: _____ Date: ___ /___/____

References

[1]   U.K. Government Department for Business, Energy & Industrial Strategy, "*Product Safety for Manufacturers*," 2015.

[2]   FDA, "Report on FDA's Approach to Medical Product Supply Chain Safety," July 2009.

[3]   EU Directive 2002/95/EC, "Use of Certain Hazardous Substances in Electrical and Electronic Equipment (RoHS) Directive," *Official Journal of the European Union,* January 27, 2003.

[4]   REACH EC 1907/2006, "European Regulation on Registration, Evaluation, Authorisation and Restriction of Chemicals," Brussels, Belgium, 2006.

[5]   EU Directive 2002/96/EC, "Waste Electrical & Electronic Equipment (WEEE) Directive," *Official Journal of the European Union,* January 27, 2003.

[6]   Chiang, W. C., A. Pennathur, and A. Mitai, "Designing and Manufacturing Consumer Products for Functionality: A Literature Review of Current Function Definitions and Design Support Tools," *Integrated Manufacturing Systems 12,* 2001, pp.430–448.

Selected Bibliography

Bolintineanu, C., and S. Loznen, "Product Safety and Third Party Certification," in *The Electronic Packaging Handbook* (ed. By G. R. Blackwell), Boca Raton, FL: CRC Press LLC, 2000.

EN 50514, "Audio, Video and Information Technology Equipment—Routine Electrical Safety Testing in Production," CENELEC, Brussels, 2014

EN 50116, "Information Technology Equipment—Routine Electrical Safety Testing in Production," CENELEC, Brussels, 1996

FDA, 21 "CFR Parts 808, 812, and 820, Medical Devices; Current Good Manufacturing Practice (CGMP); Final Rule," Federal Register, October 7, 1996.

Harris, K., and C. Bolintineanu, "Electrical Safety Design Practices Guide," Tyco Safety Products Canada Ltd, Rev 12, March 14, 2016.

IEC 62911, "Audio, Video and Information Technology Equipment—Routine Electrical Safety Testing in Production," Geneva, 2016.

http://www.aispro.com/news/hmi-touch-panel-pc-meets-iec-ul-61010-1-safety-requirements.

http://www.allaboutcircuits.com/technical-articles/designing-for-manufacturability/.

http://www.cpsc.gov/en/Business--Manufacturing/Testing-Certification/General-Use-Products-Certification-and-Testing/.

http://www.evaluationengineering.com/the-why-when-and-how-of-electrical-safety-testing.

https://www.ksl.com/index.php?sid=29667258&nid=481.

http://www.npd-solutions.com/pdforum.html.

http://www.plantengineering.com/single-article/pat-adoption-allows-for-safety-in-electrical-tes
ting/9c2cef230eb174b4f3fc808384c0625a.html.

http://www.psma.com/ul_files/forums/safety/estguide2.pdf.

Tang, C. S., "Making Products Safe: Process and Challenges," *Springer International Commerce
Review,* 2008, 8, 48–55.

Wang, X., et al., "A Production Planning Model To Reduce Risk and Improve Operations
Management," *International Journal of Production Economics,* 124, 2010, 463–474.

16

Education and Training for Compliance and Product Safety Professionals

16.1 Introduction

To yield products that satisfy the safety expectations of society, manufacturers must invest significantly in the training and professional development of technical people.

Engineers, designers, and other technical people involved in product development need to take care of the application of the principles of compliance and product safety engineering to the design, manufacturing, and marketing of products. Compliance and product safety professionals need to be instructed on the following:

- The concepts of hazard-based safety engineering and product safety theory;
- Analysis of hazardous situations;
- Basic understanding of tests;
- Fundamental knowledge of and methods;
- Risk assessment and failure analysis;
- The need for product safety to be part of the entire life cycle of the product (from idea to decommissioning);
- Writing and presenting engineering reports;

- Participation in design reviews;
- The role of standards and how they are developed and maintained;
- How product safety relates to product liability.

Building a safe and secure product requires that organizations have well-defined processes and methods for planning, designing, developing, testing, implementing, and decommissioning.

However, due to a lack of education and experience in the field of regulatory approvals in general and electrical safety in particular, many companies do not have engineering personnel with sufficient knowledge to perform and attain the required product safety objectives.

The engineer or technical personnel associated with product safety engineering must be versatile, creative, and well-informed. The question here is: How do we provide the necessary formative professional information to practitioners of product safety engineering to help advance the safety and functionality of products without compromising safety?

Over the last 30 years, engineering has made considerable technical progress, but, unfortunately, failure, product liability claims, and product safety litigation are still a problem.

Engineers need to understand the process of determining what, where, when, why, and how something could happen. Nevertheless, in many situations, they fail to estimate correctly, fail to evaluate precisely, fail to implement rigorously, fail to test adequately, fail to perform safety analysis, and fail to adequately instruct the user. It seems that despite broad efforts to train qualified product safety engineers, something is missing.

By opening a newspaper to the "Help Wanted" ads, we can determine some of the skills needed for product safety engineers, product safety officers, and compliance engineers some skills [1]. Some examples follow:

> The candidate will primarily ensure that product safety aspects are implemented and maintained in compliance with global requirements. Write, review, and maintain all product safety specifications, ensuring that the information complies with current global regulation. Keep abreast of regulatory changes and trends and take proactive measures to implement changes when required. Review and maintain a working database of relevant design specification for internal use. Assist on preparation of the products for testing in accordance with relevant standards.

> Candidates should be educated to a minimum of degree level in electrical or mechanical sciences, with a minimum of two years' experience in product safety or with relevant qualification or training.

Candidates should determine the applicable requirements to design safe products for compliance. Also need to write accurate and concise design and purchase specifications for critical components to achieve safety compliance goals.

A good working knowledge of EU requirements is needed and some experience of U.S. guidelines would be a distinct advantage. A good understanding of environmental regulations and prior knowledge of the advanced product safety principles will be an advantage.

It is difficult to predict how many suitable engineers will apply for such positions. Many will have a degree level in electrical or mechanical sciences, but basic experience in product safety is generally not obtained in university.

Perhaps some academic staff do not consider compliance engineering and product safety as examples of the leading-edge technology subjects that are desirable today. Product safety is not a top priority among schools of engineering—and the academic sector is not preparing engineering students to support or replace those engineers who are currently involved in product safety projects.

There seems to be a lack of long-term commitment to technical support. Most professional engineering associations point out that product safety is an issue of utmost importance in engineering practice and management. However, this is not enough.

Various authoritative texts, including general safety engineering literature, expressly designated product safety literature, and recommended product safety standards, are present for self-education in the field. Additionally, training sessions provided by consultants, private workshops, or by nonauthorized education units are a compromise solution. This kind of education is incomplete and sometimes superficial, due to absence of a unity in methodology and contents. Even with all of these resources, there is a limited number of resources available to engineering personnel to obtain education in the area of product safety. While there are various sources of product safety educational programs available to engineers, a comprehensive formal educational program at the university level is urgently needed. Product safety education should also be taught in business schools—schools that produce many of our business leaders—and to technical marketing professionals.

Appropriate training should be conducted to ensure that those participating in product safety activities know their responsibility and role and have the appropriate skills to properly carry out their contribution to product safety activity.

It is essential that all product safety practitioners are deemed competent in the safe and effective design, manufacturing, and/or use of the products and that they can demonstrate this competence. Furthermore, product safety practitioners need to possess the knowledge, skills, and ability to safely and effectively practice without direct supervision.

In December 2005, the U.S. Standards Strategy established standards education as a national priority:

> "Establish standards education as a high priority within the United States private, public, and academic sectors. Education programs covering the development and implementation of standards need to become a high priority within the United States. These programs must focus on the needs of leaders and top executives, those who participate in the development of standards, university and college students, and other interested parties."

Some regions, especially Asia, pay much more attention to standards and product safety education. South Korea, China, India, and Japan are beginning to see the strategic value of standards and product safety and are introducing these subjects into university curricula.

If countries intend to spend considerable resources to educate their best and brightest engineering students in the field of standardization, compliance, and product safety, these countries will gain a clear and distinct competitive advantage in the increasingly complex global marketplace of the future.

In the years to come, product safety engineering will continue to evolve from an engineering art to an engineering science. Therefore, the need to understand the theoretical and the practical application of product safety principles becomes more essential. It needs to become an integral part of the engineering curriculum. Programs in product safety engineering should be developed to provide both quality and the depth of knowledge and skills needed for entry-level and progressive positions all around the world.

16.2 Compliance and Product Safety Engineering in Senior Design Courses

In order to address product safety engineering appropriately, a wide range of knowledge and skills are needed, including the following:

- A high technical understanding and ability to assess, recognize, and prevent all types of hazards and risk factors;
- Knowledge of relevant standards, regulations, codes, acts, laws, and liability;
- An ability to deal with and motivate people, to communicate clearly, and to develop and manage plans.

Accordingly, we have performed a training needs analysis to identify the training needs of all staff in relation to product safety. This training needs analysis was carried out to ensure competencies for a product safety engineer. We believe that the proposed program in compliance and product safety engineering that resulted from this analysis has the following strengths:

- It meets the needs of industry and are market-driven and career-oriented;
- It meets the requirements for professional accreditation;
- It is based on interdisciplinary courses that include safety, legal, regulatory, economic, environmental, and ethical considerations;
- It offers a complete engineering program along with a specialized focus in business and management.

We believe that the program satisfies the criteria for accreditation and that the proposed curriculum provides the minimum practical quantitative requirements in each of the applicable compliance and product safety categories.

As part of the program, students learn and gain experience via a flexible combination of lectures, laboratory tests, computer simulations, independent research and design tasks, and individual and group projects. They also garner experience in documenting and presenting their findings to both technical and nontechnical audiences. Each student's progress and accomplishments is assessed in a variety of ways, including tests, written and oral examinations, and peer and independent evaluation of projects, reports, and presentations. Small student groups design realistic products from concept to global marketing.

The jury for estimation of achievement in this program should include representatives from academia, industry, governmental organization, and regulatory bodies.

A typical plan program in product safety engineering would cover the following issues [2]:

- New product development—safety by design;
- New product manufacture—safety by control;
- New product evaluation—safety by testing;
- Product safety hazards;
- General criteria for compliance;
- Product safety standardization;
- Basic safety concepts and considerations;
- Failure mode analysis;

- Abnormal conditions;
- Selection of components;
- Construction;
- Safety performance;
- Labeling (markings and instructions);
- EMC;
- Safety of equipment that uses radiation;
- Programmable electronic systems (software);
- Dependability;
- Risk analysis;
- Usability;
- Regulatory affairs;
- Testing for safety;
- Instrumentation for testing;
- Safety cost estimation;
- Global market access.

The proposed curriculum takes into consideration the needs of industry and guidelines established by products regulatory bodies.

The only way engineers will be well prepared to play their compliance and product safety roles is through good academic preparation and continuing education.

16.3   Training Resources Development

For manufacturers and testing houses, there needs to be a continuous program for training of the compliance and product safety professionals. The rate of changes in international regulations and in product safety standards requires a periodic updating of the knowledge of the involved personnel.

A training program should be kept up-to-date. Internal lectures, participation at seminars, conferences and congresses, webinars, and online courses represent a few of the methods for updating the information. At a minimum of once per month, compliance and product safety professionals should attend one of the above events.

A similar training program should apply to newly hired compliance and product safety personnel to introduce new employees to the specific aspects of maintaining compliance and product safety knowledge.

Before performing any work, new employees should complete specific training followed by testing in the following subjects:

1. The company overview;

2. The role of compliance and product safety overview;

3. Training in specific work for which the new employee was hired;

4. Work safety training;

5. Quality system training;

6. Code of ethics overview.

All records of periodical training and evaluation of the employees need to be maintained, as requested by the company quality system.

There are many resources available for compliance and product safety training, including books, magazines, workshops, in-house classes, online courses and webinars, and the compliance and product safety community—the IEEE-PSE Society (www.ieee.org/soc/pses/) and the IEEE-EMC Society (www. emcs.org). Another resource is found in professional events, such as symposiums, conferences, congresses, Internet forums, and websites.

The raw material of information will become the decisive performance factor. The companies with a competitive advantage are those that achieve success in the creation and distribution of information, in the efficient conversion of this information into applied knowledge, and, particularly, in the broad-based exploitation of this knowledge.

16.4   Professional Certification

Professional certification is appropriate for engineers and technicians whose training and experience has primarily focused on problems, engineering design, and corrective measures associated with minimizing or eliminating hazardous situations.

Certification provides confirmation that a person meets certain criteria in knowledge and problem-solving ability. Certification can be beneficial on multiple levels. For the certifying organization, it provides standard practices that create discipline within the industry, it provides awareness and advances in technology, and it can provide increased cooperation between organizations. For the employer, it can result in an increased level of safety, higher product yield, and increased customer and employee confidence (which produces dedication and improved teamwork). For the certified professional, it provides credibility in the industry; and it demonstrates knowledge, experience, and competency. Moreover, certification typically creates increased opportunities for career advancement and increased earnings. It is clearly a form of professional development that can improve job performance through the increased confidence that comes with knowing what you know. Becoming certified often requires extensive training and testing. This could mean, as in the case of facility certification, that the facility follows processes that meet the requirements of industry standards. Companies that become certified are looking to ensure a higher quality of product and higher product yield. In the case of individuals, certification verifies a level of technical skill that will differentiate them from those not certified.

Example of bodies which provide personal certification for compliance and product safety professionals include the following:

- The International Association for Radio, Telecommunications and Electromagnetics (iNARTE)—www.inarte.org;
- The ESD Association (ESDA)—www.esda.org.

Measurements of learning success (or failure) must be undertaken periodically during the process of professional certification. Corrections can be made every so often to improve the process. The total learning in both quantity and process should be assessed over each complete cycle of certification. With continuous improvement, professional certification programs will maintain their high quality.

References

[1] DiBiase, A. A., "The Urgent Need to Integrate EMC and Product Safety into Engineering Curriculum of Technical Universities," *Interference Technology,* March 2012.

[2] Loznen, S., "Product Safety Engineering as a Challenge for Academia," *Product Safety Engineering Newsletter,* IEEE-PSES. Vol. 10, No. 4, 2014.

Selected Bibliography

Blaise, J. C., P. Lhoste, and J. Ciccotelli, "Formalization of Normative Knowledge for Safe Design," Safety Science 41, 2003, pp.241–261.

Gambatese, J. A., "Research Issues in Prevention Through Design," Journal of Safety Research 39, 2008, pp.153–156.

In Compliance , www.incompliancemag.com.

Interference Technology (formerly ITEM), *www.interferencetechnology.com.*

Safety Link, *www.safetylink.com.*

Glossary

This glossary focuses on terms that have a specific meaning in product compliance and safety. Some related nonspecific terms are also included if they play a major role in product compliance and safety, such as terms used in quality assurance and manufacturing. This glossary aims primarily to support communication within the international product compliance and safety community by providing a harmonized vocabulary. The glossary lists alphabetically terms and their definitions or meaning in relationship to this book.

Abnormal condition   Product operating conditions (e.g., voltage, current, power, frequency, stability, environment, and other, unintended conditions.

Accessible part   Part of an electrical product that can be touched by means of the standard test finger or any human body part.

Accessory   Additional component that can be added to or integrated with a product in order to achieve the intended use or expand the products use.

Accompanying document   Documentation that is supplied with a product or accessible on the Internet or elsewhere, containing information for the user, explaining how the product is operated, and providing safety warnings, commands, and specifications of the product and its models.

Accuracy   The degree of uncertainty with which a measured value is correlated to the true value.

Accreditation   A procedure by which an authoritative body gives formal recognition that a body or person is competent to carry out specific tasks (ISO/IEC Guide 2).

Active power   A term used to describe the electrical work done by a load.

Admittance   The reciprocal of Impedance (1/Z).

Air clearance   Shortest path in air between two conductive parts.

Air discharge   A method for testing ESD-protection structures in which the ESD generator is discharged through an air gap between the generator and the tested product.

Alternating current (AC)   An electric current that reverses direction at regular intervals, with a magnitude that varies continuously in a sinusoidal manner with respect to frequency.

Ambient temperature   The temperature of the air immediately surrounding a given item.

American wire gauge (AWG)   A standard system used in the United States for designating the size of an electrical conductor based on a geometric progression between two conductor sizes.

Ampacity   The current in amperes that a conductor can carry continuously under given conditions of use without exceeding its temperature rating.

Ampere-hour capacity (storage battery)   The number of ampere-hours that can be delivered under specified conditions of temperature, rate of discharge, and voltage.

Amplitude modulation   A modulation method in which the carrier amplitude changes with the input signal amplitude.

Anode   The positive pole (the positive electrode).

Apparent power (volt-amps)   The product of the applied voltage and current in an AC circuit that is supplied to a load.

Appliance coupler   Mechanical means for connecting a power supply cord to an electrical product without the use of a tool; consists of mains connector and an appliance inlet.

Appliance inlet   Part integrated in or fixed to electrical product for connecting the detachable power supply cord.

Applicant   A submitter of the product and owner of the file. The applicant can be the manufacturer or can be represented by an agent.

Applied part (in a medical products)   Part that during the use of the product necessarily comes into physical contact with the patient to perform its function.

Arc flash   An arcing fault is the flow of current through the air between phase conductors or phases and neutral or ground. An arcing fault can release tremendous amounts of concentrated radiant energy at the point of the arcing in a small fraction of a second result.

Arrester Device that limits surge voltage by diverting it, also known as a surge arrestor.

Artwork   Drawing made to scale, of the agency mark, control number, and standard name and numbers as they will appear on the product documents.

Assessment   Activity of determination of quantitative or qualitative value of a product, service, activity, or process in regard to given quality or acceptance criteria. Similar to evaluation.

Audit An independent evaluation of products or processes to ascertain compliance to standards, guidelines, specifications, and/or procedures based on objective criteria.

Authority having jurisdiction (AHJ)   An organization, office, or individual responsible for enforcing the requirements of a code or standard or for approving equipment, materials, an installation, or a procedure—includes electrical inspectors, building officials, and code enforcement agents.

Automatic disconnection of supply   Interruption of one or more of the line conductors affected by the automatic operation of a protective device in case of a fault.

Autotransformer   A transformer in which the primary and the secondary windings have part or all of their turns in common.

Auxiliary power An alternative power source or power that is made available to supply a product.

Bandwidth   The data-carrying capacity of a transmission path, measured in bits or bytes per second.

Battery One cell or a combination of two or more chemical cells connected together electrically to furnish electric current (Merriam-Webster Dictionary)

Battery management unit   The control circuit typically used in a lithium ion battery as a protection circuit to provide information to the primary charge and discharge control circuit and/or act as the redundant control circuit to act when the primary control circuit fails.

Bleeder resistor A resistor usually connected across a capacitor to discharge the capacitor in the OFF status of the product.

Bonding   Electrically connection of conductive paths to ensure electrical continuity (the paths are at the same potential).

Breakdown voltage   The voltage at which in an insulation material's insulating properties are destroyed, permitting current flow.

Burn in Continuous operation of a product prior to putting it to use for identifying defects or failures.

Bushing   An electrically insulating lining for a hole to protect a through conductor (Merriam-Webster Dictionary)

Cable   A term generally applied to the larger sizes of bare or weatherproofed (covered) or insulated conductors. It is also applied to describe a number of insulated conductors twisted or grouped together.

Cable harness   A string of cables and/or wires that transmit informational signals or power. The cables may be bound together by clamps, cable ties, cable lacing, sleeves, electrical tape, conduit, a weave of extruded string, or a combination thereof.

Calibration   Set of operations that establish, the relationship between values indicated by a measuring instrument and the corresponding known values of the parameter measured.

Capacitance (or C, measured in farads)   The amount of electric charge that can be stored at a given voltage. Charge can, for example, be stored in a capacitor or human body.

Capacity (battery)   The quantity of electricity delivered by a battery under specific conditions and a specified time, usually expressed in ampere-hours.

Cathode   The negative pole (the negative electrode).

Cell (battery)   An electrochemical component comprised of an anode, cathode, separator, and electrolyte that converts chemical energy to electrical energy.

Charge (battery)   The conversion and storing of electrical energy from an external source, into chemical energy within a cell or battery.

Certification   Procedure by which a third party gives written assurance that a product, process, or service conforms to specified requirements (ISO/IEC Guide 2).

Circuit A conductive path through or over which electrons can flow.

Circuit board   Also known as a printed circuit board (PCB), is a nonconductive board with conductive electrical traces, connecting component together.

Circuit breaker A device that can be used to manually open or close a circuit and/or to interrupt the flow of current when the current in a circuit exceeds a specified limit.

Circuit voltage The potential difference between two points of a circuit.

Circular-mil (cmil) The area of a circle with a diameter of one mil (1/1000 inch), used to describe the cross-sectional area of a conductor. One cmil equals approximately 0.0000008 square inches.

Class I Term referring to an electrical product in which protection against electric shock includes an additional means of protection by connecting to protectively earth the accessible parts of metal or internal parts of metal, which can be energized with hazardous voltages if the basic insulation fails. (Do not confuse with Class I used in different regulations.)

Class II Term referring to an electrical product in which protection against electric shock includes means of protection such as double or reinforced insulation. There is no provision for protective earthing, but such a product can have a connection for functional earthing. (Do not confuse with Class II used in different regulations.)

Classified product A product that has been investigated and found to conform to standards for specific risks only, such as a risk of fire without consideration of other hazards (e.g., mechanical or electric shock).

Cold condition Refers to nonenergized electrical circuit or product at the ambient temperature.

Compliance The capability of the product to satisfy, for example, standards, conventions, or regulations in laws.

Common mode noise Undesired electrical signals in two or more conductors that are equal in amplitude and phase with respect to each other.

Component Constituent part of a product (can be, e.g., electrical or mechanical).

Compound An insulating or jacketing material made by mixing two or more ingredients.

Conductive part Part that can conduct electric current.

Conductivity The ability of a conductor to allow current to flow, often expressed as a percent of the conductivity of a same-sized conductor of soft copper .

Conducted Energy transmitted via cables or PCB connections.

Conductor   (1) A wire or combination of wires that can carry an electrical current. Conductors may be insulated or bare. (2) Any medium that allows electrons to flow through it.

Conductor shield   A semiconducting material, normally cross-linked polyethylene, applied over the conductor to provide a smooth and compatible interface between the conductor and insulation.

Conduit   A channel for holding and protecting conductors and cables, made of metal or an insulating material, usually circular in cross-section like a pipe. Also referred to as a duct.

Conformity assessment Systematic examination of the extent to which a product, process, or service fulfills specified requirements (ISO/IEC Guide 2).

Connector   A coupling device used to connect conductors together.

Consistency   The degree of uniformity through standardization.

Constraint   A statement of restriction that modifies a requirement or set of requirements by limiting the range of acceptable solutions.

Contact discharge   An ESD test method where the ESD generator makes direct contact with the tested product.

Cooling   Removal of heat from a product through radiation, convection, forced air, or liquid means.

Coordination   Relating to the protection of the power system, the process of coordinating the fuse, breakers, and reclosers of a system, to allow the downstream devices to operate first.

Corona discharge   An electrical discharge at the surface of a conductor accompanied by the ionization of the surrounding gasses. A corona can be visible or produce an audible noise.

Coulomb   Unit of electric charge in SI units (International System of Units). A Coulomb is the quantity of electric charge that passes any cross-section of a conductor in one second when the current is maintained constant at one ampere.

Creepage distance   The shortest distance between two conductors as measured along the device that separates them. Creepage distance is normally a design parameter of insulators or insulating bushings.

Crest value   The maximum value of a waveform. This is normally associated with electrical fault magnitude or transients (crest factor = maximum value/true RMS value.) (For sinusoidal waves, crest factor = 141/100 = 1.41.)

Crimping termination   Connection in which a metal sleeve is mechanically secured to a conductor.

Crowbar   Type of overvoltage protection in which a silicon controller rectifier (thyristor) or similar circuit, is designed to force a power supply output voltage to a designed value, when a fault or stress condition occurred.

Current-limiting   The output current is limited to a designed maximum output level, independent of the load applied to the output.

Customer   Current or potential buyer or user of products or services.

Data sheet   Document that contains the required test or measurement results of a standard test.

Decibel (dB)   A unit used to express the magnitude of change in level of electric signal or sound intensity. A voltage ratio of 1 to 10 is equal to 20 dB, 10 to 1 to 20 dB, 100 to 1 to 40 dB and 1,000 to 1 to 60 dB. A power ratio of 10 to 1 is 10 dB.

Defect   A flaw in a component or design.

Degradation   An unwanted change in expected or designed performance. Degradation does not necessarily lead to a malfunction or failure and can be associated with the end of the useful life of a product.

Derating   To lower the rated capability of a product because of deterioration or inadequacy. (At elevated temperatures, the output power rating in a power supply is reduced.)

Detachable power supply cord   Flexible cord intended to be connected to electrical product by means of an appliance coupler.

Dielectric   1) Any electrical insulating medium between two conductors. 2) The medium used to provide electrical isolation or separation.

Dielectric constant   A number that describes the dielectric strength of a material relative to a vacuum, which has a dielectric constant of one.

Dielectric test   A test that is used to verify a solid insulation system. A voltage is applied of a specific magnitude for a specific period of time.

Dielectric withstand   The ability of insulating materials and spacings to withstand specified overvoltages for a specified time (one minute unless otherwise stated) without flashover or puncture.

Differential mode noise   That component of noise measured with respect to output or input to its returns; it does not include common-mode noise.

Dip solder terminal   The terminals on a connector that are inserted into holes in the PCB and then soldered in place.

Direct current (DC)   Electric current in which electrons flow in one direction only; opposite of alternating current.

Discharge (battery)   The conversion of the chemical energy of a cell or battery into electrical energy and withdrawal of the electrical energy into a load.

Disconnect switch   A simple switch that is used to disconnect an electrical circuit.

Duct A channel for holding and protecting conductors and cables, made of metal or an insulating material, usually circular in cross-section like a pipe. Also referred to as conduit.

Earth [ground (United States)]   See ground.

Effectively grounded   Intentionally connected conductors or electric equipment to earth, where the connection and conductors are of sufficiently low impedance to allow the conducting of an intended current.

Electrical enclosure   Enclosure barrier that prevents access to energized parts to prevent electrical shock or electrocution.

Electrical safety Recognizing hazards associated with the use of electrical energy and taking precautions so that hazards do not cause injury or death.

Electric shock   Physiological effect resulting from an electric current flowing through a human or animal body.

Enclosure   Exterior surface of electrical product or parts thereof, affording the type and degree of protection suitable for the intended application.

Equipotential bonding   Provision of electric connections between conductive parts, intended to achieve the state when these parts are at the same electric potential.

Error   A human action that produces an incorrect result.

ESD protection Devices added to input and output pins on an IC to protect the internal circuitry from the damaging effect of electrostatic discharge.

Electric contact State of two or more conductive parts that touch each other accidentally or intentionally and form a single continuous conductive path.

Elicitation   The act of obtaining information from people or systems. In the context of product compliance and safety engineering, elicitation is the process of gathering requirements from other practitioners in the field (e.g., manufacturers and testing personnel).

Evaluation Similar to assessment.

Failure Deviation of the component, product, or system from its expected performance. The outcome of this condition may be benign or pose a hazard.

Fault close rating The ability, in amps, of a switching device to close into a fault of specific magnitude, without excessive arcing.

Fault current The current that flows as a result of an abnormal condition. This current may be small or large in magnitude.

Fixed Term meaning fastened or otherwise secured at a location either permanently or so that it can only be detached by means of a tool.

Flame resistance The ability of insulation or jacketing material to resist flaming combustion.

Flashover An unintended electrical discharge through air between two different potentials or to ground. Flashovers can occur between two conductors or across insulators to ground or product bushings to ground.

Floating output The output of a power supply or power converter that is ungrounded or not referenced to another output. The floating outputs are fully isolated and may be referenced positive or negative by the user. Outputs that are not floating share a common return and, as such, are referenced to one another.

Follow-up service Refers to the process of ensuring continuing conformity of the product to the specific approval requirements. The FUS is done by regular (yearly, biannually, or quarterly or at other established frequency) inspection at manufacturing facilities.

Frequency In AC systems, the frequency at which the current changes direction, expressed in hertz (cycles per second); a measure of the number of complete cycles of a waveform per unit of time.

Functional earthing Connection of a circuit to earth for functional purposes.

Functional insulation Insulation between conductive parts, necessary for the proper functioning of the product.

Fuse An electrical protection device that terminates an electric circuit once the current exceeds a designed level.

Fuse arcing time The amount of time required to extinguish the arc in a fuse when the fuse opens to clear the fault current.

Galvanic isolation Represents the isolation between two circuits that have no ohmic connection. Galvanic separation is achieved by using a transformer, optocoupler, or other means.

Ground   (1) An electrical term meaning to connect to the earth. (2) A conducting connection, whether intentional or accidental, by which an electric circuit or product is connected to the earth.

Ground fault   An undesired current path between ground and an electrical potential.

Ground plane   A conducting surface or plate used as a common electrical reference point for circuits

Guard   Part of product (e.g., casing, cover, screen, or door) used to provide protection by means of a physical barrier.

Handheld   Term referring to electrical products intended to be supported by the hand during normal use.

Harmonic   A sinusoidal wave frequency that that is a multiple of the fundamental wave frequency.

Harmonic distortion   The presence of harmonics that change an AC waveform from sinusoidal to complex.

Hazardous live part   Live part that, under certain conditions, can give a harmful electric shock.

High voltage   Voltage over 1,000-V AC or over 1,500-V DC or over 1,500-V peak value

Holdup time   Total time when an output remains active after the input has been turned OFF or switched OFF.

Impedance   (1) The total opposing force to the flow of current in an AC circuit. (2) The combination of resistance and reactance affecting the flow of an alternating current generally expressed in ohms.

Immunity   The property of a product that enables it to reject an electrical disturbance.

Induced current Unwanted or undesired current induced in a conductor from a nearby electromagnetic field.

Inductance   (1) The property of a circuit in which a change in current induces an electromotive force. (2) Magnetic component of impedance.

In-phase   A condition of two waveforms when they cross the reference line at the same time and in the same direction.

Inrush current   The initial surge of current into a product when the product is initially energized or switched ON.

Insulation coordination Mutual correlation of insulation characteristics of electrical products taking into consideration the expected micro-environment and other influencing stresses.

Insulation failure The state of the insulation in which relevant material properties (physical, chemical, electrical) are altered sufficiently to cause an unacceptable risk.

Insulator (1) A material that prevents the conduction of electricity, heat, or sound. (2) A device that is used to electrically isolate a conductor or electrical device from ground or a different electrical potential.

Intended use (purpose) Use of a product, from the functional point of view, in accordance with the specifications, instructions, information, and characteristics specified by the manufacturer.

Internal electrical power source Electrical power source for operating product that is a part of the product and that produces electrical current from some other form of energy (e.g., chemical, mechanical, solar, or nuclear).

International System of Units (SI) A universal system of units in which the following six units of measurement are considered basic: meter, kilogram, second, ampere, kelvin degree, and candela.

Inverter A device that converts DC electricity into single-phase or multiphase AC electricity.

Isolated neutral system System in which the neutral point is not intentionally earthed, except for high-impedance connections for protection or measurement purposes.

Labeling Written, printed or graphic matter affixed to a product or any of its containers or wrappers, or accompanying a product, related to identification, technical description, and use of the equipment, but excluding shipping documents.

Laboratory accreditation Formal recognition that a testing laboratory is competent to carry out specific tests.

Lay direction (1) The direction in which the wires of a conductor are twisted. (2) The twist of conductors in a cable.

Leakage current An unwanted electric current through a conductive path under normal operating conditions

Let-go threshold (current) Maximum value of electric current through a human body at which that person can release himself or herself from the current source.

Lightning   Lightning is a powerful natural electrostatic discharge produced during a thunderstorm. Lightning's abrupt electric discharge is accompanied by the ionization of air and emission of light.

Limit switch   A protective device used to open or close electrical circuits when certain conditions are met (for example, air temperature or air pressure safety levels).

Limited approach boundary   An approach limit at a distance from an exposed live part within which an electrical shock hazard exists.

Limited-current source A power source that provides a desired controlled electrical current to a circuit, irrespective of the output voltage.

Listed Equipment or materials—included in a list published by an organization acceptable to the authority having jurisdiction and concerned with product evaluation—that maintains periodic inspection of production of listed equipment or materials and whose listing states either that the equipment or material meets appropriate designated standards or has been tested and found suitable for use in a specified manner (NFPA regulations governing committee projects).

Listed component   Components that are evaluated by an accredited certification organization acceptable to the authority having jurisdiction and concerned with component evaluation that maintains periodic inspection of production.

Live part   Conductor or conductive part intended to be energized in normal operation, including a neutral conductor. A live part can also be unintentional and pose a shock or electrocution risk.

Load   (1) The amount of electrical power required by connected electrical equipment. (2) The total resistance or impedance of all the items in an electrical circuit.

Main protection The protection system that is normally expected to operate in response to a fault in the protected zone.

Mains connector   Part of a detachable power supply cord intended to be inserted into the appliance inlet for connection of the product to the supply power.

Mains part   Electrical circuit that is intended to be connected to the supply power.

Mains plug   Part, integral with or intended to be attached to a power supply of electrical product, to be inserted into a power socket or outlet.

Mains transient voltage Highest peak voltage expected at the power input to the electrical product, arising from external transients on the supply power.

Mains voltage Voltage of a supply power between two line conductors of a polyphase system or voltage between the line conductor and the neutral conductor of a single-phase system.

Mark A mark is a protected mark, applied or issued under the rules of a certification system, indicating that adequate confidence is provided that the relevant product, process, or service is in conformity with a specific standard or other normative document (ISO/IEC Guide 2).

Means of protection Means (e.g., insulation, spacings, impedances, and protective earthing, guards) for reducing the risks due to different hazards in accordance with the specific requirements.

Megohmmeter (megger) A testing device that applies a DC voltage and measures the conductor resistance or product insulation.

Multiple listee A multiple listee is a company's name that will appear in the agency directory of listed products, which is not the applicant but will be listed in addition to the applicant under the same product classification for identical products, although, the product model numbers may differ. A multiple listee markets the applicant's listed product under another brand name and model but is not responsible for the manufacture of the product or the compliance of the product to a certain standard of testing or evaluation.

Neutral Common point of a star- connected polyphase system or the earthed midpoint of a single-phase system.

Neutral conductor In multiphase circuits, the conductor used to carry unbalanced current. In single-phase systems, the conductor used for a return current path.

Nominal (value) The normal operating value quoted for reference purposes that is subject to agreed tolerances.

Nonfunctional requirement A requirement that does not relate to functionality, but relates to attributes such as reliability, efficiency, usability, maintainability, and portability.

Normal condition Condition in which all means of protection are intact and expected.

Normal use Expected usage of the product, which includes maintenance of the product (not to be confused with intended use).

Off-the-shelf software   A software product that is developed for the general market (i.e., for a large number of customers) and that is delivered to many customers in identical format.

Opening   A gap or aperture in an enclosure that exists or may be formed by the application of a test probe at the specified force

Open circuit fault   The unintended presence of a high impedance between two points in the same circuit, causing a malfunction of the circuit.

Open-frame construction   A construction technique used when the part (e.g., PCB and power supply) is not provided with an enclosure.

Output load   The total effective resistance or impedance of the circuits or apparatus connected externally across output terminals.

Overcurrent release   Protective device that causes a circuit to electrically open, with or without time delay, when the current in the device exceeds a predetermined value.

Overload   A condition that exceeds the designed limits and can result in overstress and failure.

Pareto analysis   A statistical technique in decision-making that is used for the selection of a limited number of factors that produce significant overall effect. In terms of quality improvement, a large majority of problems (80%) are produced by a few key causes (20%).

Peak to peak   The amplitude of the AC waveform, measured from its positive peak to its negative peak.

Peak working voltage   Highest peak or voltage at which work is performed in a system, not including external transients.

Pigtail   A very short patch cable or wiring adapter.

Polarity The electrical term used to denote the voltage relationship to a reference potential.

Polarized   A plug and connector formed in a way that only allows proper connection and voltage polarity.

Portable   Term referring to transportable equipment intended to be moved from one location to another while being carried by one or more persons.

Potential equalization   Direct connection (other than to protective earth or to neutral) between electrical product and the potential equalization bus bar of the electrical installation.

Power factor   The ratio of the true power delivered to the load (watts) versus the apparent power (volt-amperes).

Power supply cord   Flexible cord fixed to or assembled with electrical product to supply power to the product.

Protection   The provisions for detecting faults or other abnormal conditions in a power system for enabling fault clearance, for terminating abnormal conditions, and for initiating signals or indications.

Protective earthing   Connection of conductive parts of a Class I product to an external protective earthing system for protective purposes.

Quality The degree to which a component, product, system, or process meets specified requirements and/or user/customer needs and expectations.

Quality assurance   Part of quality management focused on providing confidence that quality requirements will be fulfilled.

Quasi   To some degree or in some manner, resembling.

Radiated   Energy transmitted through the air via wiring, antennas, or loops.

Rating   The nominal operating limits for a product, component, or material.

Reactance   The opposition of inductance and capacitance to alternating current equal to the product of the sine of the angular phase difference between the current and voltage.

Reactive power   A component of apparent power (volt-amps) that does not produce any real power (watts). It is measured in VARs volt-amps reactive.

Real power   The average value of the instantaneous product of volts and amps over a fixed period of time in an AC circuit.

Receptacle   A female flange-mounted wiring device with the conducting elements recessed behind the mating surface. Often referred to as an outlet, it provides power. Therefore, receptacles are wired to the source of power.

Recognized component A part or subassembly intended for use in products that conform to appropriate standards. A recognized component is incomplete in construction features, or restricted in performance, which necessitates evaluation of the component's acceptability in the end product. (Glossary of UL Terms and Acronyms).

Redundancy   The existence of more than one means for performing the same function.

Reliability   The ability of a product to perform its expected functions under stated conditions for a specified period of time, or for a specified number of operations.

Requirement   (1) A condition or capability needed by a user to solve a problem or achieve an objective. (2) A condition or capability that must be met or possessed by a system, product, or component to satisfy a contract, standard, specification, or other formally imposed document.

Restricted access area   Area accessible only to skilled, trained, or knowledgeable people with the proper authorization

Reversible output current   An output current that reverses polarity.

Ripple   The magnitude of AC fluctuation in a DC signal, after filtering. Ripple is usually expressed as a percentage of rated output.

RJ-11   Registered jack 11. Standard telephone connector with a tab that snaps into the socket that must be pressed to be removed from the telephone or socket; usually houses two wires but is capable of housing up to four.

RJ-45   Registered jack 45. Connectors used to connect computers to LANs or phones with many lines. It is able to house up eight wires—twice as many wires as the RJ-11.

RoHS   Restriction of hazardous substances. European directive dictating materials that may not be used in the manufacture of certain products. For example, materials restricted include: lead, mercury, cadmium, hexavalent chromium, polybrominated byphenyls, and plybrominated diphenyl ether.

Root-mean-square   The effective value of alternating current or voltage. The RMS value equates an AC current or voltage to the DC current or voltage that provides the equivalent power (same heating effect).

Safety   Freedom from unacceptable risk of harm.

Safe working load   Maximum external mechanical load (mass) on product that is permitted in normal use .

Screen   Device intended to reduce the penetration of an electric, magnetic, or electromagnetic field into a given area.

Secondary circuit   Circuit that is separated from the primary power parts by at least one means of protection and that receives its power from a transformer, converter, or equivalent isolation device, or from an internal electrical power source.

Schematic diagram   A diagram that shows, by means of graphic symbols, the electrical connections of a circuit.

Short circuit   Accidental or intentional conductive path between two or more conductive parts forcing the electric potential differences between these conductive parts to be close to zero volts.

Single-fault condition   Condition in which a single means of protection is defective or a single abnormal condition is present.

Single-phase   Single-phase electric power refers to the distribution of electric power using a system in which the voltage is taken from one phase of a three phase source. This implies a power supply or a load that uses only two wires for power. Some "grounded" single-phase devices also have a third wire used only for a safety ground, but not connected to the electrical supply or load in any other way except for safety ground.

Skin effect   In an AC system, the tendency of the outer portion of a conductor to carry more of the current as the frequency of the AC increases.

Slitting The designation to separate insulated parallel wires.

Snap-on   The easy and quick attachment or detachment of one part from another.

Spark test   A high-voltage test performed on certain types of conductors during manufacture to ensure that the insulation is free from defects.

Stability   The property of a system to return to its original state after having been displaced from a steady state by a disturbance.

Stationary   Term referring to equipment that is not intended to be moved from one place to another.

Storage conditions   The conditions defined by means of ranges of the influence quantities, such as temperature, or any special conditions, within which the product may be stored (nonoperating) without damage.

Stripping   The designation of the removal of the insulation or jacket from a conductor/wire.

Supply mains   Electrical power derived from the electrical grid.

Temperature rating   The maximum temperature at which insulation will maintain its integrity.

Temperature rise   The increase in temperature that results when electrical load is carried by electrical equipment.

Tensile strength The greatest longitudinal force that a substance can bear without tearing apart or rupturing; also called ultimate tensile strength.

Terminal   A terminal is the point at which a conductor from an electrical component, device, or network comes to an end and provides a point of connection to external circuits.

Thermal cutoff Device that, during an abnormal condition in which the temperature exceeds a predetermined limit, electrically opens the circuit to terminate current flow.

Touch current   The current that will flow through a person, to earth or to another part of the enclosure, when the person touches one or more accessible parts of a product. The touch current is a function of the skin resistance at the contact points and also human body capacitance and resistance.

Three-phase   Three-phase refers to one circuit consisting of three conductors where the current and voltage in each conductor (phase) is 120° out of phase with each other phase.

True RMS   (1) The effective value of an AC current or voltage value regardless of the waveform distortion. (2) An AC measurement that has equal power transfer capability to a corresponding DC current or voltage.

Total load   Maximum total loading of a product, including the maximum safe working load, where applicable, and the static and dynamic forces occurring in normal use.

Trapping zone Accessible location within the product or in the product environment where a human body or a part of the human body is exposed to a trapping, crushing, shearing, impact, cutting, entanglement, drawing in, stabbing, or abrasion hazard

Unlisted component   Component that is separately investigated in accordance with requirements applicable to the type of component and that is investigated for that product only as a component of the complete product.

Usability   Characteristic that establishes effectiveness, efficiency, and user learnability and satisfaction.

Validation   Confirmation by examination and through provision of objective evidence that the requirements for a specific intended use or application have been fulfilled.

Verification   Confirmation by examination and tests that specified requirements have been fulfilled.

V-model   A framework to describe the software development life cycle activities, from requirements specification to maintenance. The V-model illustrates how testing activities can be integrated into each phase of the software development life cycle.

Voltage to ground during a short circuit   The voltage measured between a specified point and a reference point.

Warm-up time   The time interval from when a product is turned on until its outputs comply with all performance specifications.

Wire A strand or group of strands of electrically conductive material, normally copper or aluminum.

Working voltage The designed voltage to which the insulation or the component under consideration is, or can be, subjected when the electrical product is operating under normal conditions.

Yield strength   The force required to stretch a material.

List of Acronyms and Abbrevations

AAC All-aluminum conductor

AC Alternating current

A/D Analog-to-digital

ADC Analog-to-digital convertor

AFI Arc fault interrupter

AHJ Authority having jurisdiction

AKA Also known as

AIC Arc-interrupting current

AM Amplitude modulation

ANSI American National Standards Institute

AQL Acceptable quality level

ASME American Society of Mechanical Engineers

ASTM American Society for Testing and Materials

ATE Automatic test equipment

ATM Asynchronous transfer mode

AUI Attached unit interface

AWG American wire gauge

BEAB British Electronic Approvals Board for Household Equipment

BMU Battery management unit

BW Bandwidth

CAD Computer-aided design

CAG   Chairman advisory group

CAM   Computer-aided manufacturing

CASE   Conformity assessment systems evaluation

CAT   Computer-aided test

CB   Certification body

CCA   CENELEC Certification Agreement

CCITT Consultative Committee of International Telephony and Telegraphy

CCTV Closed-circuit television

CDF   Construction data form

CENELEC   European Committee for Electrotechnical Standardization (Commission Européenne de Normalisation Électrique)

CFM   Cubic feet per minute

CISPR Comité International Spécial de Perturbations Radioélectriques

COTS Commercial off-the-shelf

CRT   Cathode ray tube

CSA   Canadian Standards Association

CW   Continuous wave

dBm   Decibels referenced to one milliwatt

dBmV Decibels referred to 1 mV across 75Ω

D/A   Digital-to-analog

DAC   Digital-to-analog converter

DBA   Doing business as

DC   Direct current

DFS   Dynamic frequency selection

DIN   Deutsches Institut fur Normung (German Institute for Standardization)

DMM Digital multimeter

DoC   Declaration of conformity

DSO   Digital storage oscilloscope

DUT   Device under test

DVM   Digital voltmeter

ECITC European Committee for Information Technology Testing and Certification

ECN   Engineering change notice

ECO	Engineering change order
ECR	Engineering change request
EEPCA	European Electrical Products Certification Association
EFTA	European Free Trade Association
EIA/J	Electronic Industries Association (USA/Japan)
ELF	Extremely low frequency (below 3 kHz)
EMC	Electromagnetic compatibility
emf	Electromotive force
EMF	Electromagnetic field
EMI	Electromagnetic interference
EN	Européenne Norme (European standard)
ENEC	European Norms Electrical Certification (mark for electrical products that demonstrate compliance with ENs)
ESD	Electrostatic discharge
ETICS	European Testing, Inspection, and Certification System
ETSI	European Telecommunications Standards Institute
EU	European Union
EUT	Equipment under test
FA	Failure analysis
FCC	Federal Communications Commission
FFI	First factory inspection
FIT	Fault isolation test or failures in testing time
FM	Frequency modulation
FUS	Follow-up service
GF	Ground fault
GFCI	Ground fault circuit interrupter
GMP	Good manufacturing practices
GND	Ground
GUI	Graphical user interface
HALT	Highly accelerated life test
HAR	Harmonized European cables
HASS	Highly accelerated stress screening
HAST	Highly accelerated stress test

HBM	Human body model
HD	Harmonic distortion
HF	High-frequency (3–30 MHz)
hipot	High-potential
HV	High-voltage
I/O	Input/output
IEC	International Electrotechnical Commission
IECEE	IEC System for Conformity Assessment Schemes for Electrotechnical Equipment and Components
IEE	Institution of Electrical Engineers (U.K.)
IEEE	Institute of Electrical and Electronics Engineers
IPI	Initial product inspection
IR	Infrared radiation
ISA	Instrument Society of America
ISM	Industrial, scientific, and medical equipment
ISO	International Standards Organization
ITE	Information technology equipment
ITU	International Telecommunication Union
JEDEC	Joint Electron Device Engineering Council
JIS	Japan Industrial Norm
JSA	Japanese Standard Association
LCC	List of critical components
LED	Light-emitting diode
LF	Low-frequency (30–300 kHz)
LNA	Low-noise amplifier
LPC	Limited product certification
MDA	Manufacturing defects analyzer
MF	Medium frequency (300–3 MHz)
MOP	Means of protection
MOU	Memorandum of understanding
MRA	Mutual recognition agreement
MTBF	Mean time between failures
MTTR	Mean time to repair

mW/cm2	Unit for power density 1 mW/cm2 = 10 W/m2
N/C	Normally closed
N/O	Normally open
NCB	National certification body
NEC	National Electrical Code (NFPA-70).
NEMA	National Electrical Manufacturers Association
NFPA	National Fire Protection Association
NIST	National Institute of Standards and Technology
NRTL	Nationally recognized testing laboratory
NTC	Negative temperature coefficient
OCV	Open-circuit voltage
OEM	Original equipment manufacturer.
OSHA	Occupational Safety and Health Administration.
OVP	Overvoltage protection
p-p	Peak-to-peak
PCB	Printed circuit board
PCM	Power control module
PDN	Power distribution network
PE	Professional engineer
PEBS	Protective-equipotential-bonding system
PF	Power factor
PLC	Programmable logic controller
POV	Peak operating voltage
ppm	Parts per million
psi	Pounds per square inch (unit for pressure)
PTB	Physikalisch-Technische Bundesanslalt
PTC	Positive temperature coefficient
PWB	Printed wiring board
QA	Quality assurance
QC	Quality control
QMS	Quality management system
RCA	Radio Corporation of America

REACH	Registration, Evaluation, Authorization, and Restriction of Chemicals
RH	Relative humidity
RFI	Radio-frequency interference
RMS	Root mean square
RTD	Resistance temperature detector
SFC	Single-fault condition
SELV	Safety extra low voltage
S/N	Signal-to-noise ratio
SQC	Statistical quality control
SWR	Standing wave ratio
TC	Thermocouple, temperature coefficient; or technical committee
TAG	Technical advisory group
THD	Total harmonic distortion
TMB	Technical management board
TQM	Total quality management
TÜV	Technische Überwachungs Verein
UHF	Ultra high frequency (300 MHz–3 GHz)
UL	Underwriters Laboratories
UPS	Uninterruptible power supply
USB	Universal serial bus
UUT	Unit under test
UV	Ultraviolet
V/m	Unit of electric field strength
VA	Volt-ampere
VAR	Volt-ampere reactive
VDE	Verband Deutscher Electrotechniker
VHF	Very high frequency (30–300 MHz)
VLF	Very low frequency (3–30 kHz)
WG	Working group
XTALK	Crosstalk
XMTR	Transmitter

About the Authors

Steli Loznen was born in Romania in 1952. He received his M.Sc. in electronics from the Polytechnic University of Bucharest in 1974. In Romania, he worked for the Tehnoton and Iassy University of Medicine–Physiology Department, laying the foundations of bioengineering activities together with Prof. Dr. Florin Topoliceanu. In Israel, he works for Tel Aviv University in the Department of Biomedical Engineering as a lecturer on clinical engineering and medical ethics. He has also served as managing director of Stelco-Bioengineering and was a lecturer for the standardization of electrical and electronic equipment at the Center for Technological Education Holon. He was also chief engineer at the Standards Institution of Israel Telematics Laboratory and Quality Assurance and Certification Manager at Israel Testing Laboratory Ltd. He is also the coordinator of the ETL and TUVRNA Inspections Center in Tel Aviv. His work focuses on international regulations and the safety of medical and laboratory electrical equipment. His main areas of expertise are the following:

- International standardization (ISO, IEC, UL, EN, and ANSI) for medical devices and laboratory and information technology equipment;
- Product safety, international regulatory procedures, and quality assurance;
- Risk management programs (hazard identification, risk analysis, risk evaluation, and risk control);
- CE mark (MDD, IVDD, LVD, and EMC);
- FDA procedures;

- ISO 9001 (Quality Systems), ISO 18001 (Environmental), ISO/IEC 17025 (Testing and Calibration), ISO/IEC 17065 (Certification), ISO 13485 (Medical Devices manufacturing), and ISO 14155-1 (Clinical Trials).

Loznen is the convener for IEC subcommittee 62A/MT62354 (General Testing Procedures for Medical Electrical Equipment) and SC62A/MT 29 (Mechanical Hazards), and he is the project leader for the IEC/TR 62354 "General Testing Procedures for Medical Electrical Equipment." He is also a member of the IECEE—RMETFMED (Risk Management Experts Task Force for Medical Equipment).

He holds the following certifications:

- Lead and technical assessor for IECEE-CB scheme;

- QMS lead auditor included in the International Register of Certificated Auditors (IRCA).

Loznen is one of the charter members of the IEEE-Product Safety Engineering Society (2005), and since 2012, he has been a member of the board of govenors of IEEE-PSES. He is also a member of A2LA accreditation council.

Loznen has written six books and more than 62 papers and presented at conferences more than 90 times on various topics relating to product compliance and safety engineering.

Constantin Bolintineanu is currently working within the DSC Testing Laboratory part of Tyco Safety Products Canada-Johnson Controls, a 17025-accredited testing laboratory for IT Equipment. Bolintineanu has been working in the compliance regulatory area since 1977. He specializes in testing and equipment evaluations, global regulatory approvals, and product requirements and standards (electrical safety).

Bolintineanu worked as technical manager of the electrical division for Intertek Testing Services, Missisauga, Canada, providing services including testing, evaluation, and certification of diverse equipment in the area of EMC, electrical safety, and telecom, from 1995 to 1998. In 1998, he became the direct approval liaison engineer for the BABT for all technically related issues within Digital Security Controls .

Since 2001, Bolintineanu has served as the supervisor of the DSC Testing Laboratory. As a technical supervisor of the A2LA-accredited testing laboratory, he is responsible for developing and managing all testing and evaluation activities related to electrical safety, telecom, and environmental testing performed under the accreditation of the laboratory.

Bolintineanu has extensive experience (over 35 years) in electrical safety testing and evaluation in accordance with European, North American, South American, South African, and Australia/New Zealand requirements and standards for IT equipment.

Bolintineanu received an M.S. degree in electronics engineering from the Polytechnic University of Bucharest Romania in 1972 and graduated the ASQ-accredited program at Ryerson Polytechnic University in Toronto in 1997, obtaining a degree in quality assurance. Since 1997 he has been licensed as a professional engineer in Ontario, Canada, and since 2004 he has been certified as a NARTE electrical safety engineer.

From 1972 to 1994, Bolintineanu worked as a researcher at the Center of Research of Electrotechnical Engineering in Bucharest, Romania, under the direction of Florin Teodor Tanasescu.

Bolintineanu is author of several technical books and over 40 scientific papers published worldwide, related to medical electrical equipment and electrical safety, and he holds several patents in this field. His patents are recognized in Romania, the United States, and Japan. Along with his colleague Loznen, he wrote the chapter "Product Safety and Third Party Certification," in *The Electronic Packaging Handbook,* edited by G. R. Blackwell (CRC Press, 2000).

Jan Swart received his master's in electrical engineering from the Cape Peninsula University of Technology in Cape Town, South Africa, and his Ph.D. in engineering management from California Coast University in the United States. Swart has published and presented internationally and has lectured on electronics and control systems in South Africa. In addition, he has served as a member of a tertiary college executive council.

Swart has held various technical and research positions in South Africa, Germany, and the United States. He is currently a consultant in the United States. Dr. Swart applies engineering and scientific principles to failure analysis and investigation of consumer product failures and utilizes his failure analysis experience to advise clients on safety risk mitigation during the design phase of new products. He specializes in battery systems specific to medical devices, portable consumer products, backup power systems for the telecommunication industry, energy storage for the utility industry, and battery systems for automotive applications.

Index

Successful Proposal Strategies for Small Businesses: Using Knowledge Management to Win Government, Private Sector, and International Contracts, Sixth Edition, Robert S. Frey

Systems Approach to Engineering Design, Peter H. Sydenham

Systems Engineering Principles and Practice, H. Robert Westerman

Systems Reliability and Failure Prevention, Herbert Hecht

Team Development for High-Tech Project Managers, James Williams

For further information on these and other Artech House titles, including previously considered out-of-print books now available through our In-Print-Forever® (IPF®) program, contact:

Artech House
685 Canton Street
Norwood, MA 02062
Phone: 781-769-9750
Fax: 781-769-6334
e-mail: artech@artechhouse.com

Artech House
16 Sussex Street
London SW1V 4RW UK
Phone: +44 (0)20 7596-8750
Fax: +44 (0)20 7630-0166
e-mail: artech-uk@artechhouse.com

Find us on the World Wide Web at: www.artechhouse.com